D1158261

DIURETICS

Chemistry and Pharmacology

MEDICINAL CHEMISTRY

A Series of Monographs

EDITED BY

GEORGE DESTEVENS
CIBA Pharmaceutical Company
Division of CIBA Corporation
Summit, New Jersey

Volume 1. GEORGE DESTEVENS. Diuretics: Chemistry and Pharmacology. 1963

In Preparation

E. J. ARIËNS (ED.). Molecular Pharmacology: The Mode of Action of Biologically Active Compounds. (In two volumes)
MAXWELL GORDON (ED.). Psychopharmacological Agents
RODOLFO PAOLETTI (ED.). Lipid Pharmacology
GEORGE DESTEVENS (ED.). Analgetics

DIURETICS

Chemistry and Pharmacology

GEORGE deSTEVENS

CIBA Pharmaceutical Company
Division of CIBA Corporation
Summit, New Jersey

1963

ACADEMIC PRESS · New York and London

ACADEMIC PRESS INC.
111 Fifth Avenue, New York 3, New York

United Kingdom Edition published by
ACADEMIC PRESS INC. (LONDON) LTD.
Berkeley Square House, London W.1

LIBRARY OF CONGRESS CATALOG CARD NUMBER: 63-22326

PRINTED IN THE UNITED STATES OF AMERICA

To my wife Ruby

Preface

The search for clinically useful diuretics has been a continuing effort ever since the early days of organic chemistry. Throughout this whole period of development the cumulative research efforts of many dedicated chemists, pharmacologists, and clinicians have done much to advance our knowledge of diuresis and diuretics. This is evidenced by the literature which abounds with many reports on renal function and dysfunction, and the use of drugs to facilitate kidney performance. A number of reviews have also been written on specific groups of compounds which cause diuresis, and in the past few years several reviews have been published on the pharmacological and clinical aspects of newer diuretics. These chapters, although excellently executed, have covered only restricted areas of this broad field of research, and in many cases the emphasis has been biologically oriented. Thus, there has been a need for a monograph critically surveying the field in its entirety, with particular emphasis on the chemistry of diuretically active compounds and their structure–activity relationships. Consequently, the purpose of this book is to satisfy this need and in so doing to familiarize the chemist and biologist with the significant developments in this area of medicinal research. In addition, it is hoped that this survey will act as a catalyst for further developments.

The first chapter was purposely written in a relatively uncomplicated and concise manner so that all those not well versed in the field could readily understand the dynamics of renal function. Chapter II on xanthines and pyrimidines, and Chapter III on triazines were accordingly situated since they are necessary for the historical development leading to organomercurials and sulfonamides. The sulfonamides (Chapter V) and the thiazides and hydrothiazides (Chapter VI) represent the most important advance in diuretic therapy and consequently are appropriately treated. In Chapter VI I have endeavored to correlate the data derived from the work of my colleagues and myself in the CIBA Laboratories in addition to the published data from other research groups. Chapter VII on aldosterone antagonists also was dealt with intensively because of the growing interest in this specific area. The chapter on miscellaneous compounds was included to serve as a catch-all for some interesting but not clinically useful compounds and also to indicate new and potentially useful compounds. Finally, it was felt that some particular emphasis should be given to the clinical importance of diuretics in the treatment of hypertension, thus accounting for the last chapter.

In each section I have surveyed the literature up to August, 1963, and have attempted to include primarily what appeared to me to be the most pertinent findings. It is inevitable that in some cases omissions might have been committed. To those so overlooked, I wish to extend my sincere apologies.

Summit, New Jersey GEORGE DESTEVENS

October, 1963

Acknowledgments

Many kind people have helped me enormously during the months of writing. First of all, I would like to extend my deepest gratitude to Dr. E. Schlittler, Executive Vice President, Research and Production, CIBA, for his continual interest and encouragement during the execution of this work, and also for reading the entire text and making many helpful suggestions. Special thanks are also extended to Dr. R. Gaunt, Dr. A. Plummer, and Dr. L. Werner for reading the text and for their many critical comments.

Dr. W. Bencze, Dr. J. J. Chart, and Dr. A. Renzi also were very helpful in the preparation of the chapter on aldosterone antagonists.

I wish to acknowledge the assistance of Miss A. Halamandaris in accumulating the literature and reference materials. I also wish to thank Miss R. Farina for typing the final manuscript, Miss Y. Schaefer and Mrs. B. Rex for their assistance in various ways.

I am grateful to many authors, and to the editors and publishers of the following books and journals for permission to reproduce the following figures and tables:

Chapter I. "Anatomy of the Human Body" (H. Gray), Lea and Febiger, Philadelphia, Pennsylvania, 1959: Figures 1, 2, 4. "Textbook of Histology" (H. Maximow and W. Bloom): Figure 3. "Comparative Biochemistry" (E. Baldwin), Cambridge Univ. Press, London and New York, 1949: Figure 5.

Chapter II. "Medicinal Chemistry" (F. F. Blicke and R. H. Cox, eds.) Vol. III, Wiley, New York, 1959: Tables II–X.

Chapter IV. *Journal of Clinical Investigation:* Figure 1. *Annals New York Academy of Science:* Figure 2.

Chapter V. "Water, Electrolyte and Acid-Base Syndrome" (E. Goldberger), Lea and Febiger, Philadelphia, Pennsylvania, 1959: Figure 1. Dr. R. O. Roblin, American Cyanamid Company: Figure 2.

The Biochemical Journal: Table I. *Journal of the American Chemical Society:* Table II. *Journal of Organic Chemistry:* Table III.

Chapter VI. Toxicology and Applied Pharmacology: Table I, Figures 1–4. *Annals New York Academy of Science:* Tables II, III.

Chapter VII. Journal of Chronic Diseases: Figure 1. *Journal of Medicinal and Pharmaceutical Chemistry:* Tables III–V.

Chapter IX. "Hypertension" (J. H. Moyer, ed.), Saunders, Philadelphia, Pennsylvania, 1959: Table I, Figure 1. "Edema" (J. H. Moyer and M. Fuchs, eds.), Saunders, Philadelphia, Pennsylvania, 1960: Tables II, III. *Annals New York Academy of Science:* Figure 2.

Contents

CHAPTER I

General Physiological and Pharmacological Considerations

Animals have really two environments: a *milieu extérieur* in which the organism is situated, and a *milieu intérieur* in which the tissue elements live. The living organism does not really exist in the *milieu extérieur* (the atmosphere if it breathes, salt or fresh water if that is its element) but in the liquid *milieu intérieur* formed by the circulating organic liquid which surrounds and bathes all tissue elements; this is the lymph or plasma.... The *milieu intérieur* surrounding the organs, the tissues and their elements never varies; atmospheric changes cannot penetrate beyond it and it is therefore true to say that the physical conditions of environment are unchanging in a higher animal: each one is surrounded by this invariable *milieu* which is, as it were, an atmosphere proper to itself in an ever-changing cosmic environment. Here, we have an organism which has enclosed itself in a kind of hothouse. The perpetual changes of external conditions cannot reach it; it is not subject to them, but is free and independent.... All the vital mechanisms, however varied they may be, have only one object, that of preserving constant the conditions of life in the internal environment.

Claude Bernard, 1857

A little more than a century has elapsed since Claude Bernard first pointed out that the true medium in which we live is neither air nor water, but the plasma or liquid part of the blood that bathes all the tissue elements. In Bernard's time the science of the chemistry of living organisms was only in its infant stage and accordingly afforded only a meager insight into the complexity of the internal environment. However, within the past 50 years the sciences of biochemistry and physiology have revolutionized our thinking related to life processes. New concepts have broadened our horizons and given us a new perspective of the chemical and biological interactions at the cellular level. This new knowledge has only emphasized the fundamental importance of Bernard's generalization concerning the internal environment. The internal environment is a consequence of the nature of the kidney and thus the study of the physiology of this organ has done much to advance our knowledge of the *milieu intérieur*. Thus, a study of the phenomenon of diuresis and the drugs which influence it presupposes an understanding of renal function.

A. Renal Function

Diuresis can be defined as an increase in the rate of urine formation. It may be caused by copious fluid intake (water), by pathological states, or by the action of certain drugs. Such drugs are referred to as diuretics. Regardless of the cause of urine formation the site of action of this phenomenon is centered in the kidney. Thus, a detailed discussion of renal function must be considered before turning to other factors.

Man is equipped with a pair of kidneys (see Fig. 1) which are located in the posterior part of the abdomen. The right kidney is usually slightly lower than the left, probably due to the presence of the liver. In an adult male the average dimension of the kidney is 12 cm in length, 6 cm in breadth, and 4 cm in thickness. Each kidney weighs approximately 150 gm. Situated directly above the kidney and resembling the form of a hat, is the suprarenal gland—also known as the adrenal gland. The effect of this organ on renal function is not a direct one since it is not physiologically bound to the kidney. Its influence is exerted through the blood stream and this aspect will be considered later in this monograph (see Chapter VII).

The kidney plays an important role in maintaining the constancy of the internal environment of the organism. It does this by eliminating the waste products of metabolism and thus maintaining a constant volume and composition of the body fluids. This process is known as *homeostasis*. The dynamics whereby this constancy is achieved and maintained will now be examined.

In Fig. 2 is outlined a longitudinal cross section of one side of a kidney. It is a vitally complex system whose most important parts are the external cortical and the internal medullary substance, the renal pelvis, and the ureter. The medullary substance (see Fig. 3 for an enlargement of this subsection) consists of a series of striated conical masses termed renal pyramids the bases of which are directed toward the circumference of the kidney (cortical substance) and the apices converge toward the renal sinus. The pyramids in turn are made up of single, identical, secretory units called nephrons which commence in the cortical substance and terminate at the end of the pyramid. A typical nephron is outlined in Fig. 4. It is this unit which is the work-horse of the kidney.

Each of the two human kidneys contains approximately one

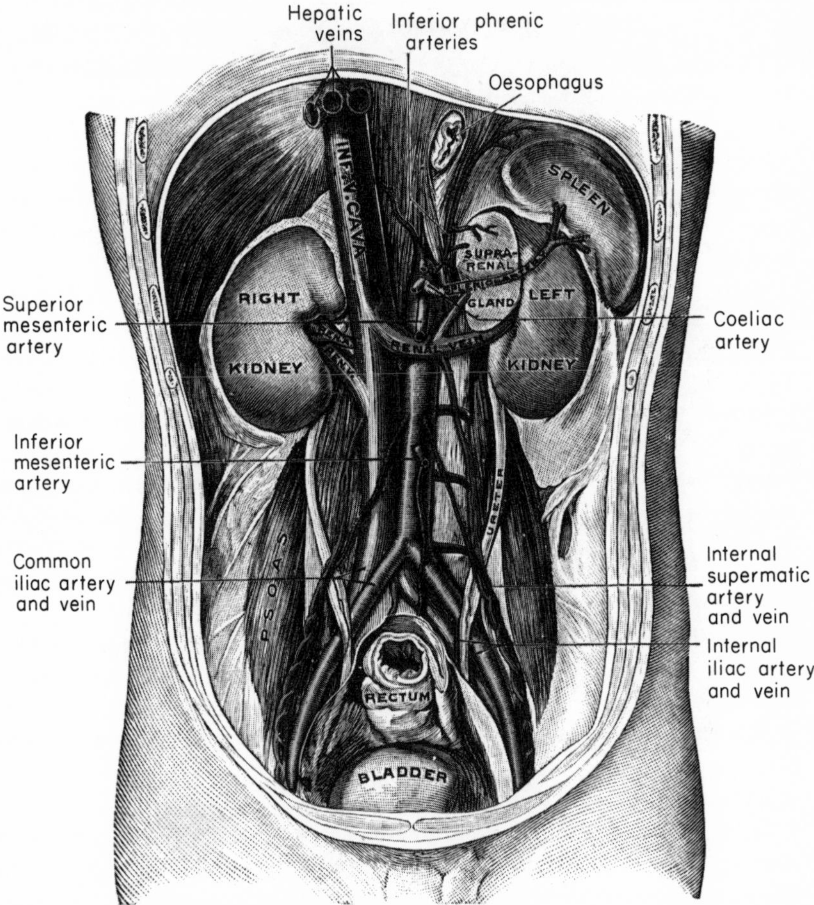

FIG. 1. Posterior abdominal wall, after removal of the peritoneum, showing kidneys, suprarenal capsules, and great vessels.

million nephrons. The task of studying kidney function is simplified by the remarkable fact that the mode of action of each nephron may be considered representative of the action of the kidney as a whole. Each of these nephrons consists of a glomerulus, tubules (both

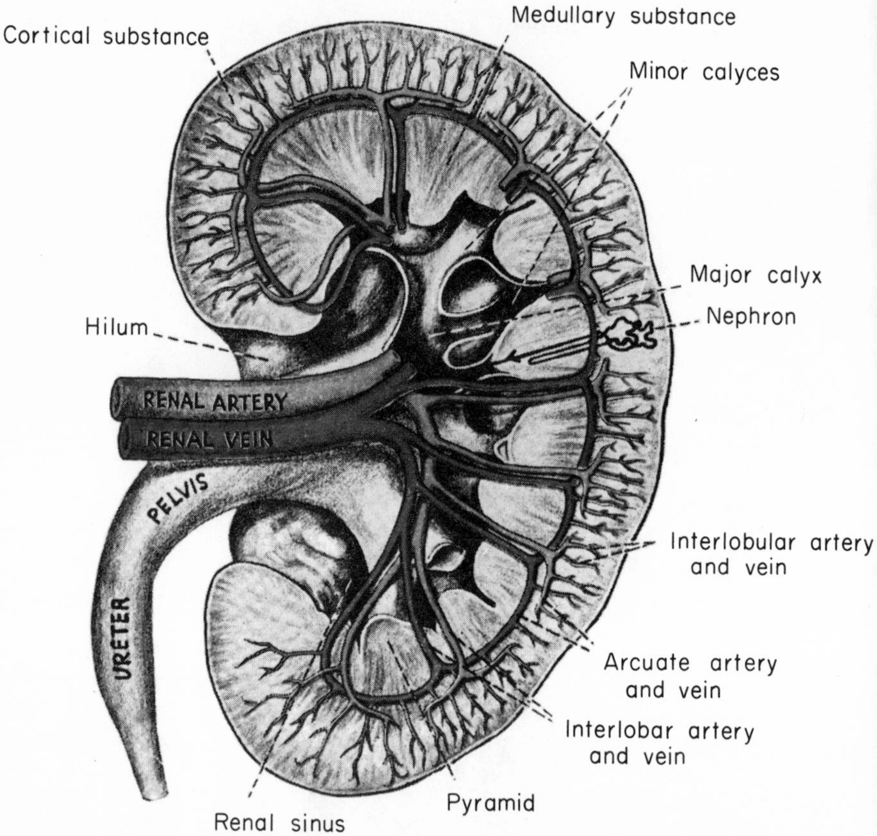

Medullary substance
Cortical substance
Minor calyces
Major calyx
Nephron
Hilum
RENAL ARTERY
RENAL VEIN
PELVIS
URETER
Interlobular artery and vein
Arcuate artery and vein
Interlobar artery and vein
Pyramid
Renal sinus

FIG. 2. Diagram of a vertical section through the kidney. Nephron and blood vessels greatly enlarged.

INNER ZONE
OUTER ZONE
MEDULLA
CORTEX

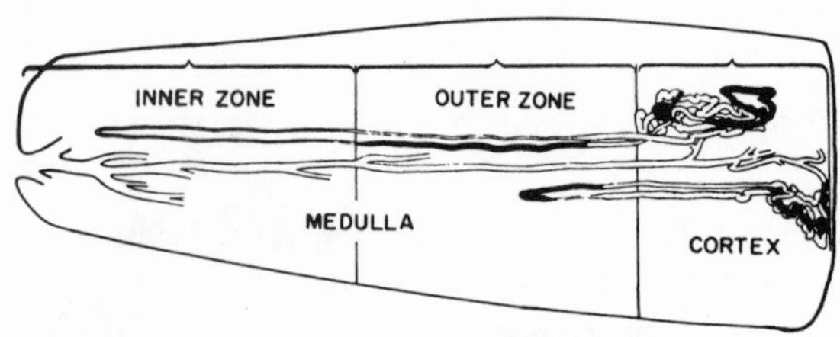

FIG. 3. The nephron and its relative positions in the medulla and cortex.

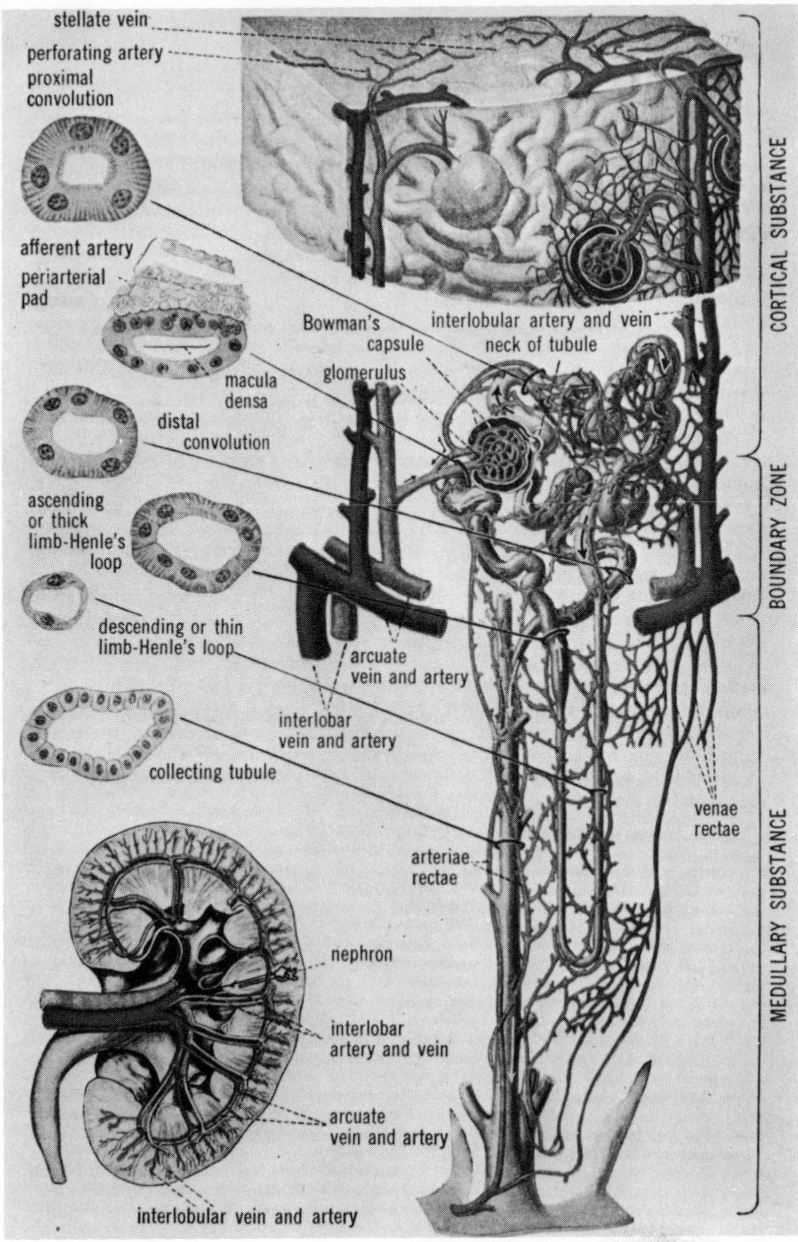

FIG. 4. Diagram of a portion of kidney lobule illustrating a nephron, typical histological sections of the various divisions of a nephron, and the disposition of the renal vessels. The section of the collecting tubule is reproduced at a lower magnification than the divisions of the nephron.

proximal and distal), the loop of Henle, and the collecting tubule—all of which participate in the elaboration of urine. Therefore, the important factors which determine the volume and composition of urine are: (*1*) glomerular filtration, (*2*) proximal and distal tubular reabsorption, and (*3*) tubular excretion.

Within a 24-hour period, approximately 1700 liters of blood flow through the human kidney. This blood enters the nephron through the afferent arteriole which leads to a filtration chamber (Bowman's capsule) made up of conglomerated capillary blood vessels. This area is known as the glomerulus. The blood is filtered by the glomeruli at the rate of 180 liters per day, or approximately 120 ml per minute. The energy to run this efficient filtration pump is supplied by the beating heart. The unfiltered blood consisting of cellular elements and plasma constituents, passes out of the glomerulus via the efferent arteriole which breaks up again into a second set of capillaries, which ramify around the tubules.

The filtrate, on the other hand, passes into Bowman's capsule before going on into the tubules. The filtered components are water, electrolytes [NaCl, $(NH_4)_2HPO_4$, KCl, $NaHCO_3$, etc.], and low molecular weight organic substances such as glucose, essential nutrients, and urea. These must be largely reabsorbed to maintain the volume and composition of the extracellular fluid. Although glomerular filtration separates a large amount of fluid,* the necessity for homeostasis demands that a considerable amount of the filtrate be reabsorbed during its passage through the proximal tubule, the loop of Henle, and the distal tubule. As a matter of fact, in the act of tubular reabsorption 98–99% of the water of the glomerular filtrate plus electrolytes and organic compounds are reabsorbed through the cell walls of the tubules and back into the blood stream. Obviously the composition of the reabsorbate must closely approximate that of the extracellular fluid to prevent distortions in fluid composition. Otherwise considered, the reabsorption process, the energy for which is supplied by the kidney cells, serves to accomplish two purposes, namely, to control electrolyte balance and to maintain a constant hydrostatic pressure. As a result, physiologically necessary amounts of water, sodium, potassium, and chloride ions are reabsorbed into the blood stream, and urea, uric acid, creatinine, water, and excess

* It has been determined that each day the total aqueous filtrate from the glomeruli contains about 1100 gm of sodium chloride, 5–10 gm of which is excreted, 450 gm of sodium bicarbonate, and 145 gm of glucose.

electrolytes are rejected. This residue of the filtrate which is not reabsorbed enters the collecting tubule and is eventually eliminated from the kidney via the ureter as urine.

In the past decade a new theory has evolved to explain urine concentration in the collecting tubule. This revolutionary idea is due to Wirz, Hagetay, and Kuhn and incorporates a "hairpin countercurrent multiplier system." It also provides new functional concepts of the role of the loops of Henle in the mammalian kidney.

These investigators examined frozen sections of the rat kidney to determine the osmotic pressure at various areas from the cortex to the papilla. They observed by melting-point depression studies that the osmotic pressure increased from the corticomedullary junction to the tip of the papilla. Thus, the kidney appears to be composed of concentric shells with respect to points of equal osmotic concentration. Wirz and colleagues explained this result by applying the principle of a countercurrent system. In such a system two streams flowing in opposite directions and lying close together assist one another in the exchange of heat or energy of some sort. In the kidney the system is the nephron with the descending (proximal) tubule, the ascending (distal) tubule, and the descending (collecting) tubule. The driving force of this exchange system is the sodium ion. This ion is transported from the ascending distal tubule to the descending proximal tubule. Thus, the fluids in the descending limb become more concentrated with sodium ions and a hypertonic state exists in the loop. Then as this concentrated fluid begins to ascend to the distal tubule, the fluid becomes less concentrated due to the transport of sodium ions again to the descending tubule. Thus, the fluid entering the ascending limb experiences a progressive dilution during its ascent, ultimately appearing in the early distal convolution as a hypotonic fluid which then flows over to the collecting duct. In the presence of antidiuretic hormone (see Chapter VIII) the collecting ducts are considered permeable to water and a concentrated urine is delivered through the hypertonic medullary region. Conversely, in the absence of antidiuretic hormone a dilute urine is eliminated from the collecting ducts. This is influenced by the fact that in the loop of Henle, sodium chloride is abstracted in excess of water so that urine leaving the loop is hypotonic. In the absence of antidiuretic hormone, this hypotonicity is maintained throughout the nephron.

The Wirz–Hagetay–Kuhn theory has now been widely accepted and has opened a new chapter in renal physiological research.

It is by this over-all process that the internal environment (the *milieu intérieur* so prophetically described by Bernard) is maintained. Homer Smith has indicated the importance of the kidney in a more succinct manner. "The kidney is not so important in what it excretes as in what it retains." This organ controls and regulates electrolyte concentration in the internal environment thus directly influencing healthy cellular function. Any marked change in this environment, the electrolyte concentration of which is similar to the one existent in the primitive ocean at the beginning of life (see Fig. 5), acts as a

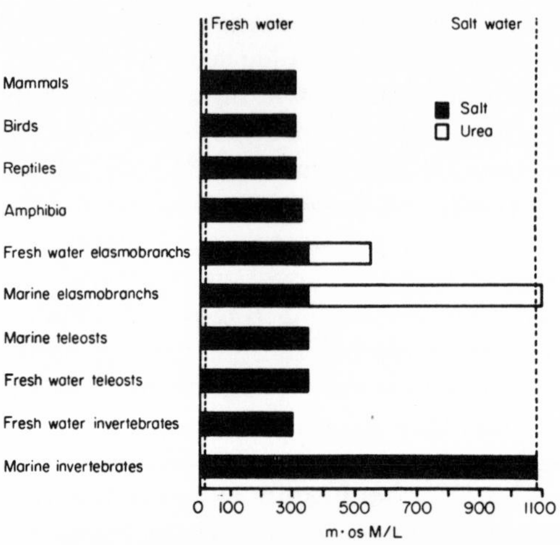

FIG. 5. Osmotic pressures of bloods of various animals compared with those of fresh and sea waters.

warning signal that owing to internal or external factors, the kidney is not able to fulfill its primary function; i.e., regulation of electrolyte concentration and acid-base balance. As a result, a state of renal dysfunction (either glomerular or tubular in origin, or both) exists which reduces the capacity of the body to excrete sodium and chloride ions and water. That is, if the glomerular filtration is reduced to a much greater extent than the capacity for the tubules to reabsorb sodium chloride and water, there results a relatively higher percentage of absorbed salts to the amount excreted. The increased salt reabsorbed retains with it an osmotic equivalent of water, thus leading to excessive retention of body fluids. This renal disease is known as glomerular nephritis and is commonly associated with an abnormal increase in the volume of the extracellular fluid. When the increase is of the order of 50%, it becomes manifest as *edema*.

Renal insufficiency can also occur in spite of a properly functioning glomerulus. The imbalance leading to increased absorption of salt and water is due in some cases to the elaboration of mineralocorticoids, i.e., aldosterone from the adrenal cortex into the blood stream. The effect now is directly on the tubules. The resulting shifts in electrolyte imbalance cause edema which can predispose congestive heart failure. Diseased tubules can also cause excessive loss or absorption of salt. These glomerulotubular imbalances in turn affect the kidney's role in regulating blood flow and maintaining blood pressure, the consequence of which usually is hypertension.

It is, therefore, essential to interrupt this vicious cycle somewhere. Since it is apparent that a slight deviation from the normal 99% tubular reabsorption results in a large increase in urine volume, one method of alleviating these pathological conditions has been to facilitate the removal of the excess water and sodium and chloride ions from the body. This has been accomplished with the use of diuretic agents. *Diuretic drugs* serve to decrease the reabsorption of water, electrolytes, and low molecular weight organic compounds into the blood stream, and as a consequence, to promote the formation of urine. A *saluretic agent* is one which primarily increases the excretion of sodium chloride which, in turn, induces diuresis in the edematous patient. Generally, it is believed that these drugs act somewhere in the tubules, but the particular tubule acted upon varies with the chemical nature of the drug.

B. Pharmacological Evaluation of Diuretics

Before going on to discuss the chemistry and pharmacology of these compounds, it is of interest to record how these compounds are tested for their diuretic effects in experimental animals.

Claude Bernard, the father of experimental medicine, laid down many of the basic principles upon which this science is based. He emphasized to the medical scientists of his day and of the future that the only rational attack on disease was to observe and study it in the clinics, then return to the laboratory and set up the same diseased condition in animals and investigate its causes, cures, and prevention. Under such conditions and with proper controls, Bernard predicted the curbing of some, and the eradication of many, of man's diseases.

Thus, when diuretic studies were commenced in our Laboratories over a decade ago, it was decided that the compounds should be tested in animals whose diseased state approximated as closely as possible that found in humans. Whereas in some laboratories, it has been reported that *anesthetized* dogs were used, it was decided by the CIBA group that such a condition did not simulate the clinical situation.* Consequently, a method was developed whereby *unanesthetized* dogs were used. It should be indicated that the initial observations on diuretic activity were made on male rats, fasted 18 hours, and given 5 ml/100 gm body weight of a 0.2–0.9% sodium chloride solution by stomach tube. The diuretic drug then was given also by stomach tube at the time of fluid loading. The rats were placed in metabolism cages and urine volumes measured at 30-minute intervals over a 3-hour period. In those series of compounds tested in rats where it was unequivocally established that comparable activities were obtained in dogs, the rat test† served as a useful, rapid screening method for the selection of substances to be tested in dogs.

Unanesthetized mongrel dogs were usually used in these experiments. At the start of each experiment the dogs received a subcutaneous injection of 100 ml of 0.9% saline. Immediately before the saline injection they received the compound by injection, as is the case with the mercurials, or orally by capsules. Urine was then collected by catheterization at intervals of 2, 4, and 6 hours after the administration of the drug. Urinary sodium and potassium concentrations were measured by means of a Baird flame photometer and expressed in milliequivalents of sodium and potassium excreted in 6 hours or in each of the three successive 2-hour intervals. Urinary chloride was determined polargraphically and the concentration was expressed in the same units as for sodium and potassium. The results of such an experiment are expressed as the average volume of urine in milliliters and average milliequivalents of electrolyte excreted per dog in the

* The author is indebted to Dr. A. Plummer and his colleague Dr. Barrett for the many helpful discussions during the preparation of this section.

† Among the group of substances which act as sodium and water diuretics in rats but which have little or no activity in dogs and human subjects are: (a) many but not all antihistamines, the diuretic activity of which, however, is not proportional to antihistaminic activity; (b) analeptics, e.g., Ritalin® and amphetamine; (c) some analgesics, e.g., Su-4432 (4-piperidinomethyl-tetrahydrobenzothiazole-2-one hydrobromide); (d) stilbesterol and some related stilbenes; (e) amphenone and related adrenal corticol inhibitors; (f) epinephrine, norepinephrine, and hypertensin; and (g) glucocorticoids. (R. Gaunt, in "Diuresis and Diuretics," p. 176.)

6-hour period or for each 2-hour interval. The saline control experiments were run prior to the drug experiments and also at intervals during the course of the drug studies. During a control or drug experiment, water and food were withheld from the dogs.

A method derived by Lipschitz and co-workers (1943) has been used with suitable success. They fed small volumes of 0.9% sodium chloride solution to their rats and then tested urea, saline diuretics, xanthine derivatives, and mercurials and calculated the relative efficiency of the drugs by plotting their dose–effect curves against that of urea. Lipschitz's results are remarkable in that the sequence of potencies in the rat was the same as that established in man.

Beyer (1961) in turn has evaluated the efficacy of some compounds in dogs made edematous by giving them mineralocorticoids (e.g., 9α-fluorohydrocortisone) and sodium chloride, potassium chloride, and water. During this regime, the animals gained weight to such a degree that pitting edema was demonstrable. At this stage, the dogs were treated with a diuretic agent in order to effect water diuresis to the level of healthy controls.

General References

Bernard, C., "An Introduction to the Study of Experimental Medicine" (Translated by H. C. Greene). H. Schumann, 1927.

Beyer, K. H. and Baer, J. E., *in* "Progress in Drug Research" (E. Jucker, ed.), Vol. II pp. 10–69. Birkhäuser Verlag, Basel, Switzerland, 1961.

Colby, F. H., "Essential Urology." Williams and Wilkins, Baltimore, Maryland, 1950.

Gaunt, R., *in* "Diuresis and Diuretics" (H. Schwiegk, ed.), pp. 170–190. Springer Berlin, Germany, 1959.

Goodman, L. S., and Gilman, A., "The Pharmacological Basis of Therapeutics," 2nd ed., pp. 835–839. Macmillan, New York, 1955.

Gray, H. "Anatomy of the Human Body" (C. M. Goss, ed.), 27th ed., pp. 1326–1340. Lea and Febiger, Philadelphia, Pennsylvania, 1959.

Grollman, A., "Pharmacology and Therapeutics." Lea and Febiger, Philadelphia, Pennsylvania, 1960.

Lipschitz, W. L., Hadidian, Z., and Kerpcsar, A., *J. Pharmacol. Expt. Therap.* **79**, 97 (1943).

"Of Water, Salt and Life," Lakeside Laboratories, Milwaukee, Wisconsin, 1956.

Schroeder, H. A., "Hypertensive Diseases: Causes and Control." Lea and Febiger, Philadelphia, Pennsylvania, 1953.

Smith, H., "From Fish to Philosopher." Little, Brown, Boston, Massachusetts, 1959.

White, H. G., "Clinical Disturbances of Renal Function." Saunders, Philadelphia, Pennsylvania, 1961.

CHAPTER II

Xanthines and Pyrimidines

A. Xanthines

It should be noted that with the exception of calomel used by Paracelsus in the 16th century, the xanthines also have been used extensively as diuretics for centuries. However, this class of compounds was used only in the form of extracts; that is, in coffee and tea. Although it was known from antiquity that these beverages influenced the flow of urine, it was not until 1864 that Koschlakoff (1) and later Schroeder (1887) (2) identified caffeine (I) as the active diuretic principle in coffee. Theophylline (II), found in tea was shown by Minkowski (3) to be a more potent diuretic than caffeine and also

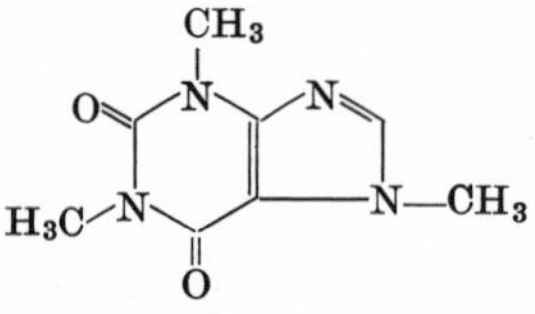

I
caffeine

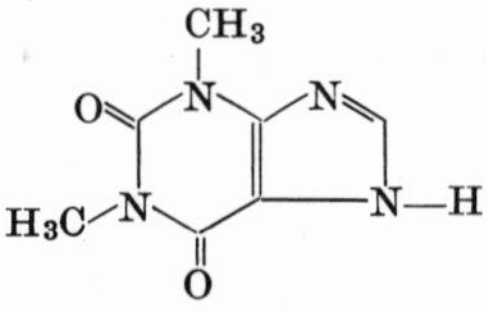

II
theophylline

caused less central-nervous-system stimulation. All these findings were in turn complemented by the fundamental studies of Emil Fischer and Wilhelm Traube and their collaborators in elaborating general synthetic procedures for the preparation of pyrimidines and purines. Thus, before considering the clinical utility of this group of substances, some brief consideration will be given to some general principles involved in their synthesis. Since in many instances it is essential that a 4,5-disubstituted pyrimidine serves as a platform on which to form the bicyclic purine, some principal syntheses of pyrimidines will be considered initially.

Pyrimidines are available by many general methods. However, in essence the problem involves the proper disposition of two nitrogen atoms in the components undergoing condensation. This then requires the following fundamental arrangements:

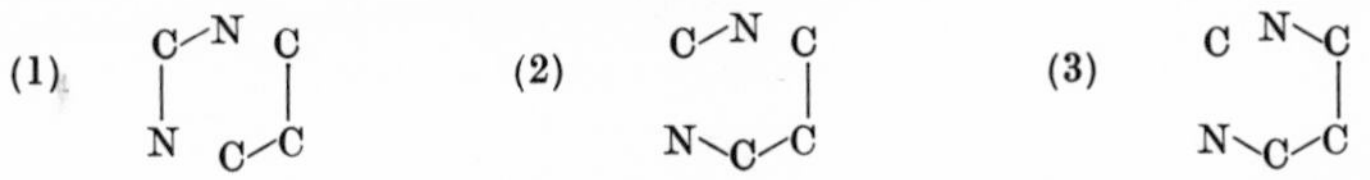

(1) C–N C / N C–C (2) C–N C / N–C–C (3) C N–C / N–C–C

The first is by far the most versatile and useful of these schemes. The three-carbon component can be provided by compounds such as ethyl malonate, ethyl acetoacetate, ethyl cyanoacetate, or acetylacetone, and the nitrogen component by urea, thiourea, guanidine, or amidines, with urea the least active; e.g.,

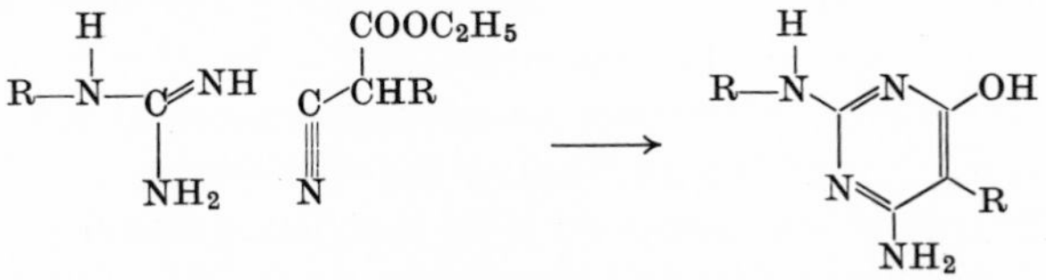

R—NH—C(=NH)—NH_2 + N≡C—CHR—$COOC_2H_5$ ⟶ R—NH—(pyrimidine)—OH, R, NH_2

The second method usually involves the self-condensation of an aliphatic nitrile, or the reaction of formamidine with malononitrile, or the combination of an isocyanate with an α,β-unsaturated amino ester; e.g.,

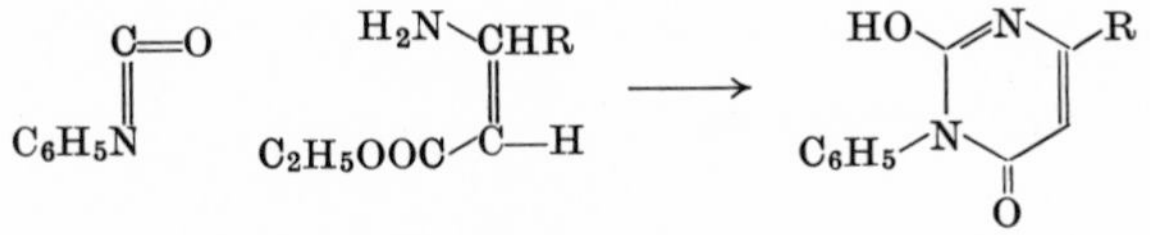

C_6H_5N=C=O + H_2N—CHR=C(H)—$COOC_2H_5$ ⟶ HO, R, C_6H_5—N, O (pyrimidine)

Ethyl formate is used generally as the condensing agent in the third synthetic method. For example, ethyl formate and malonodiamidine derivatives combine to form diaminopyrimidines, e.g.,

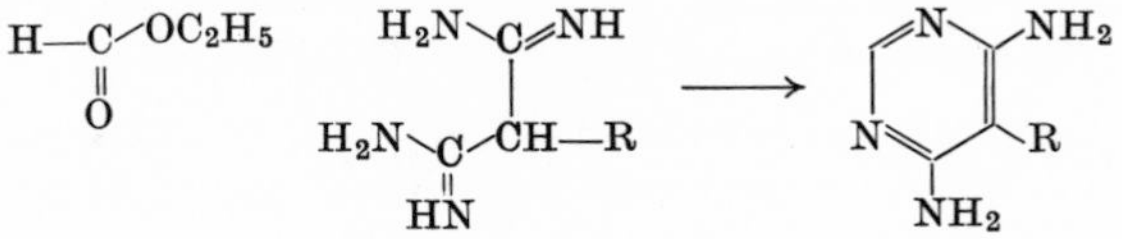

H—C(=O)—OC_2H_5 + H_2N—C(=NH)—CH(R)—C(=NH)—NH_2 ⟶ (pyrimidine) NH_2, R, NH_2

There are many variations of the above described condensations and some of these will be discussed in the course of elaborating the preparation of some compounds in this series which have shown diuretic effects.

The synthesis of theophylline and caffeine is carried out according to a modification of the original method devised by Traube (4) (Scheme I). Symmetrical dimethylurea was allowed to react with

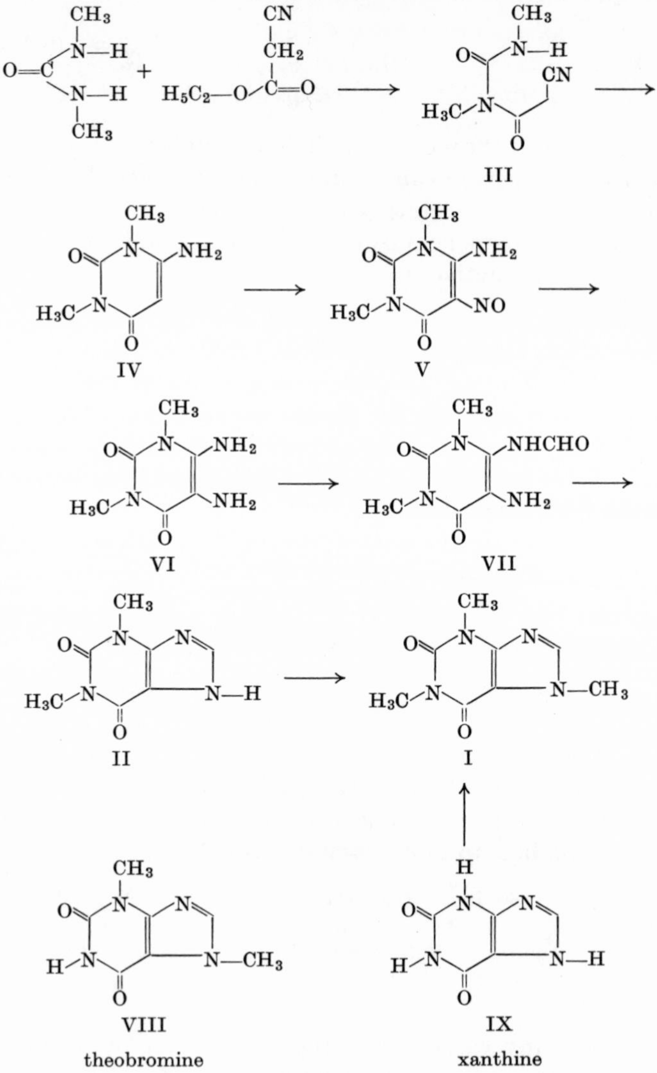

III

IV

V

VI

VII

II

I

VIII

theobromine

IX

xanthine

SCHEME 1

cyanoacetic acid ethyl ester in phosphorous oxychloride to yield cyano-acetyl-*N*-*N*′-dimethylurea (III) which is then treated with alkali to form 1,3-dimethyl-4-amino-2,6-pyrimidinedione (IV) (5). Nitrosation followed by catalytic reduction afforded the diamine (VI) which was then allowed to undergo condensation with formic acid to give VII. The formyl derivative on heating in aqueous alkali forms theophylline (6) which is converted to caffeine with dimethyl sulfate. Caffeine can also be formed directly by the methylation of xanthine (IX). The structural isomer theobromine (VIII) is extracted from the hull of the cocoa bean and is reported to be intermediate in diuretic activity between theophylline and caffeine.

However, theophylline still is considered to be the most effective of the three. It is used primarily in the form of double compounds for solubilization, the most widely used combination being ethylene-diaminetheophylline, otherwise known as aminophylline. The diuresis produced by this preparation is probably due to a renal tubular effect. It inhibits those enzymes in the renal tubule necessary for the re-absorption of sodium and chloride with a resultant increase in water excretion. It also increases the glomerular filtration rate due to the increased renal blood flow which results from an improved cardiac output. In Table I are outlined some of the theophylline compositions which have been used clinically.

TABLE I

XANTHINE COMBINATIONS

Proprietary name	Generic name and composition
Aminophylline	Theophylline ethylenediamine
Aminodrox	Aminophylline + aluminum hydroxide
Bromth	2-Amino-2-methyl-1-propanol-8-bromotheophyllinate
Cardalin	Aminophyllin + aluminum hydroxide + ethyl aminobenzoate
Choledyl	Choline theophyllinate
Diuretin	Theobromine sodium salicylate
Glucophyllin	Theophylline methylglucamine
Monotheamin	Theophylline ethanolamine
Piperophyllin	Theophylline piperazine
Theocin soluble	Theophylline sodium acetate
Theoglycinate	Theophylline sodium glycinate
Theopropanol	Theophylline 1-amino-2-propanol

Because the methylated xanthines exhibit a certain amount of central-nervous-system stimulation along with diuretic effects, a tremendous effort has been made since the turn of the century to prepare derivatives with improved diuretic properties. Some of the results of this work are outlined in Tables II–IX. Although these studies are only a small fraction of the total effort channeled in this direction, it is significant that no compound has emerged with diuretic properties superior to theophylline.

TABLE II

MONO- AND DIMETHYLXANTHINES

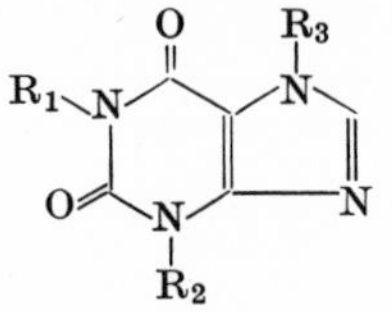

No.	R_1	R_2	R_3	Ref.	Remarks (diuretic activity)
1.	H	H	H	7	Inactive. Hematuria on intravenous injection in rabbits
2.	CH_3	H	H	8	Slight activity
3.	H	CH_3	H	7, 9	Slight activity in rabbits. Strong diuretic in rabbits
4.	H	H	CH_3	7, 9	Heteroxanthine. Slightly active. Strong diuretic in rabbits
5.	CH_3	CH_3	H	10	Theophylline. Strongly active
6.	H	CH_3	CH_3	11, 12	Theobromine. Less active than theophylline
7.	CH_3	H	CH_3	10	Paraxanthine. Diuretic in humans

TABLE III

HOMOLOGS OF CAFFEINE (13)

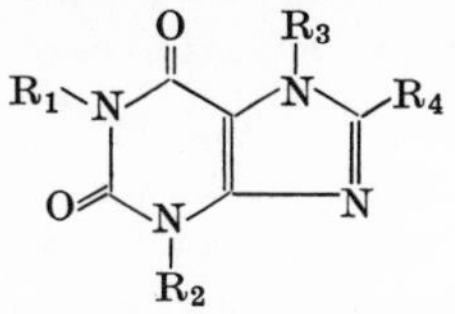

No.	R_1	R_2	R_3	R_4	Activity	Diuretic effect[a]
1.	C_2H_5	CH_3	CH_3	H	+ + +	Stronger than caffeine. Toxic
2.	n-C_3H_7	CH_3	CH_3	H	+ +	
3.	iso-C_3H_7	CH_3	CH_3	H	+ +	
4.	n-C_4H_9	CH_3	CH_3	H	+ +	
5.	iso-C_4H_9	CH_3	CH_3	H	+ +	
6.	iso-C_5H_{11}	CH_3	CH_3	H	+	
7.	C_2H_5	C_2H_5	C_2H_5	H	—	
8.	C_2H_5	C_2H_5	C_2H_5	CH_3	—	
9.	H	C_2H_5	C_2H_5	CH_3	+ +	

[a] Tested in rabbits made nephritic through uranium poisoning.

TABLE IV

1-SUBSTITUTED THEOBROMINE DERIVATIVES (14)

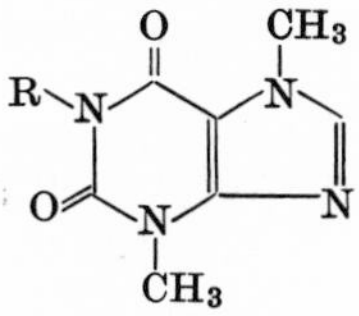

No.	R	Average urine[a] output in 90 min. (ml)	Emesis	Approx. LD_{50} (intraven. in mice, mg/kg)
1.	Control	61.5	—	—
2.	H (theobromine)	53.4	0/8	—
3.	CH_3	94.0	0/10	101
4.	C_2H_5	114.0	0/6	61
5.	C_3H_7	117.3	0/6	126
6.	C_4H_9	83.6	2/7	167
7.	iso-C_5H_{11}	74.6	1/7	200
8.	$CH_2{=}CHCH_2$	80.7	0/6	40
9.	$CH_2{=}C(CH_3)CH_2$	85.9	3/6	254
10.	$CH_3CH{=}CHCH_2$	40.6	4/5	95
11.	$CH_3OCH_2CH_2$	74.8	0/4	272

[a] In dogs, treated by intravenous injection with 10 mg/kg of the appropriate compound.

TABLE V

ALKANOIC ACID DERIVATIVES OF XANTHINE

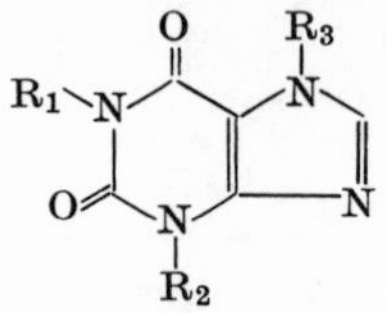

No.	R_1	R_2	R_3	Ref.	Remarks
1.	CH_3	CH_3	CH_2COOH	15, 16	Therapeutic activity
2.	CH_2COOH	CH_3	CH_3	15, 17	is claimed for compounds
3.	H	CH_3	CH_2COOH	15	1 to 3
4.	H	CH_3	CH_2CH_2COOH	15	No data on this compound

TABLE VI

ACYL DERIVATIVES OF THEOBROMINE AND THEOPHYLLINE

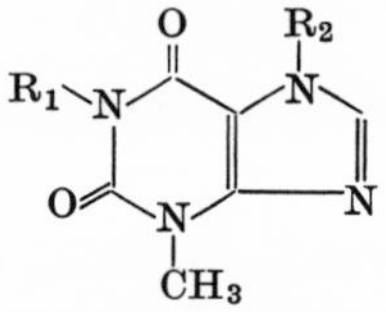

No.	R_1	R_2	Ref.	Diuretic activity
1.	CH_3CO	CH_3	18, 19	Stronger than theobromine
2.	C_6H_5CO	CH_3	18, 19	No increase over theobromine
3.	*o*-HOC_6H_4CO	CH_3	20	Compounds 3 to 6 are active and nonirritating to the stomach
4.	*o*-$CH_3COOC_6H_4CO$	CH_3	21	
5.	*o*-$CH_3OCOC_6H_4CO$	CH_3	21	
6.	*o*-$C_6H_5COOC_6H_4CO$	CH_3	21	
7.	$C_6H_5CH{=}CHCO$	CH_3	18	Albuminuria
8.	CH_3OCO	CH_3	18	Albuminuria
9.	C_2H_5OCO	CH_3	18	Compounds 9 to 12 were active, but no better than theobromine
10.	C_3H_7OCO	CH_3	18	
11.	iso-C_4H_9OCO	CH_3	18	
12.	iso-$C_5H_{11}OCO$	CH_3	18	
13.	CH_3	CH_3OCO	18	Compounds 13 to 15 were active, but no better than theophylline
14.	CH_3	C_2H_5OCO	18	
15.	CH_3	C_6H_5OCO	18	

TABLE VII

7-Phenacyl Derivatives of Theophylline (22)

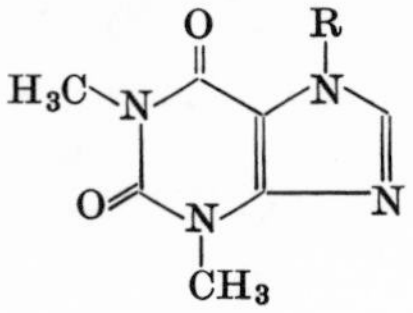

No.	R	Remarks
1.	$CH_2COC_6H_5$	Compounds 1 to 6 are inactive as diuretics
2.	$CH_2COC_6H_3(OH)_2$	
3.	$CH_2COC_6H_3(OCH_3)_2$	toxic
4.	$CH_2CH(OH)C_6H_5$	
5.	$CH_2CH(OH)C_6H_3(OH)_2$	
6.	$CH_2CH(OH)C_6H_3(OCH_3)_2$	

TABLE VIII

8-Aminoxanthines and Related Compounds

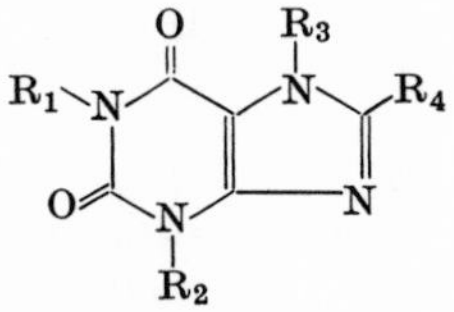

No.	R_1	R_2	R_3	R_4	Ref.	Remarks
1.	CH_3	CH_3	H	NH_2	23	
2.	CH_3	CH_3	H	$N(CH_3)_2$	23	
3.	CH_3	CH_3	H	NHC_6H_5	23	Compounds 1 to 11 (inclusive) are said to be very effective diuretics
4.	H	CH_3	CH_3	NH_2	24	
5.	H	CH_3	CH_3	$N(CH_3)_2$	24	
6.	H	CH_3	CH_3	NHC_6H_5	24	
7.	CH_3	H	CH_3	NH_2	25	
8.	CH_3	H	CH_3	$NHCH_3$	25	
9.	CH_3	H	CH_3	$N(CH_3)_2$	25, 26	Compound 9: paraxin. As active as theobromine but causes gastric disturbance (25)
10.	CH_3	H	CH_3	NHC_6H_5	25	
11.	CH_3	CH_3	CH_3	$NHCH_2CH_2NH_2$	27	

TABLE IX

THEOPHYLLINE HOMOLOGS AND RELATED COMPOUNDS (28)

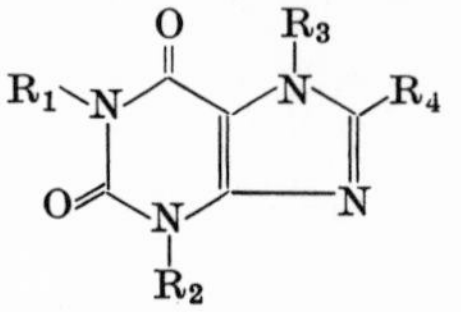

No.	R_1	R_2	R_3	R_4	%Na^+ excretion over control
1.	C_2H_5	C_2H_5	H	H	400
2.	CH_3	CH_3[a]	H	H	200–300 (for compounds 2 to 5)
3.	C_2H_5	C_2H_5	H	Br	
4.	C_2H_5	CH_3	H	H	
5.	C_4H_9	C_4H_9	H	H	
6.	H	C_4H_9	H	H	150–200 (for compounds 6 to 9)
7.	C_2H_5	CH_3	H	Cl	
8.	CH_3	C_2H_5	H	H	
9.	C_2H_5	C_2H_5	H	H (2-thio)	
10.	H	CH_3	H	H	Weak or inactive (for compounds 10 to 18)
11.	CH_3	C_4H_9	H	H	
12.	C_2H_5	C_4H_9	H	H	
13.	C_3H_7	C_3H_7	H	H	
14.	CH_3	CH_3	H	Cl	
15.	C_2H_5	C_2H_5	H	Cl	
16.	CH_3	CH_3	CH_3CO	H	
17.	CH_3	CH_3	H	CH_3CONH	
18.	CH_3	CH_3	CH_3	iso-$C_5H_{11}O$	

[a] As Ca salt.

Recently, a caffeine derivative, Xanturil, has been introduced in France and is reported to be an effective diuretic agent. Xanturil is purported to be more effective than the sulfonamides (see Chapter V) and shows less potassium depletion. It is prepared by carrying out a Mannich reaction on theophylline (29):

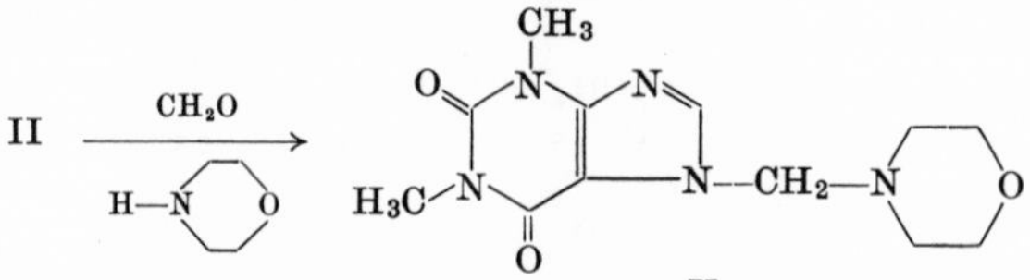

II $\xrightarrow[\text{H–N(morpholine)}]{CH_2O}$ X

X

Xanturil

Another group of compounds which has shown diuretic effects in experimental animals are methylated xanthine isosters prepared by Schmidt (30) and co-workers. These substances are termed generally as pyrazolo[3,4-*d*]pyrimidines, and the synthetic pathways leading to isosters of caffeine, theophylline, and theobromine are outlined in Schemes 2A–D. In the caffeine series, two isosters are possible as outlined in Schemes 2A, 2B.

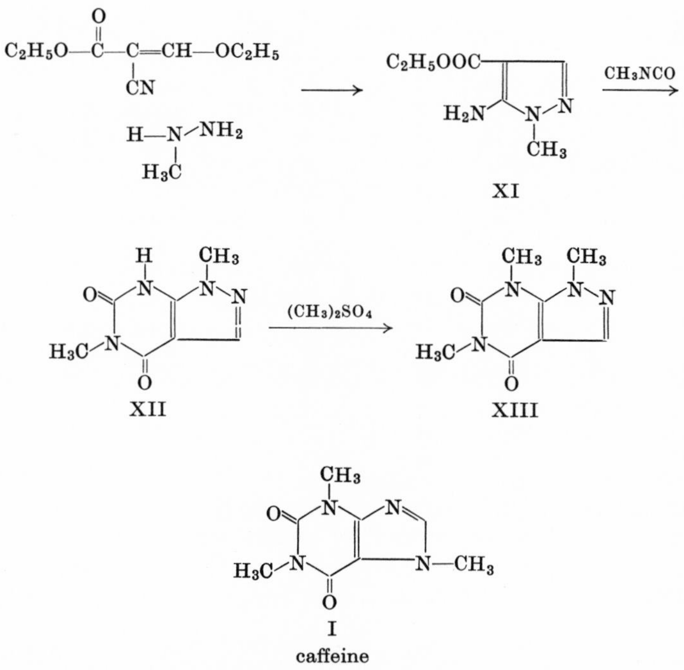

caffeine

Scheme 2A. Caffeine isoster

The starting material in each case is the ethyl ester of ethoxymethylene cyanoacetic acid. In Scheme 2A this compound is allowed to react with methylhydrazine to yield the 2-methyl-3-amino-4-carbethoxypyrazole (XI) which on condensation with methyl isocyanate affords XII. Methylation of this substance gives rise to XIII, whose relationship to caffeine is immediately obvious.

In Scheme 2B the ethyl ester of ethoxymethylene cyanoacetic acid was condensed with benzalmethylhydrazine to form under acid conditions 1-methyl-3-amino-4-carbethoxypyrazole (XIV). The conversion of XIV to XVI follows pathways previously described.

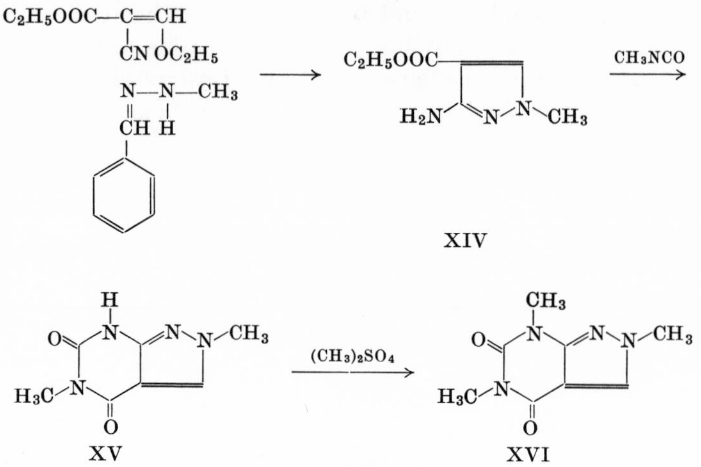

XIV

XV

$(CH_3)_2SO_4$

XVI

SCHEME 2B. Caffeine isoster

The methylated pyrazolo[3,4-*d*]pyrimidine related to theophylline is shown in Scheme 2C.

In this reaction sequence ethoxymethylene malononitrile undergoes condensation with benzylhydrazine to yield 2-benzyl-3-amino-4-cyanopyrazole (XVII) which is in turn converted to the amide XVIII. Compound XVIII undergoes ring closure with urea to give XIX. Methylation of XIX followed by hydrogenolysis yielded the desired 5,7-dimethyl-4,6-dioxo-4,5,6,7-tetrahydropyrazolo[3,4-*d*]pyrimidine (XX).

Finally, the conversion of 4-mercapto-6-oxo-6,7-dihydropyrazolo-[3,4-*d*]pyrimidine (XXI) to the theobromine isoster XXIII is briefly noted in Scheme 2D.

These compounds were evaluated in the CIBA Basel Research Laboratories (31) for their diuretic effects. Compound XIII had properties indistinguishable from caffeine. It caused some diuresis but it was also observed to be a strong central-nervous-system stimulant. Isoster XVI caused a diuretic effect comparable to caffeine but it was also a stimulant. Compound XX was not quite as effective as theophylline in its diuretic action and the theobromine isoster XXIII was almost inactive.

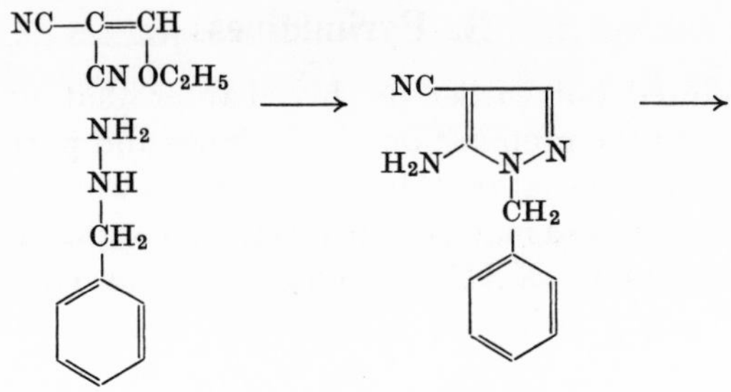

NC—C=CH | CN OC$_2$H$_5$ + NH$_2$—NH—CH$_2$—C$_6$H$_5$ → XVII →

XVII

H$_2$NCONH$_2$

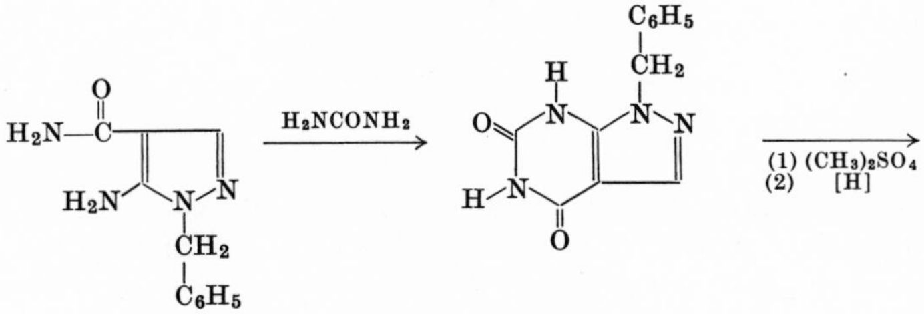

XVIII

XIX

(1) $(CH_3)_2SO_4$
(2) [H]

XX

II
theophylline

SCHEME 2C. Theophylline isoster

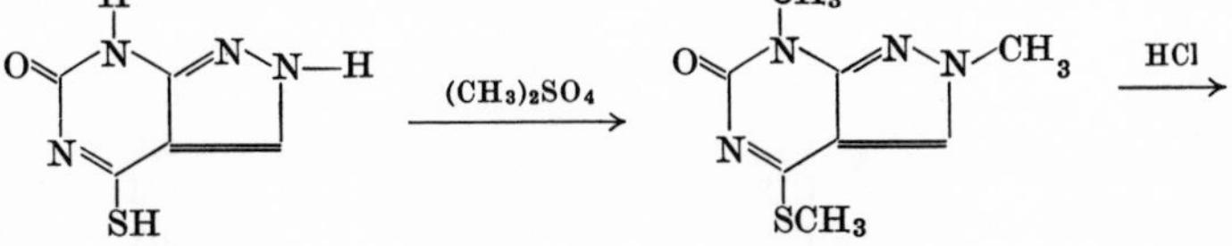

$(CH_3)_2SO_4$

HCl

XXI

XXII

XXIII

theobromine

SCHEME 2D. Theobromine isoster

B. Pyrimidines

It was pointed out earlier in this chapter that pyrimidines are intermediates in the preparation of xanthines and purines in general. Thus, it was not unusual that diuretic research would be extended to these heterocycles. As a matter of interest, Levene (32) in 1907 reported that 5-methyluracil (XXIV) produced a marked diuresis when administered orally to dogs. It is quite surprising that this observation

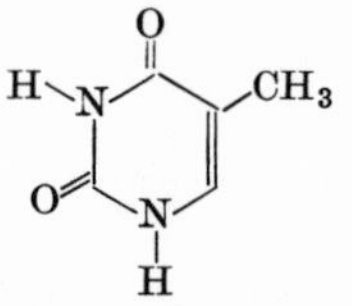

XXIV

should have gone relatively unnoticed and unexploited for almost 40 years since it was not until 1944 that Lipschitz and Hadidian (33) checked this and other uracil derivatives for their diuretic effects.

TABLE X

1, 3-DISUBSTITUTED 6-AMINOURACILS (34)

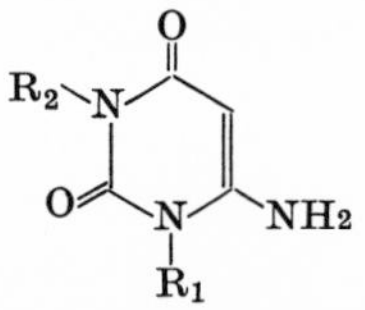

No.	R_1	R_2	T/C,[a] urine volume	T/C Na	Emesis	LD_{50} mg/kg mouse[b]
1.	CH_3	C_3H_7	1.46	3.54	0/3	2000
2.	C_2H_5	C_3H_7	2.35	4.80	1/6	1440
3.	C_2H_5	$CH_2{=}CHCH_2$	1.72	2.62	0/3	1740
4.	C_3H_7	CH_3	2.13	3.30	0/3	1640
5.	C_3H_7	C_2H_5	1.78	2.95	0/3	1310
6.	$CH_2{=}CHCH_2$	CH_3	1.54	1.63		1240
7.	$CH_2{=}CHCH_2$	C_2H_5	2.38	2.83	0/3	1290
8.	Theophylline (as aminophylline)		2.53	2.51	0/3	600

[a] Duration of test was 5 hours. T/C is the ratio of treated-to-control animals in volume of urine and sodium ion excreted.

[b] Stomach tube.

These investigators also reported that uracil, 5-aminouracil (XXV), and isocytosine (XXVI) are weakly diuretic in rats.

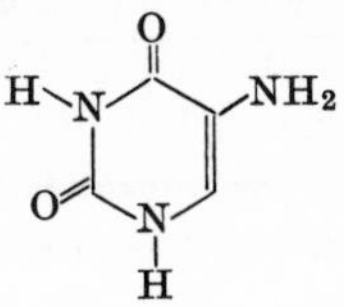

XXV

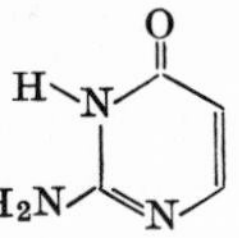

XXVI

In 1951 Papesch and Schroeder (34, 35) reported that a series of 1,3-disubstituted 6-aminouracils produced strong diuresis in rats and dogs, comparable in some cases with that of theophylline. Some typical results obtained in dogs with several of the more active compounds, at an oral dose level of 100 mg/kg, are shown in Table X. The toxicity of these compounds appears to be considerably less than that of the xanthines. Additional 6-aminouracils have also been extensively studied by Kattus *et al.* (28) (Table XI). In dogs they were found, in

TABLE XI

6-Aminouracils (28)

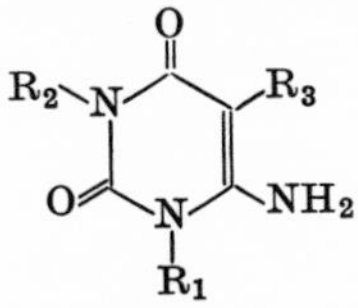

No.	R_1	R_2	R_3	%Na^+ excretion over control
1.	C_2H_5	CH_3	H	150–200 (for compounds 1 to 4)
2.	C_2H_5	C_2H_5	H	
3.	C_3H_7	C_2H_5	H	
4.	iso-C_3H_7	CH_3	H (2-thio)	
5.	CH_3	CH_3	H	Low activity or inactive (for compounds 5 to 15)
6.	$HOCH_2CH_2$	H	H	
7.	$HOCH_2CH_2$	CH_3	H	
8.	$HOCH_2CH_2$	C_2H_5	H	
9.	C_3H_7	C_3H_7	H	
10.	iso-C_3H_7	C_2H_5	H	
11.	C_4H_9	CH_3	H	
12.	C_4H_9	C_4H_9	H	
13.	$C_6H_5CH_2$	$C_6H_5CH_2$	H	
14.	CH_3	CH_3	NH_2	
15.	$HOCH_2CH_2$	H	NH_2	

general, to be less potent than the xanthines, but there was also a much lower incidence of gastrointestinal disturbance. It was observed that, generally, 1,3-disubstitution was necessary for activity. 6-Aminouracil itself ($R_1 = R_3 = H$) was inactive; the 1-monosubstituted derivatives ($R_2 = H$) were likewise either not active or of very low potency. The same was true also for several 5,6-diamino derivatives. The 2-thio analogs of the 1,3-disubstituted 6-aminouracils frequently exhibited good activity. Clinical studies carried out with one of the active uracils, 1-*n*-propyl-3-ethyl-6-aminouracil (Table X, compound 5) indicated that a good diuresis could also be obtained in man when the substance was administered orally. However, a rather high incidence of undesirable side effects (nausea, vomiting) led to its withdrawal from further clinical studies. Nevertheless, further research in this series by Papesch and Schroeder led to the clinical utility of aminometradine (XXVII) and amisometradine (XXVIII).

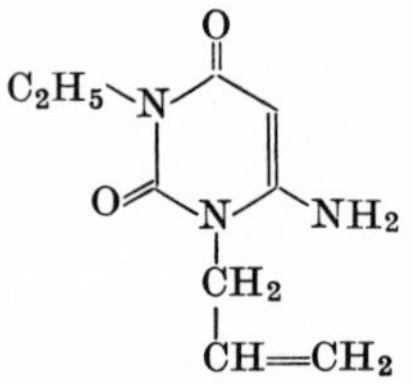

XXVII
aminometradine

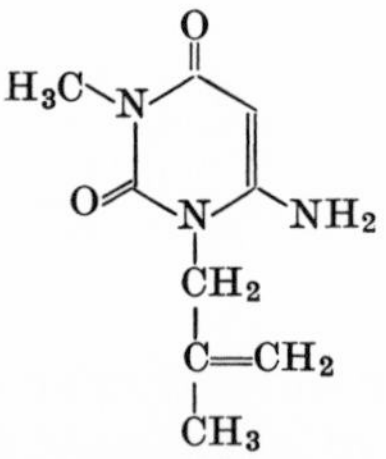

XXVIII
amisometradine

The diuretic action of these two aminouracils is attributed to inhibition of tubular reabsorption of sodium and chloride ions which are excreted in increased amounts although the glomerular filtration rate does not change. Potassium excretion rises slightly but there appears to be no change in bicarbonate, phosphate, and ammonia excretion. However, daily administration of aminometradine and amisometradine for 5 consecutive days leads to a loss of effectiveness. Since Spencer and Lloyd-Thomas (36) have found that in sodium depleted patients aminometradine is ineffective, it has been suggested that a decrease in plasma sodium may be the cause of the loss of diuretic response. This proposal, although reasonable, has not been experimentally verified. Amisometradine is about one-half as potent as aminometradine (500–1000 mg/day) but gastrointestinal disturbances occur less frequently. Single oral doses of amisometradine up to 2400 mg have been well tolerated.

Van Arman (37) has reported on a group of isocytosine derivatives that are fully substituted on all the carbons of the pyrimidine ring system. These compounds were found to be orally effective diuretics in experimental animals. The most potent of these, 2-amino-4-hydroxy-5-methyl-6-phenylpyrimidine (XXIX) is reported to be active in man.

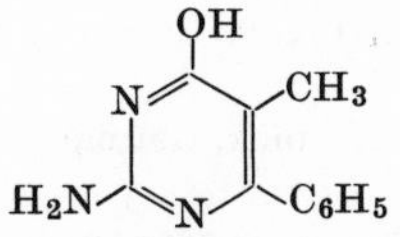

OH, CH_3, H_2N, N, N, C_6H_5

XXIX

In 1952 Whitehead (38) synthesized a series of uracil-5-carboxylic acids and amides, some of which are reported to be active in dogs at oral doses of 0.5–1.0 gm and with intravenous injections of 5–10 mg/kg.

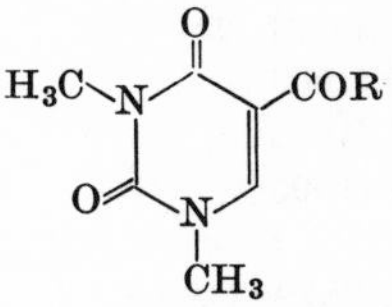

O, H_3C, N, COR, O, N, CH_3

R = OH
R = NHC_2H_5
R = $NHCH_2CH_2OH$
R = $NHCH_2CH(CH_3)_2$
R = $N(CH_2CH_2OH)_2$

Further work by Whitehead (39, 40) and co-workers has led to the synthesis of a variety of 6-alkylamino-4-aminopyrimidines, 4-amino-6-arylaminopyrimidines, and their amide and sulfamide derivatives.

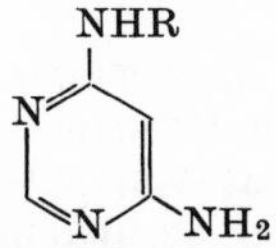

NHR, N, N, NH_2

R = alkyl, aryl
R = CH_3CO
R = $C_6H_5SO_2$ and others

The 6-*n*-amylamino derivative (R = C_5H_{11}) was the most active of the simple aliphatic members. It was reported to be more active than aminometradine when administered orally to the dog. The greatest activity was seen with 6-toluidino-, 6-anilino-, 6-phenoxyethylamino-, and 6-benzylaminopyrimidines. These were active in the dogs at 5–10 mg/kg.

References

1. Koschlakoff, *Virchow's Arch.* **31**, 438 (1864); through A. Vogl, "Diuretic Therapy." Williams and Wilkins, Baltimore, Maryland, 1953.
2. von Schroeder, *Arch. Exptl. Pathol. Pharmakol.* **22**, 39 (1887).

3. K. Minkowski, *Therap. Gegenwart*, p. 490 (1902).
4. W. Traube, *Ber. Deut. Chem. Ges.* **33**, 3052 (1900).
5. A. H. Homeyer, U.S. Pat. 2,444,023 (1948); *Chem. Abstr.* **42**, 7328a (1948).
6. J. C. Ballantyne, U.S. Pat. 2,564,351 (1951); *Chem. Abstr.* **46**, 2574c (1952).
7. N. Ach, *Arch. Exptl. Pathol. Pharmakol.* **44**, 319 (1900).
8. M. Englemann, *Ber. Deut. Chem. Ges.* **42**, 177 (1909).
9. M. Albanese, *Arch. Exptl. Pathol. Pharmakol.* **43**, 305 (1900).
10. H. Dreser, *Arch. Ges. Physiol.* **102**, 1 (1904).
11. von Schroeder, *Arch. Exptl. Pathol. Pharmakol.* **24**, 85 (1888).
12. Rost, *Arch. Exptl. Pathol. Pharmakol.* **36**, 70 (1895).
13. P. Bergell and P. F. Richter, *Z. Exptl. Pathol. Therap.* **1**, 655 (1905).
14. C. C. Scott, R. C. Anderson, and K. K. Chen, *J. Pharmacol. Exptl. Therap.* **86**, 113 (1946).
15. E. Merck, O. Wolfes, and E. Kornick, German Pat. 352,980 (1920); *Chem. Abstr.* **17**, 1307 (1923).
16. J. Baisse, *Bull. Soc. Chim. France*, p. 769 (1949).
17. Poulenc and Behal, French Pat. 556,365, (1924).
18. H. Vieth, and E. Leube, *Biochem. Z.* **163**, 13 (1925).
19. Knoll and Co., German Pat. 252,641 (1911); *Chem. Abstr.* **7**, 402 (1913).
20. E. Merck, German Pat. 291,077 (1915); *Chem. Abstr.* **11**, 870 (1917).
21. E. Merck, German Pat. 290,205 (1913); *Chem. Abstr.* **10**, 2784 (1916).
22. C. Mannich and S. Kroll, *Ber. Deut. Pharm. Ges.* **31**, 291 (1921).
23. C. H. Boehringer Sohn, German Pat. 156,900 (1903).
24. C. H. Boehringer Sohn, German Pat. 164,425 (1904).
25. C. H. Boehringer Sohn, German Pat. 156,901 (1903).
26. J. Forschbach and S. Weber, *Arch. Exptl. Pathol. Pharmakol.* **56**, 186 (1907).
27. Meister, Lucius and Bruening, German Pat. 142,896 (1902).
28. A. Kattus, E. V. Newman, and J. Franklin, *Bull. Johns Hopkins Hosp.* **89**, 1 (1951).
29. *Prod. Pharm.* **17**, No. 1, 52 (1962).
30. P. Schmidt, K. Eichenberger, and M. Wilhelm, *Angew. Chem.* **73**, No. 1, 15 (1961).
31. Personal communication from Dr. P. Schmidt, CIBA, Basel, Switzerland.
32. P. A. Levene, *Biochem. Z.* **4**, 316 (1907).
33. W. L. Lipschitz and Z. Hadidian, *J. Pharmacol. Exptl. Therap.* **81**, 84 (1944).
34. V. Papesch and E. F. Schroeder, *J. Org. Chem.* **16**, 1879 (1951).
35. V. Papesch and E. F. Schroeder, U.S. Pat. 2,567,651 (1951); *Chem. Abstr.* **46**, 2585c (1952); U.S. Pat. 2,615020 (1952); *Chem. Abstr.* **47**, 10013a (1953); U.S. Pat. 2,602,795 (1952); *Chem. Abstr.* **47**, 4920f (1953).
36. A. G. Spencer and H. G. Lloyd-Thomas, *Brit. Med. J.* **I**, 957 (1953).
37. C. G. Van Arman, B. A. Jenkins, S. A. Wahls, J. P. Zehren, and R. G. Bianchi, *J. Pharmacol. Exptl. Therap.* **113**, 285 (1954).
38. C. W. Whitehead, *J. Am. Chem. Soc.* **74**, 4367 (1952).
39. C. W. Whitehead and J. J. Traverso, *J. Am. Chem. Soc.* **80**, 2185 (1958).
40. J. J. Traverso, E. B. Robbins, and C. W. Whitehead, *J. Med. Pharm. Chem.* **5**, 808 (1962).

CHAPTER III

Triazines

Early in 1943 Lipschitz and co-workers (1) at the Lederle Research Laboratories described a method using rats for the bioassay of diuretics (see Chapter I). With this method it was possible not only to estimate the diuretic activity of drugs from their dose–response curves but also to obtain information on side effects produced by them. Using urea as a standard, Lipschitz was able to confirm the reproducibility of his method by evaluating several nitrogen-containing compounds known to have diuretic effects (e.g., biuret, xanthine derivatives).

Lipschitz and Hadidian (2) then noted that urea, biuret, and the xanthines have in common the following arrangement (form a) of atoms:

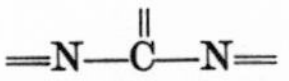

$$=N-\overset{\|}{C}-N=$$

form a

This observation prompted these investigators to test approximately seventy compounds containing this grouping for their diuretic effects. In principle, they found that acid amides are diuretically active but that simple amides are weaker diuretics than urea (control activity = 1) and with increasing molecular weight the potencies of the homologs

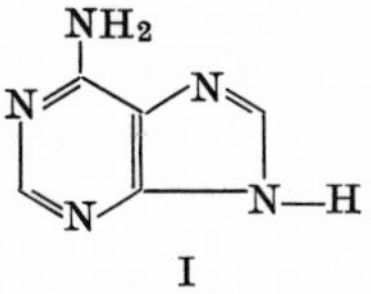

I adenine

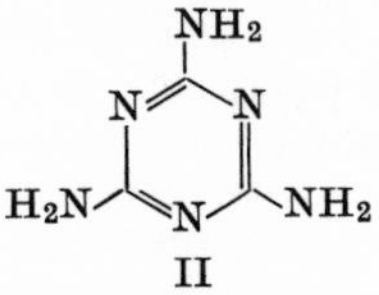

II melamine

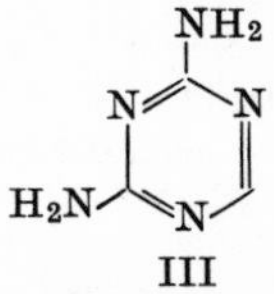

III formoguanamine

of acetamide decrease. Introduction of a hydroxyl group in the α-position of an amide led to an increase of activity. It was also noted that amidines were more potent than amides. Finally, some heterocyclic compounds containing the "form a" group were evaluated.

Three compounds in this group were shown to have equal or greater diuretic activity than the xanthines: adenine (I) (a purine in the same

TABLE I

TRIAZINES (2)

Substance	Useful diuretic dose range (total dose range tested) (mM/kg)	No. of expts. util. for comput.	Activity of substance[a]	Observations about mode of action (at mM/kg)
Cyanuric acid	2.91–9.68	4	1.7	—
Trimethyl-n-cyanurate	(0.18–2.92)		0	Depressant
Trimethyl-iso-cyanurate	0.73–2.19 (0.73–7.31)	3	11.0	3.66 mM: depressant
Ammelide	(1.95–19.52)	3	0	—
Ammeline	(3.93–19.66)	2	0	—
Melamine	0.1–1.0 (0.1–20.0)	9	76.5	> 1.0 mM: 140—160% of fluid fed excreted; crystalluria
Formoguanamine	0.023–0.09 (0.023–2.23)	6	347.1	—
Acetoguanamine	1.0–5.0 (0.2–10.0)	5	4.5	5.0 mM: diarrhea
Carboxyaceto-guanamine	1.85–11.83	2	0	—
Levulinoguanamine	(3.45)	1	0	—
α-Furoguanamine	(0.107–5.65)	5	0	Depressant, diarrhea
α-Furoacrylo-guanamine	0.62–1.23 (0.62–6.16)	4	11.1	> 1.23 mM: lethal within several days
4-Aminobenzo-guanamine	2.46–4.92	1	3.5	—
2-Phenylcinchono-guanamine	(1.99–3.98)	1	0	—
Acetoguanide	(4.96–19.84)	3	0	—
Aminoacetoguanamine	4.46–10.71	2	1.7	—
Varia:				
Allantoin	(7.91–36.64)	2	0	—
Urazol	(7.43–24.75)	2	0	—
Barbituric acid	(9.76–19.51)	2	0	Diarrhea

[a] 0 means doubtful or insignificant diuretic activity. These activities are compared to urea which at equivalent doses has a value of unity.

heterocyclic class as the xanthines), melamine (II), and formoguanamine (III). Melamine and formoguanamine represent the first triazines showing diuretic effects in animals. The other triazines tested by these authors are listed in Table I.

The following flow sheet summarizes the structure–activity relationship studies of Lipschitz and Hadidian.

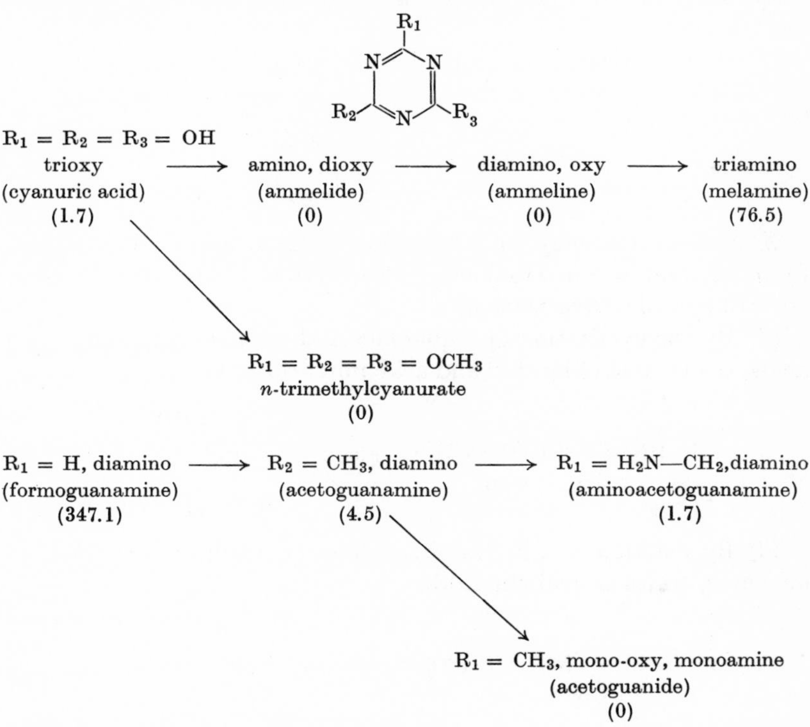

SCHEME 1. Structure-activity relationships. Figures in parentheses represent diuretic activity compared to urea = 1.

Lipschitz and Hadidian reported that melamine had a urea-type of diuretic action in that "it has a linear dose–response curve which begins to flatten only at levels of excretion considerably greater than 100% of the administered water. On the other hand, formoguanamine, with activity greater than melamine, was not able to drain tissue water from the rat, thus being similar to theobromine in its diuretic action." Formoguanamine was studied in man by Ludwig (3) who found it to be an orally effective diuretic at a dosage of 1 gm. However, further clinical studies uncovered several undesirable side effects, including anuria (4), crystalluria (5), and poor sodium excretion (6). Nevertheless, this discovery of Lipschitz and Hadidian stimulated further research in 1:3:5 triazines, the results of which will be considered after a brief outline of the principal modes of synthesis of this class of heterocycles.

Symmetrical triazines are prepared by three general preparative methods (7):

(*1*) By trimerization of cyano derivatives of the type X—CN.

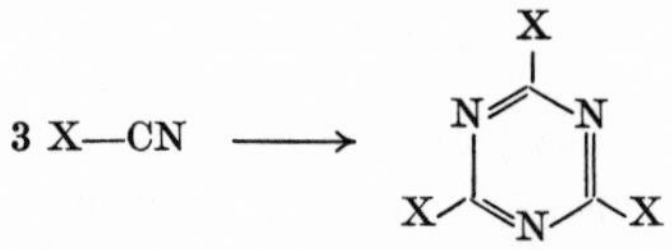

$$3\ X\text{—}CN \longrightarrow \text{(1,3,5-triazine ring with X at positions 2, 4, 6)}$$

X in this case may be hydrogen, halogen, alkyl, aryl, amino, hydroxy, and so on. Obviously, this method lends itself to great versatility and derivatization.

(*2*) By the cyclization of biguanides and related compounds with acids, esters, acid chlorides, and acid anhydrides (8).

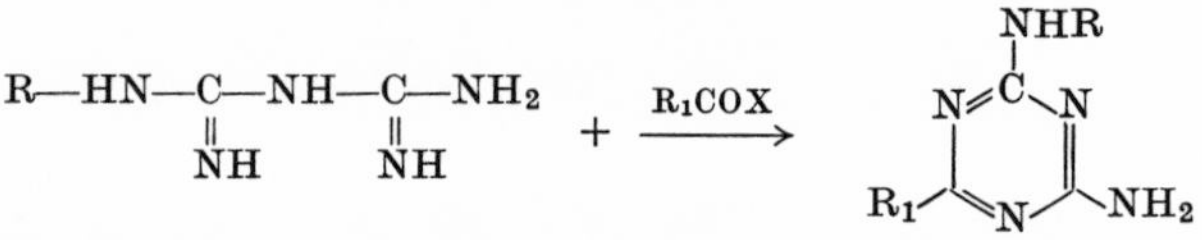

$$R\text{—}HN\text{—}\underset{\underset{NH}{\|}}{C}\text{—}NH\text{—}\underset{\underset{NH}{\|}}{C}\text{—}NH_2 + \xrightarrow{R_1COX} \text{(triazine ring with NHR, } R_1\text{, } NH_2\text{)}$$

(*3*) By reaction of 2 moles of amidines or nitriles with 1 mole of acid anhydrides or acid chlorides.

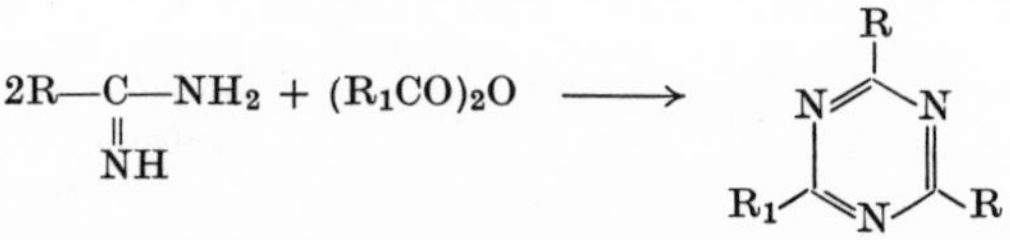

$$2R\text{—}\underset{\underset{NH}{\|}}{C}\text{—}NH_2 + (R_1CO)_2O \longrightarrow \text{(triazine ring with R, } R_1\text{, R)}$$

One of the first modifications made of formoguanamine in an attempt to eliminate or diminish its side effects was the preparation

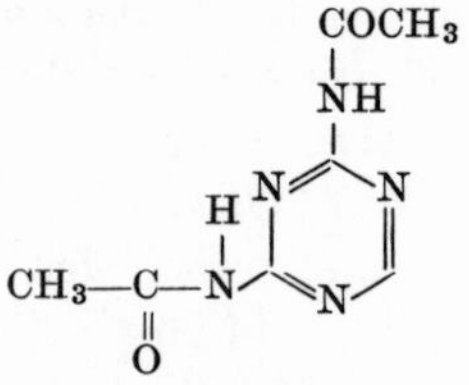

$$\text{(triazine ring with } NH\text{—}COCH_3 \text{ and } CH_3\text{—}\underset{\underset{O}{\|}}{C}\text{—}\overset{H}{N}\text{—)}$$

IV

diacetylformoguanamine

of its diacetyl derivative (IV). This substance was reported by Newman *et al.* (9) to be a potent oral diuretic in dogs. However, it had very little effect on sodium excretion and it also produced crystalluria. Newman and his group (10) later also tested 2,4,6-trimethoxy-*s*-triazine and 2,4-bis(propionylamino)-*s*-triazine, but these were only weakly active.

Then in 1951 Clauder and Bulcsu (11) announced the preparation of twenty derivatives of formoguanamine to be evaluated for their diuretic effects. Their method of synthesis follows procedure (*2*) as previously outlined, and the diuretic effects of some compounds prepared are outlined in Table II.

TABLE II

TRIAZINE DERIVATIVES (11)

No.	R_1	R_2	R_3	R_4	R_5	Diuretic activity[a]
1.	CH_3	CH_3	H	H	H	25
2.	C_2H_5	C_2H_5	H	H	H	288
3.	CH_3	CH_3	CH_3	H	H	50
4.	C_6H_5	H	H	H	H	2600
5.	*o*-$CH_3C_6H_4$	H	H	H	H	800
6.	*p*-$CH_3C_6H_4$	H	H	H	H	1500
7.	2,4,5-trimethylphenyl ($(CH_3)_3C_6H_2$—, drawn as ring with CH_3, H_3C, H_3C)	H	H	H	H	1250

[a] Diuretic activity was measured in rats by the Lipschitz method (1). Their activities are compared at equivalent doses to urea equal to unity.

Several of these compounds showed excellent diuretic effects. As reported later by Clauder and co-workers (12), 2-amino-4-anilino-*s*-triazine (V) (amanozine) and 2-amino-4-(*p*-chloroanilino)-*s*-triazine (VI) (chlorazanil) were found to be the most potent compounds in the series. Of further interest is the fact that substitution at position 6 with an alkyl group completely destroys diuretic activity. Also, it is worthy of note that the substitution of a substituted phenyl group other than a *p*-bromo derivative at position 4 leads to a marked diminution in activity. Moreover, a disubstituted amino group at

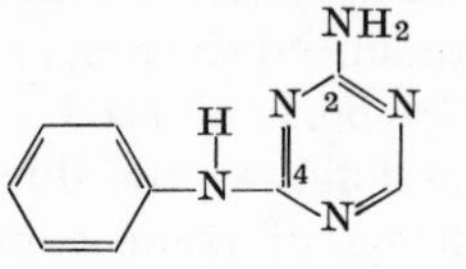

V
amanozine

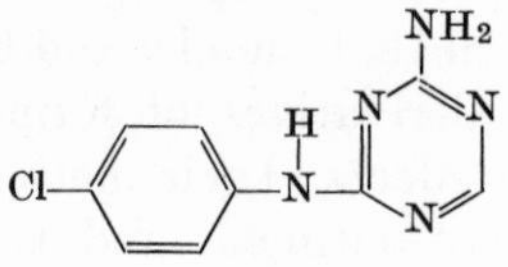

VI
chlorazanil

position 4 results in a compound with greatly reduced activity. Ten years later, Shah, Mhasalkar, and Deliwala (13) prepared 2-amino-4-(*m*-chloroanilino)-*s*-triazine and stated that it produced marked natriuresis and chloruresis in rats and in dogs at an oral dosage of 10 mg/kg. No clinical data have been forthcoming on this compound.

Kagawa and Van Arman (14) reported 2-amino-4-(*p*-fluoranilino)-*s*-triazine to be about twice as active as chlorazanil.

Other 2-amino-4-arylamino-substituted *s*-triazines have been reported by Szabo and co-workers (15) who have shown that the diuretic activity is diminished with the replacement of halogen with carbethoxy, sulfamyl, or acetyl groups in the *para* position of the 4-aryl moiety.

Shapiro *et al.* (16) prepared a large number (eighty-six) of 2-alkyl- and 2-aralkyl-substituted guanamines and although many of the substances had diuretic properties, the 2-amino-4-isoamylamino-*s*-triazine (UX-6) (VII) was diuretically active in dogs, causing water and sodium diuresis at a dose of 2.5 mg/kg intravenously. In humans, UX-6 is somewhat less potent than chlorazanil (17). Some patients

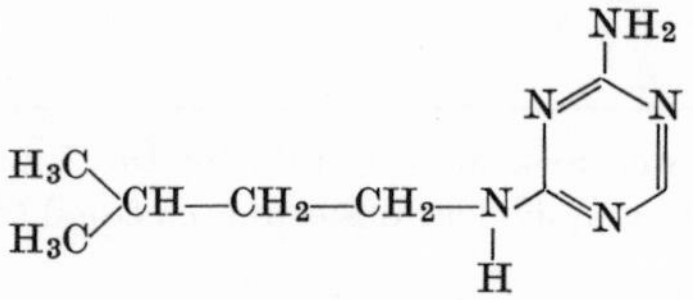

VII
UX-6

could only be maintained in a state of compensation at dosages as high as 800 mg/day whereupon serious side effects such as anorexia, nausea, fatigue, and drowsiness were observed.

Clinically, chlorazanil is still the most effective and least toxic of the triazine diuretic agents. It has very little effect on potassium excretion; however, this is most likely owing, not to a specific mode of action, but to the fact that it does not have a marked sodium-excreting activity when compared to the thiazide diuretics (see Chapter VI). Nevertheless, its water-excreting effect is quite pronounced. The daily clinical dosage of chlorazanil is from 300 to 600 mg.

REFERENCES

1. W. L. Lipschitz, Z. Hadidian, and A. Kerpcsar, *J. Pharmacol. Exptl. Therap.* **79**, 97 (1943).
2. W. L. Lipschitz and Z. Hadidian, *J. Pharmacol. Exptl. Therap.* **81**, 84 (1944).
3. H. Ludwig, *Schweiz. Med. Wochschr.* **76**, 822 (1946).
4. R. S. Mach and J. P. Dubois, *Praxis* (*Bern*) **37**, 317 (1948).
5. V. Papesch and E. F. Schroeder, *in* "Medicinal Chemistry" (F. F. Blicke and R. H. Cox, eds.), Vol. III, p. 175. Wiley, New York, 1956.
6. A. Turchetti, *Riforma Med.* **64**, 405 (1950).
7. E. Hoggarth, *in* "Chemistry of Carbon Compounds" (E. H. Rodd, ed.), Vol. IVc p. 1568. Elsevier, Amsterdam, 1960.
8. C. G. Overberger and S. J. Shapiro, *J. Am. Chem. Soc.* **76**, 93 (1954).
9. E. V. Newman, J. Franklin, and J. Genest, *Bull. Johns Hopkins Hosp.* **82**, 409 (1948).
10. A. H. Kattus, E. V. Newman, and J. Franklin, *Bull. Johns Hopkins Hosp.* **89**, 1 (1951).
11. O. Clauder and G. Bulcsu, *Magy. Kem. Folyoirat* **57**, 68 (1951); *Chem. Abstr.* **46**, 4023 (1952).
12. O. Clauder, B. Zemplen, and G. Bulcsu, Austrian Pat. 168,063 (April 10, 1951); *Chem. Abstr.* **47**, 8097 (1953).
13. M. H. Shah, M. Y. Mhasalkar, and C. V. Deliwala, *J. Sci. Ind. Res.* (*India*) **19C**, 282 (1960); D. J. Mehta, U. K. Sheth, and C. V. Deliwala, *Nature* **187**, 1034 (1960).
14. C. M. Kagawa and C. G. Van Arman, *J. Pharmacol. Exptl. Therap.* **124**, 318 (1958).
15. L. Szabo, L. Szporny, and O. Clauder, *Arch. Pharm. Hung.* **31**, 163 (1961).
16. S. Shapiro, V. A. Parrino, K. Geiger, S. Kabrin, and L. Freedman, *J. Am. Chem. Soc.* **79**, 5064 (1957).
17. J. H. Moyer, R. Ford, C. Handley, K. Pevey, and R. Seibert, *Antibiotic Med. Clin. Therapy* **4**, 685 (1957).

CHAPTER IV

Organomercurials

A. Chemistry

During the medical renaissance which began in the 16th century, one of the important contributions made by Paracelsus, the leading medical experimentalist of his day, was the use of calomel (mercurous chloride) as a diuretic. Although this use was forgotten shortly thereafter, it was rediscovered and re-established in therapy by Jendrássik (1) in 1885. In addition, calomel was also combined with equal parts of squill and digitalis and became well known as "Guy's Hospital Pills." The second part of the 19th century also saw the acceptance of the germ theory of disease, and in this respect several heavy metals and their salts were used as antiseptics and disinfectants. Thus, metallic mercury as blue ointment or blue pills and also calomel were widely employed during the first decade of the 20th century in the treatment of syphilis. The principle behind this antisyphilitic treatment was *drug saturation* which inevitably produced systemic mercury poisoning in a relatively large proportion of the patients. Thus, although the spirochete could be destroyed to some extent, the untoward side effects resulting from the use of these compounds seriously curtailed their widespread utility. Presently, it should also be emphasized that this was the era of Ehrlich's great success with Salvarsan, and the development of organometallic compounds as chemotherapeutic agents was an intensively active area of medicinal research. In this connection, the chemists of the Bayer Company synthesized an organic mercurial which was shown to be relatively nontoxic but effective when administered parenterally for the treatment of syphilis. The compound was known as merbaphen (I) and consisted of sodium mercuric *o*-chlorophenoxyacetate chemically combined to 5,5-diethyl barbituric acid.

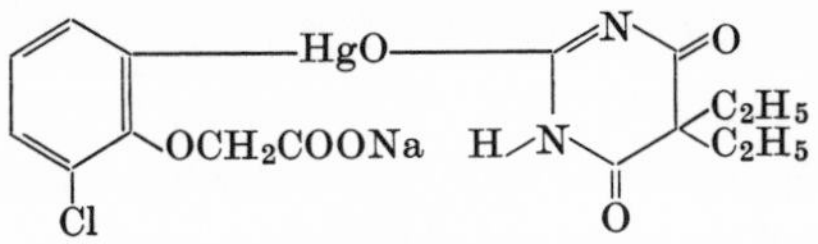

—HgO— N O
C_2H_5
OCH_2COONa H–N C_2H_5
Cl O

I
merbaphen

Until 1919 no one suspected that this drug also had diuretic properties. In that year, Vogl (2), a third-year medical student at the University of Vienna, observed that 1 ml of merbaphen, administered parenterally, induced marked water loss in a nonedematous girl with congenital neurosyphilis. This chance finding by Vogl led Saxl and Heilig (3) to study the effect of merbaphen in edematous patients, the results of which clearly established this antisyphilitic drug as a diuretic and saluretic agent. The general use of merbaphen in edematous disorders was short-lived because of the toxicity of the drug (e.g., cardiac arrest, local tissue irritation). However, its importance lies in the fact that it opened a new area in medicinal research which was vigorously pursued between the years 1920 and 1950 leading to the synthesis of thousands of organomercurials to be evaluated as diuretic agents. One of the earliest of these compounds to achieve some measure of success was mersalyl (see Table I) which was introduced as a parenteral mercurial diuretic in 1924 (4). Mersalyl was found to be equal to merbaphen in activity but less toxic, and consequently was more widely used. Moreover, its method of synthesis was the forerunner for the preparation of many of the organomercurial diuretics which followed. The general method of synthesis is outlined in Scheme 1, and the compounds which have achieved clinical importance are presented in Table I.

There are several general principles associated with the compounds derived by these synthetic routes. If one considers these substances to be essentially derivatives of mercuripropanol,

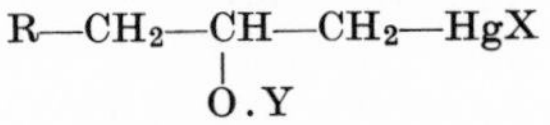

$$R\text{—}CH_2\text{—}\underset{\substack{|\\ O.Y}}{CH}\text{—}CH_2\text{—}HgX$$

then the following necessary structural features evolve: (*1*) a chain of not less than three carbon atoms; (*2*) a mercury atom at the end of the chain; and (*3*) a hydrophilic group of not less than three carbon atoms removed from the mercury. Kessler, Lozano, and Pitts (5)

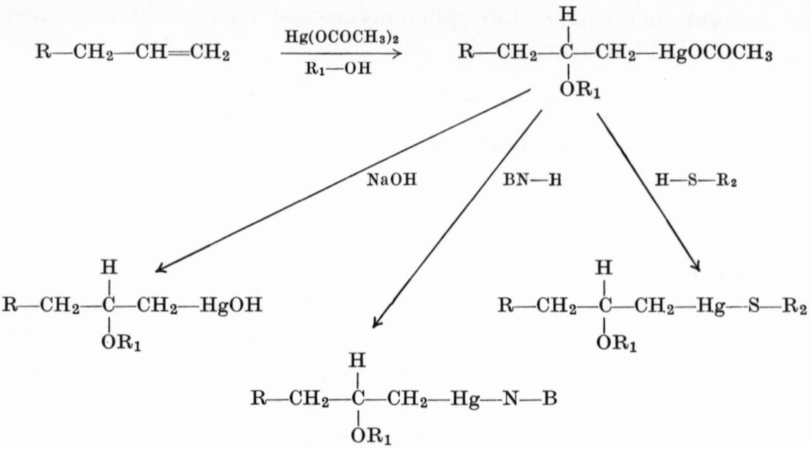

$$R{-}CH_2{-}CH{=}CH_2 \xrightarrow[R_1{-}OH]{Hg(OCOCH_3)_2} R{-}CH_2{-}\underset{OR_1}{\overset{H}{C}}{-}CH_2{-}HgOCOCH_3$$

$$\xrightarrow{NaOH} R{-}CH_2{-}\underset{OR_1}{\overset{H}{C}}{-}CH_2{-}HgOH$$

$$\xrightarrow{BN{-}H} R{-}CH_2{-}\underset{OR_1}{\overset{H}{C}}{-}CH_2{-}Hg{-}N{-}B$$

$$\xrightarrow{H{-}S{-}R_2} R{-}CH_2{-}\underset{OR_1}{\overset{H}{C}}{-}CH_2{-}Hg{-}S{-}R_2$$

R = alkyl, aryl, aralkyl amides
R_1 = CH_3, C_2H_5, etc.
R_2 = alkyl, substituted alkyl, alkanoic acids
BN—H = nitrogen-containing substance with acidic hydrogen

SCHEME 1. General method for synthesis of organomercurials.

demonstrated experimentally that a high diuretic potency was associated with these features. Moreover, they suggested that a critical "lock and key relationship" of substrate to enzyme exists, as shown in Fig. 1, which is responsible for the diuretic action of these

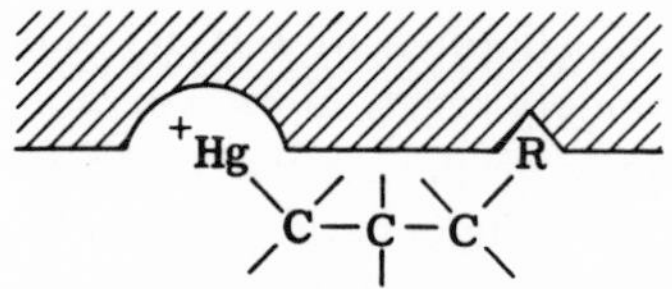

FIG. 1. Schematic representation of enzyme–substrate relation.

compounds. Thus the shape of these molecules is such that they can combine with two appropriately located sites on an enzyme which are essential for normal renal function. However, as attractive as this hypothesis appears, the authors also appreciated its tenuity since substances such as mercuric chloride and merbaphen which lack these structural features also show a significant diuretic effect.

Several other important features are associated with the mercuripropanol derivatives; namely, the groupings R, X, and Y. The Y substituent is determined by the solvent in which the mercuration is

TABLE I

STRUCTURE OF MERCURIAL DIURETICS

$$R\text{—}CH_2\text{—}\underset{\underset{Y}{|}}{\underset{O}{|}}{CH}\text{—}CH_2\text{—}HgX$$

Name	R	Y	X	Hg (in mg) per tablet
Mersalyl	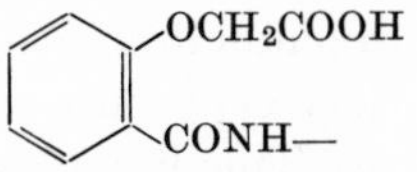 OCH_2COOH CONH—	CH_3	Theophylline	32
Merethoxylline	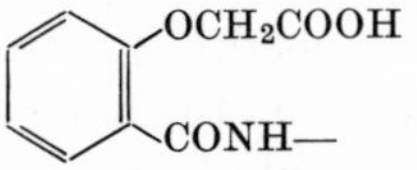 OCH_2COOH CONH—	$CH_2CH_2OCH_3$	Theophylline	39.3
Merdroxone	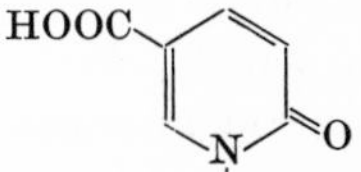 HOOC O N	CH_3	Theophylline	38
Esidron	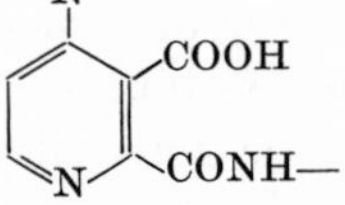 COOH CONH— N	CH_3	Theophylline	40
Mercumatilin	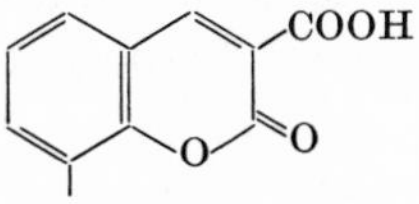 COOH O O	CH_3	Theophylline	20
WY-1204	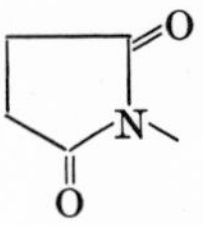 O N O	CH_3	Theophylline	—
Mercurophylline	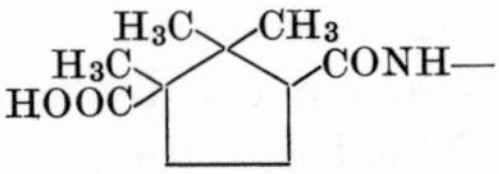 H_3C CH_3 H_3C CONH— HOOC	CH_3	Theophylline	28
Mercaptomerin	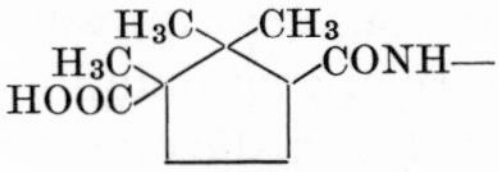 H_3C CH_3 H_3C CONH— HOOC	CH_3	$\text{-S-}CH_2COOH$	43
Merelluride	CH_2—CONH—CONH— CH_2—COOH	CH_3	Theophylline	39
Chlormerodrin	H_2N—CONH—	CH_3	Cl	10
Merbiurelidin	H_2N—CONH—CONH—	CH_3	OH	15

carried out (6), being —OH where the solvent is water and a methoxy or ethoxy group where the solvent is the corresponding alcohol. Secondary amines have also been employed in the mercuration step leading to compounds containing a tertiary amino group at the central carbon of the propyl chain (7). It can be safely stated that a variation of this group has little effect on the diuretic action as well as on toxicity. Most of the mercurial diuretics in use today contain a methoxyl at the central carbon atom.

The group R exerts a pronounced effect on both the toxicity and the diuretic activity of mercuripropanol derivatives (8, 9). In many of these compounds R contains a carboxyl group which is believed to be necessary for solubilizing purposes. This R group is also linked to the mercuripropyl chain through a carbamyl group. Many variations of R have been made including the aromatic, heterocyclic, alicyclic, and aliphatic groups. As outlined in Table I, the potencies of these substances are approximately in the same range (10). However, the unsubstituted urea compound, chlormerodrin, was considerably more potent than the substituted compound, meralluride. In addition chlormerodrin was orally effective. Merbiurelidin, an unsubstituted biuret derivative, was also found to be quite effective orally.

Finally, the nature of group X is of paramount importance in altering the acute toxicity and local tissue irritation effects of the drug when given intravenously, even though it has little influence on diuretic potency. Theophylline has been most widely used as X primarily because it causes decreased local irritation, it is eliminated rapidly from the kidney, and also it enhances the diuretic effect of the mercurials (9, 11).

In 1949 Lehman *et al.* (12) observed that the replacement of theophylline in mercurophylline with mercaptoacetic acid led to a far less toxic compound. This change markedly reduced cardiac toxicity and local tissue irritation. This led to the synthesis of other thiol-containing derivatives (13–15) (e.g., mercaptosuccinic acid).

Werner and Scholz (16) prepared a thiol-containing organomercurial incorporating a sugar moiety as well as a dioxane grouping which contains the mercuripropanol arrangement of atoms. The synthesis of this compound is illustrated on Scheme 2.

The diacetonide of mannitol (III) was allowed to react with allyl bromide in alkali to form the allyl derivative IV. Mercuration with mercuric acetate of this substance led to the formation of the carbon–mercury bond concomitant with intramolecular addition of oxygen to the central carbon atom to form a dioxane derivative V. This compound in turn was de-acetonized and then treated with thiosorbitol to yield diglucomethoxane (VII). Thus, Werner's aim to prepare a

II mannitol $\xrightarrow{CH_3COCH_3}$ III $\xrightarrow{CH_2{=}CH{-}CH_2Br}$

IV $\xrightarrow{Hg(OCOCH_3)_2}$ V $\xrightarrow{\text{de-acetonized}}$

VI $\xrightarrow{\text{thiosorbitol}}$ VII diglucomethoxane

SCHEME 2

polyhydroxy organomercurial containing a thiol group linked to mercury in order to increase solubility and lower toxicity was achieved. Diglucomethoxane has undergone extensive clinical trials and is reported to be a very potent mercurial diuretic with low toxicity. However, this substance is effective only parenterally (17, 18).

Parenteral administration is characteristic of the mercurial diuretics in order to achieve an effective diuresis. Their weak oral activity is due to their poor absorbability. However, WY-1204 (see Table I) has been reported to be orally active in man (19). The most extensively studied orally effective organomercurial is chlormerodrin (10, 20). This compound was designed for oral administration and is only given by this route. It is better tolerated than other mercurials when given by mouth and has been used successfully to maintain an edema-free state in patients with congestive heart failure after the initial "drying-out" by intramuscular administration of the drug. However, it is not devoid of untoward side effects when taken orally and many patients cannot tolerate it.

B. Pharmacology

The organomercurials, in general, have a slow onset of action reaching peak activity within 2 hours and maintaining a steady diuretic action over several hours. Their action is characterized by an increase in the excretion of sodium and chloride ions followed by water. The extent of increase of chloride excretion is greater than for sodium. The potassium excretion is variable depending on the electrolyte balance although clinically potassium excretion is minimal.

The mode of action and fate of mercury have been matters of paramount importance associated with the use of the organomercurials. Since mercury has an intrinsic affinity for sulfhydryl groups (—SH), it has been assumed that the diuretic action is intimately connected with the association of the mercury with the sulfhydryl-containing enzyme or enzymes. Several theories have evolved, but none fit the experimental findings completely.

The original belief that the organomercurial undergoes a metabolic change to release mercuric ion which is responsible for diuresis is no longer tenable since equivalent amounts of mercuric ion given directly and alone have not produced diuresis (21). Mudge and Weiner (22) have suggested that the organomercurials are degraded to the mercuric ion at a rate dependent on the pH, and this ion in turn combines with cysteine (see Fig. 2). Also, they found mercuric cysteine itself to be a potent diuretic. Mudge and Weiner explained that mercuric ion itself is a poor diuretic because it becomes concentrated in organs other than the kidney and thus cannot come in ready contact with sulfhydryl-containing intermediates. However, the evidence (23) that only a minute fraction of the mercury excreted in urine is in the inorganic form does not support the view of these investigators. In fact, Weiner and Muller (24) found that following an injection of mersalyl most of the mercury in the urine was present as a mersalyl–cysteine complex.

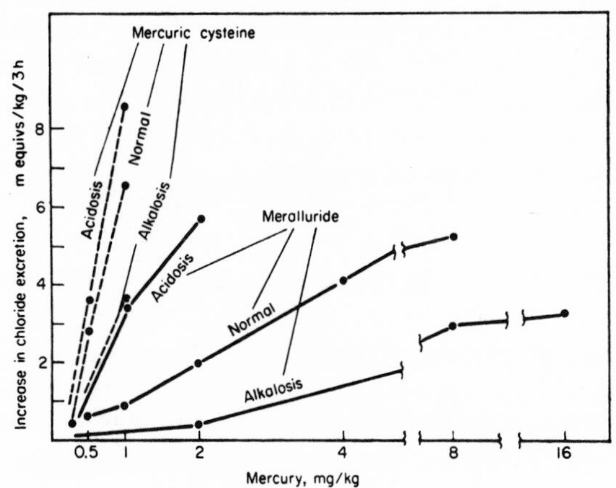

Fig. 2. Dose–response relationship of an organic mercurial (meralluride) and an ionic mercury complex (mercuric cysteine) in normal, acidotic, and alkalotic dogs.

The steric configuration theory of Kessler, Lozano, and Pitts (5) supports the view that the intact organomercurial acts as the diuretic agent through the substrate–enzyme complex. These investigators explained the diuretic effect of mercuric cysteine as arising from a complex of mercuric ion with cysteine in a 1:1 molar ratio in the kidney. The resulting compound would then possess the configurational features necessary for insertion into their postulated enzyme receptor (see Fig. 3). In this hypothesis it is necessary to assume that a methylene group can be replaced with a sulfur atom. Under these circumstances the chain of one sulfur and two carbon atoms between the mercury and the hydrophilic amino group would constitute the usual three units necessary for their postulated "lock and key relationship" of substrate–enzyme complex. As stated earlier in this chapter, several exceptions to this theory are known and thus limit its scope. A compromise between these two views was outlined by Heller and Ginsburg (25). They suggest that when mercury is combined in a suitable organic structure its intracellular penetration is facilitated and that liberation of relatively small amounts of mercuric ion in tubular cells, dependent on intracellular pH, impairs some part of the sodium reabsorption process. This would explain the experimental fact that the diuretic effect often persists beyond the time of maximum excretion of the organomercurial agent. In any event, it is well established that the sulfhydryl group plays a significant part in organomercurial induced diuresis. Farah (26) was able to inhibit the diuretic action of mersalyl by the use of *p*-chloromercuribenzoate which readily complexes with sulfhydryl groups. Treating the dog

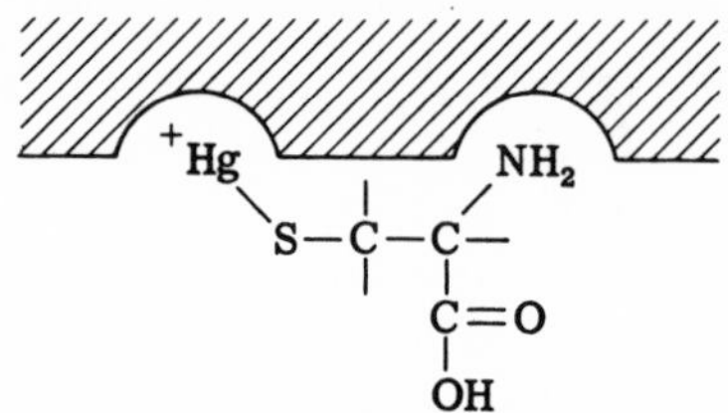

FIG. 3. Schematic representation of enzyme–substrate relation with sulphur replacing the methylene group.

with graded doses of 2,3-dimercaptopropanol deactivated the complex and liberated the sulfhydryl-containing substance (enzyme or enzymes) which then interacted with mersalyl resulting in diuresis. Excessive amounts of 2,3-dimercaptopropanol were shown to inhibit diuresis.

A precise definition of the site or sites of action of organomercurial diuretics is quite difficult at the present time. The available evidence indicates that these agents act directly on the kidney but the specific effect must be considered by the influence of these drugs on (a) filtration rate (glomerulus), (b) tubular re-absorption (proximal tubule), or (c) tubular secretion (distal tubule). It is known that organomercurials do not increase the rate of filtrate formation in experimental animals or in the edematous subject during mercurial diuresis. Thus, the glomerulus is not implicated.

However, it is difficult at present to ascertain whether the mercurials act in the proximal or distal tubules or both. In a recent review Pitts (27) has stated: "Because mercurial diuretics interfere with the extrusion of sodium and the retention of potassium, they reduce the polarization of proximal tubular cells.... Accordingly, the re-absorption of chloride as well as that of sodium is inhibited. Proximal tubular cells are freely permeable to water. The re-absorption of sodium and chloride ions creates an osmotic force which causes the re-absorption of water. Mercurial diuretics, by blocking the active re-absorption of a fraction of the filtered sodium, secondarily block the re-absorption of an equivalent quantity of chloride and an osmotically equivalent quantity of water. More sodium and chloride ions and water are delivered to the distal tubules. Here a part of the sodium is re-absorbed in exchange for potassium and hydrogen ions. Accordingly, mercurial diuretics may induce the excretion of more chloride than sodium ions, although they primarily block sodium re-absorption."

In summary then, the field of mercurial diuretics was investigated very actively between 1920 and 1950 and considerable progress was made in reducing toxicity and irritation at the site of injection. However, most mercurial diuretics are effective only when given parenterally (intravenously or intramuscularly). This factor plus the toxicity usually associated with organomercurials has prompted the search for nontoxic, orally active, nonmercurial diuretic drugs. The most important group of organic compounds found to date which fulfill these conditions are the sulfonamides and related compounds.

References

1. E. Jendrássik, *Deut. Arch. Klin. Med.* **38**, 499 (1885).
2. A. Vogl, *Am. Heart J.* **39**, 881 (1950).
3. P. Saxl and R. Heilig, *Wien. Klin. Wochschr.* **33**, 943 (1920).
4. W. Wobbe, *Arch. Pharm.* **262**, 70 (1924).
5. R. H. Kessler, R. Lozano, and R. F. Pitts, *J. Clin. Invest.* **36**, 656 (1957).
6. H. L. Friedman, *Ann. N.Y. Acad. Sci.* **65**(5), 461 (1957).
7. G. E. Wright, *Ann. N.Y. Acad. Sci.* **65**(5), 436 (1957).
8. H. L. Friedman, *in* "Edema" (J. H. Moyer and M. Fuchs, eds.) pp. 208–213. Saunders, Philadelphia, Pennsylvania, 1957.
9. J. M. Sprague, *Ann. N.Y. Acad. Sci.* **71**(4), 328 (1958).
10. L. S. Goodman and A. Gilman, "The Pharmacological Basis of Chemotherapeutics," pp. 850–852. Macmillan, New York, 1960.
11. K. H. Beyer and J. E. Baer, *in* "Progress in Drug Research" (E. Jucker, ed.) Vol. II, p. 30. Birkhauser Verlag, Basel, Switzerland, 1960.
12. R. A. Lehman, E. E. King, and H. Taube, *Proc. Soc. Exptl. Biol. Med.* **71**, 1 (1949).
13. C. A. Handley, D. Chapman, and J. H. Moyer, *Proc. Soc. Exptl. Biol. Med.* **78**, 433 (1951).

14. S. White and P. A. Nuhfer, *J. Pharmacol. Exptl. Therap.* **101**, 38 (1951).
15. J. H. Moyer, C. A. Handley, R. A. Seibert, S. Mitchell, and D. Papandrianos, *Am. Heart J.* **44**, 281 (1952).
16. L. H. Werner and C. R. Scholz, *J. Am. Chem. Soc.* **76**, 2453 (1954).
17. R. V. Ford, *G. P., J. Am. Acad. Gen. Pract.* **14**, 118 (1956).
18. R. H. Chaney and R. F. Maronde, *Am. J. Med. Sci.* **231**, 26 (1956).
19. W. J. Posnanski and B. W. Cromie, *Brit. Med. J.* **1**, 1553 (1959).
20. W. A. Leff and H. E. Nussbaum, *Brit. Med. J.* **1**, 883 (1959).
21. T. Sollmann, N. E. Schrieber, and H. N. Cole, *Arch. Internal Med.* **58**, 1067 (1956).
22. G. H. Mudge and I. M. Weiner, *Ann. N.Y. Acad. Sci.* **71**(4), 344 (1958).
23. J. H. Moyer, C. A. Handley, and R. A. Seibert, *Ann. N.Y. Acad. Sci.* **65**(5), 511 (1957).
24. I. M. Weiner and R. Muller, *J. Pharmacol. Exptl. Therap.* **113**, 241 (1955).
25. H. Heller and M. Ginsburg, *in* "Progress in Medicinal Chemistry" (G. P. Ellis and G. B. West, eds.), Vol. I, pp. 132–186. Butterworths, London, 1961.
26. A. Farah, *in* "Edema" (J. H. Moyer and M. Fuchs, eds.), pp. 214–223. Saunders, Philadelphia, Pennsylvania, 1960.
27. R. F. Pitts, *Prog. Cardiovascular Diseases* **3**, 537 (1961).

Sulfonamides

A. Historical Development

As it often happens in research, a chance unexpected observation, keenly interpreted, can lead to notable progress in an area of potential development. This certainly was the case for the sulfonamides. The exploration of sulfonamide chemistry has yielded a rich return in drugs of therapeutic value. The key compound in all of this work has been sulfanilamide (I). The initial finding by Domagk (1) that animals

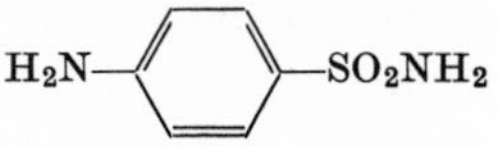

$$H_2N-C_6H_4-SO_2NH_2$$

I

infected by the deadly hemolytic *Streptococcus* B survived when treated with Prontosil (II), led Trefouël and co-workers (2) to study

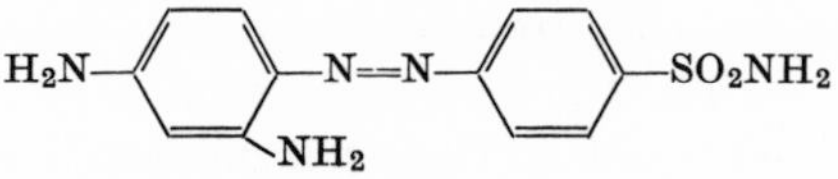

$$H_2N-C_6H_3(NH_2)-N{=}N-C_6H_4-SO_2NH_2$$

II

the structure–activity relationship of various analogs of this substance. Their observation that animals treated with Prontosil excreted *p*-acetamidobenzenesulfonamide as a metabolite, resulted in their correct hypothesis, verified later by experiment, that the active moiety of the sulfonamide dye was sulfanilamide.

The key role of sulfanilamide in diuretic research began in 1940 in connection with a study of the side effects of sulfa drugs. Clinical studies revealed that some patients treated with sulfanilamide developed acidosis, a condition in which the hydrogen ion concentration (pH) in the blood drops below the normal 7.35. Shortly thereafter,

Mann and Keilin (3) discovered that this side effect resulted from the inhibition of carbonic anhydrase, the enzyme responsible for the conversion of carbon dioxide and water to hydrogen ion and bicarbonate ion. Pitts and Alexander (4), in a brilliant study on the effect of sulfanilamide on urinary pH in the dog, elucidated the cause of the acidosis. Their findings will be considered after a brief description of the regulation of the pH by the kidneys (5, 6).

During the course of normal metabolism, the body produces an excess of acids. The kidneys compensate for this by excreting acids and returning bicarbonate to the plasma and extracellular water. Therefore, the urine is usually acid (pH 5.5 to 6.5), whereas the pH of the plasma and extracellular water is slightly alkaline (pH 7.35 to 7.45). The acid–base balance is maintained as follows:

$$CO_2 + H_2O \xrightleftharpoons{\text{carbonic anhydrase}} H_2CO_3 \rightleftharpoons H^+ + HCO_3^- \qquad (1)$$

$$Na_2HPO_4 \longrightarrow Na^+ + NaHPO_4^- \longrightarrow \text{glomerular filtrate} \qquad (2)$$

$$NaHPO_4^- + H^+ \longrightarrow NaH_2PO_4 \longrightarrow \text{urine} \qquad (3)$$

$$HCO_3^- + Na^+ \longrightarrow NaHCO_3 \longrightarrow \text{plasma and urine} \qquad (4)$$

Normally, all the bicarbonate ions which pass the glomeruli and enter the tubular urine (glomerular filtrate) are reabsorbed. This occurs by means of an exchange of hydrogen ions (which the renal tubular cells secrete) for sodium ions in the tubular urine.

Hydrogen ions are available in the tubular cells because the enzyme carbonic anhydrase is able to convert water and the carbon dioxide present in all cells into carbonic acid which in turn is ionized to hydrogen ions and bicarbonate ions [Eq. (1)].

In the tubular urine, the hydrogen ions combine with the bicarbonate ions of the tubular urine to form carbonic acid. This then forms water and carbon dioxide. The water is excreted and the carbon dioxide is reabsorbed by the tubular cells. At the same time, sodium ions pass from the tubular urine into the tubular cells where they unite with the bicarbonate ions there to form sodium carbonate. The bicarbonate then passes into the plasma and extracellular water where its concentration is maintained. This interrelationship of carbon dioxide, water, carbonic acid, hydrogen ions, and bicarbonate ions is schematically outlined in Fig. 1.

A similar exchange mechanism occurs between hydrogen ions of the renal tubular cells and disodium phosphate (Na_2HPO_4) which dissociates into sodium ions and sodium monohydrogen phosphate ions

($NaHPO_4^-$) [Eq. (2)]. The sodium ion moves into the tubular cells and a hydrogen ion moves from the cells and unites with the sodium monophosphate ion to form a dihydrogen phosphate salt (NaH_2PO_4) which is excreted [Eq. (3)]. In this way a hydrogen ion is removed from the body.

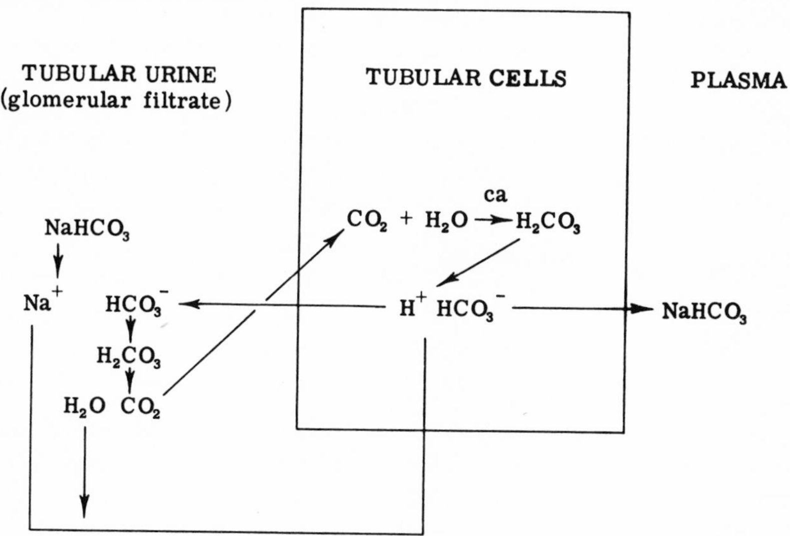

FIG. 1. Diagram showing the mechanism by which bicarbonate is conserved by the kidneys.

Pitts and Alexander were able to show that the presence of a carbonic anhydrase inhibitor, in this case sulfanilamide, led to a decrease in the hydrogen ion concentration, available for interaction. Therefore, the transformation of disodium phosphate into monosodium phosphate is slowed down owing to the nonavailability of hydrogen ions. Consequently, inhibition of the enzyme carbonic anhydrase depresses the hydrogen–sodium exchange and results in a more alkaline urine since a larger amount of sodium bicarbonate ions are excreted. Thus the metabolic acidosis caused clinically by sulfanilamide was explained. Schwartz (7) took advantage of the increased sodium excretion caused by sulfanilamide to promote a diuretic action in patients suffering from congestive heart failure. He reasoned that the natriuretic effect of the compound should in turn facilitate water excretion. Schwartz was able to show clinically that the diuretic action of sulfanilamide was caused by its inhibition of carbonic anhydrase. He also pointed out that the chronic use of sulfanilamide led to excessive excretion of sodium and bicarbonate ions and concomitant acidosis rendering the carbonic anhydrase inhibitor ineffective for further diuretic action. Moreover, the amount of sulfanilamide necessary to produce a diuretic effect was too high and caused toxic side effects.

During this time, Krebs (8) reported on his evaluation of a number

TABLE I

INHIBITION OF CARBONIC ANHYDRASE *in Vitro* BY SULFONAMIDES[a]

Formula	Concentration causing 50% inhibition ($\times 10^{-7}M$)	
	At 0° C	At 15° C
C_6H_5—SO_2NH_2	4.6	—
C_6H_5—$CH_2SO_2NH_2$	150	—
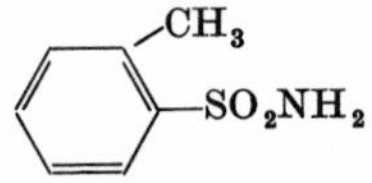 o-CH_3—C_6H_4—SO_2NH_2	6.3	7.7
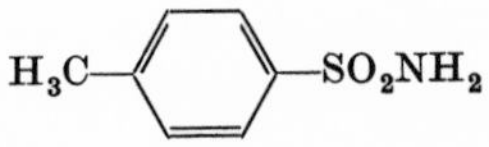 H_3C—C_6H_4—SO_2NH_2	1.0	2.4
H_3C—C_6H_4—SO_2NHCH_2—COOH	4400	7600
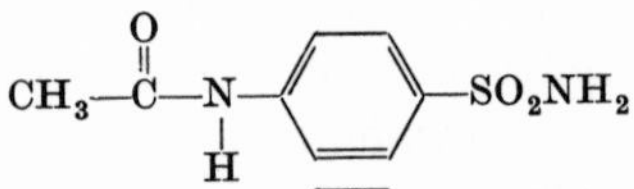 CH_3—C(=O)—N(H)—C_6H_4—SO_2NH_2	1.2	2
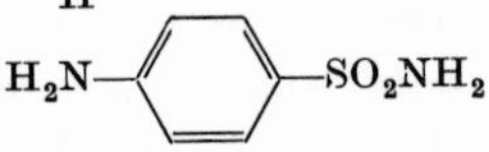 H_2N—C_6H_4—SO_2NH_2	9.0	19
H_2N—C_6H_4—$SO_2NHCOCH_3$	6500	19000
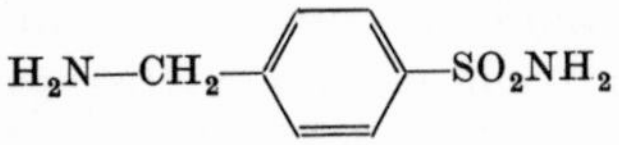 H_2N—CH_2—C_6H_4—SO_2NH_2	25.0	—

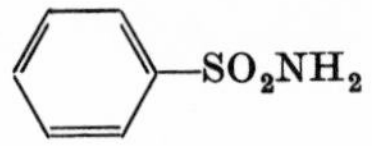

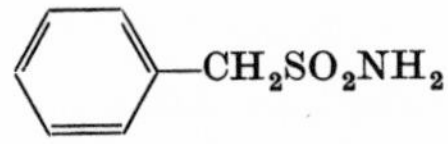

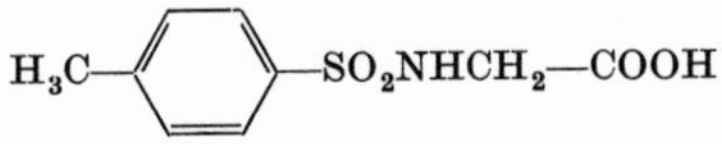

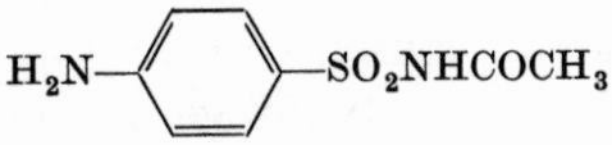

[a] Data from Krebs (8).

TABLE I—*continued*

Formula	Concentration causing 50% inhibition ($\times 10^{-7} M$)	
	At 0° C	At 15° C
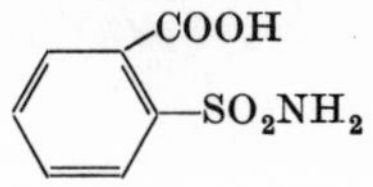 COOH, SO_2NH_2	5.3	15
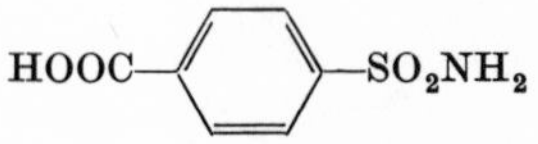 HOOC—, —SO_2NH_2	2.0	2.7
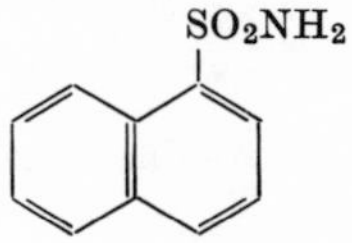 SO_2NH_2	1.6	2.0
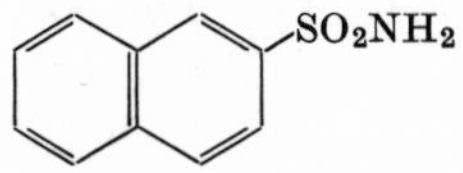 SO_2NH_2	1.0	2.7
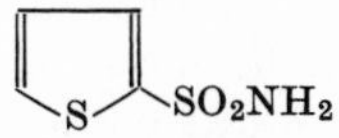 S, SO_2NH_2	3.0	3.8
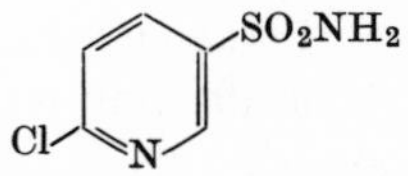 SO_2NH_2, Cl, N	1.2	—
Prontosil (II)	0.06	—
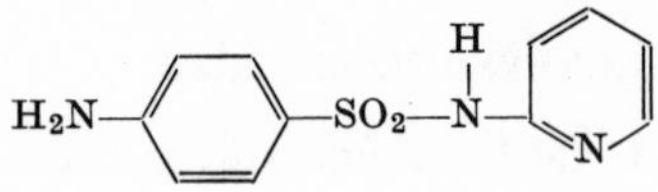 H_2N—, —SO_2—N(H)—, N	510	1400
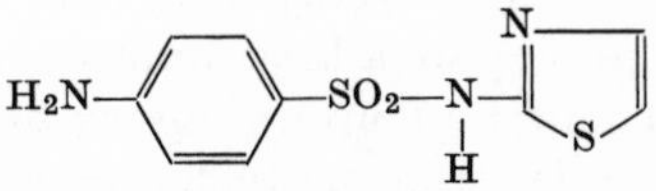 H_2N—, —SO_2—N(H)—, N, S	6600	7700
CN—CH_2—CH_2—SO_2NH_2	380	

of sulfonamides as carbonic anhydrase inhibitors. The results of this study are outlined in Table I. The most pertinent feature of this study is that an unsubstituted sulfamyl group is necessary for maximum activity. This has been explained as a result of the similar spatial relationship of the sulfamyl group and carbonic acid and their competitive interaction with the active center of the enzyme as represented in Fig. 2.

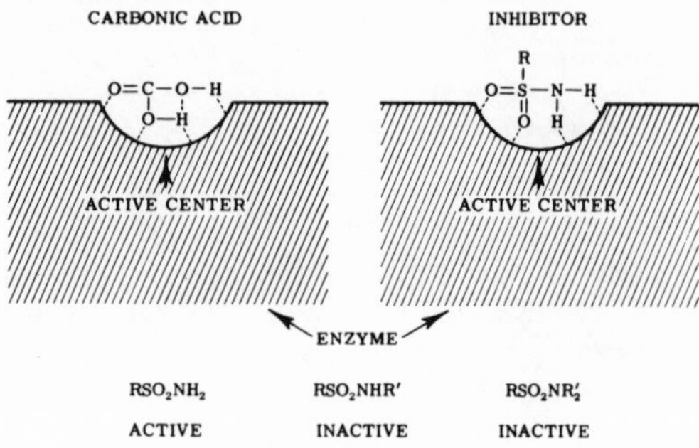

FIG. 2. Schematic representation of the enzyme–inhibitor relationship.

It was also observed that high carbonic anhydrase inhibition was obtained in those compounds where the unsubstituted sulfamyl group was attached directly to an aromatic group (phenyl, naphthyl, or heterocycle). Substitution of various groups on the aromatic ring did not affect markedly the activity. In some cases (e.g., compounds substituted with CH_3, COOH) the activity was increased several fold over that of benzenesulfonamide. Finally, it was significantly noted that acetylation of the amino group of sulfanilamide resulted in an increase of activity over the parent compound.

B. 1,3,4-Thiadiazolesulfonamides

Roblin and Clapp (9) of the Lederle Laboratories capitalized on these fundamental findings emanating initially from the report of Mann and Keilin and proceeded to prepare a large number of heterocyclic compounds containing a sulfamyl group for evaluation as carbonic anhydrase inhibitors. At the time they began their work relatively few heterocyclic sulfonamides in which the sulfur atom is joined directly to a carbon of the heterocyclic ring had been described. In part this was owing to the restriction of the methods of synthesis: that is, chlorosulfonation of the ring or conversion of the sulfonic acid to the acid chloride, followed by amidation, are not generally applicable to the preparation of heterocyclic sulfonamides.

Roblin and Clapp prepared their compounds according to the method outlined for 2-acetylamino-1,3,4-thiadiazole-5-sulfonamide in Scheme 1. 2-Amino-1,3,4-thiadiazole-5-thiol (III) was first acetylated to form IV which was oxidatively chlorinated to the sulfonyl chloride and then amidated with anhydrous liquid ammonia to yield

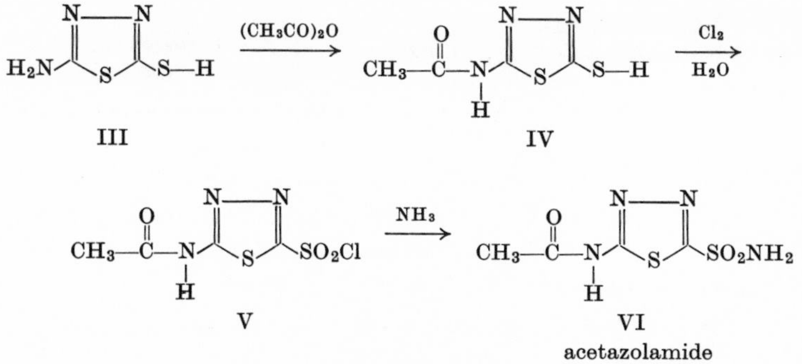

III $\xrightarrow{(CH_3CO)_2O}$ IV $\xrightarrow[H_2O]{Cl_2}$ V $\xrightarrow{NH_3}$ VI

VI
acetazolamide

SCHEME 1

compound VI, generically known as *acetazolamide.* Other heterocyclic sulfonamides prepared by Roblin and Clapp, and the relative carbonic anhydrase inhibitory activity of these substances as determined by Miller *et al.* (10), are listed in Table II.

They found several of the heterocyclic sulfonamides to be substantially more potent than sulfanilamide when tested *in vitro.* One of these compounds, 2-benzothiazole sulfonamide, was by far the most potent of the group in this test. However, it was virtually devoid of carbonic anhydrase inhibitory activity when tested *in vivo.* Clapp (11) was able to explain this on the basis of its rapid metabolism by the dog. A metabolic product accounting for 25% of the administered drug was isolated and identified as the glucuronide of 2-mercaptobenzothiazole.

Recently, 6-ethoxy-2-benzothiazolesulfonamide (VII) (12) has been reported to be effective as a diuretic in man and it is, therefore, apparently more resistant to metabolic inactivation than the 6-unsubstituted substance. Ethoxzolamide, however, has not gained much prominence as a carbonic anhydrase inhibitor or as a mild diuretic because of its side effects (13).

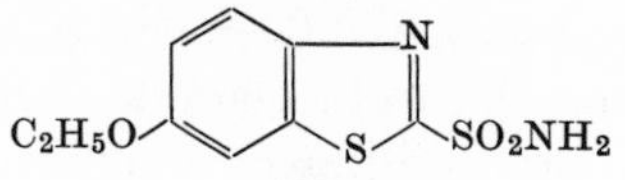

VII
ethoxzolamide

Another interesting observation noted by Miller and co-workers was that acetylation of the free amino group enhanced activity—a generalization which was initially reported by Krebs for sulfanilamide.

TABLE II

RELATIVE CARBONIC ANHYDRASE INHIBITORY ACTIVITY OF HETEROCYCLIC SULFONAMIDES

Sulfonamide	Inhibitory activity[a] (sulfanilamide ratio) 50%	100%	Ratio 100%/50%
p-aminobenzene- (Sulfanilamide)	1	1	25
Imidazole-2-	5	—	—
1-Methylimidazole-2-	20	3	150
1-Phenylimidazole-2-	2	—	—
Benzimidazole-2-	14	—	—
1, 2, 4-Triazole-3-	3	—	—
Pyrido [2, 1-*c*]*s*-triazole-3-	30	30	25
3-Hydroxy-4-phenyl-4,1,2-triazole-5-	30	—	—
4-Phenyl-4,1,2-triazole-3,5-di-	18	5	75
1-Methyltetrazole-5-	14	—	—
1-Phenyltetrazole-5-	190	650	10
Pyrimidine-2-	3	—	—
4,6-Dimethylpyrimidine-2-	0.4	—	—
5-Chloropyrimidine-2-	16	—	—
Pyrazine-2-	18	40	15
1,3,4-Thiadiazole-2,5-di-	800	870	20
2-Acetylamino-1,3,4-thiadiazole-5-	330	440	15
2-Amino-1,3,4-thiadiazole-5-	25	—	—
Benzothiazole-2-	730	2500	7
Thiazole-2-	120	240	10
4-Methylthiazole-2-	50	70	15
2-Acetylaminothiazole-5-	15	6	50
2-Aminothiazole-5-	3	—	—

[a] Values indicate approximate number of times as active as sulfanilamide on a molar basis. From Miller *et al.* (10).

The most important compound to come out of the investigations of Roblin and co-workers is acetazolamide. This substance is considered an important accomplishment in diuretic therapy since it was the first clinically effective, nonmercurial, orally active diuretic drug.

For a number of years (1951–1958) acetazolamide was considered the drug of choice when a mild diuretic effect was desired. Unlike most mercurials, it is well tolerated when given by the oral route at a daily dosage of 250–375 mg, but its diuretic action is not as rapid or as dramatic as that observed after organic mercurial therapy. It has also had wide use for the treatment of glaucoma. However, the

TABLE III

ACETAZOLAMIDE ANALOGS (14)

(Structure: 2-R-1,3,4-thiadiazole-5-SO_2NH_2 ring, N—N, S, R, SO_2NH_2)

Name	R	*In vitro*[a] carbonic anhydrase activity
Formamido-	HCONH-	0.62
Propionamido-	CH_3CH_2CONH-	1.2
n-Butyramido- (butamide)	$CH_3CH_2CH_2CONH$-	1.2
Isobutyramido-	$(CH_3)_2CHCONH$-	0.55
Isovaleramido-	$(CH_3)_2CHCH_2CONH$-	1.6
Chloroacetamido-	$ClCH_2CONH$-	0.6
Trifluoroacetamido-	F_3C-CONH-	0.31
Benzamido-	C_6H_5CONH-	2.1
Phthalimido-	$H_4C_6<(CO)_2>N$-	3.1
2-Carboxybenzamido	H_4C_6(CONH-)(COOH)	1.9
Carbobenzoxamido-	$C_6H_5CH_2OCONH$-	2.6
Carbobenzoxyaminoacetamido-	$C_6H_5CH_2OCONHCH_2CONH$-	0.48
Aminoacetamido-HBr	H_2NCH_2CONH-	0.03
Benzenesulfonamido-	$C_6H_5SO_2NH$-	5.1
4-Methylbenzenesulfonamido-	4-$CH_3C_6H_4SO_2NH$-	4.4
4-Chlorobenzenesulfonamido-	4-$ClC_6H_4SO_2NH$-	3.7
3,4-Dichlorobenzenesulfonamido-	3, 4-$Cl_2C_6H_3SO_2NH$-	2.6
4-Bromobenzenesulfonamido-	4-Br-$C_6H_4SO_2NH$-	2.3
4-Acetamidobenzenesulfonamido-	4-$CH_3CONHC_6H_4SO_2NH$-	2.6
4-Aminobenzenesulfonamido-	4-$H_2NC_6H_4SO_2NH$-	1.7

[a] Carbonic anhydrase inhibition compared to acetazolamide as 1.0, on a weight basis.

carbonic anhydrase inhibitory effect of the drug eventually causes acidosis which then renders the compound ineffective. In an attempt to prepare more effective and less toxic substances, Vaughan *et al.* (14) prepared a series of analogs of acetazolamide in which the 2-acetamido group in the parent compound was replaced by other 2-acylamido and by 2-sulfonamido groups. These compounds and their relative *in vitro* activities are listed in Table III (p. 55). The 5-*n*-butyramido-1,3,4-thiadiazole-2-sulfonamide (butamide) was shown to be a clinically effective diuretic. Still another modification of acetazolamide was made by Young and co-workers (15). They prepared the two isomeric methyl derivatives VIII and IX. These compounds are

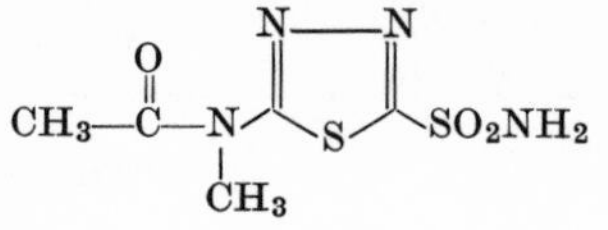

VIII

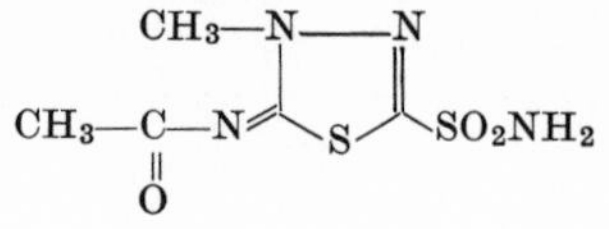

IX
methazolamide

more potent carbonic anhydrase inhibitors *in vitro* than acetazolamide. In addition, methazolamide, the more stable of the two isomers,

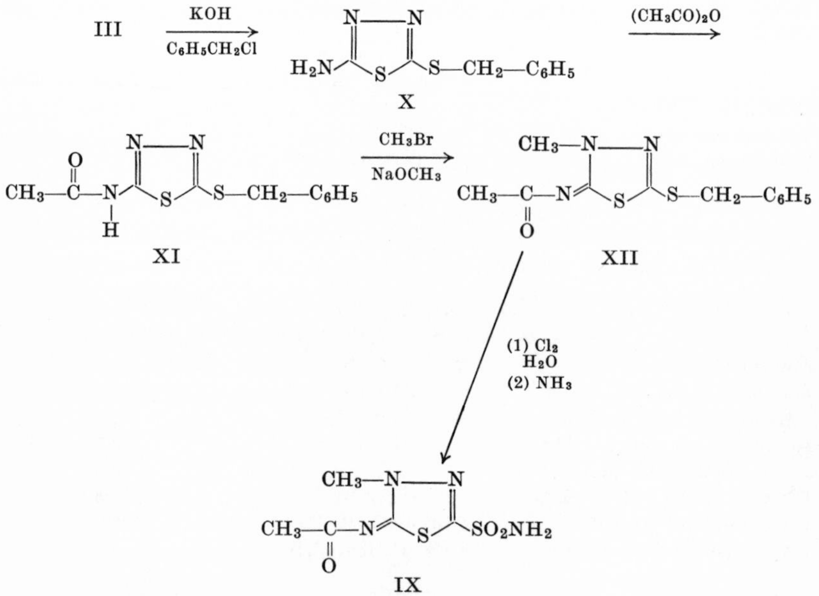

III $\xrightarrow[C_6H_5CH_2Cl]{KOH}$ X $\xrightarrow{(CH_3CO)_2O}$ XI $\xrightarrow[NaOCH_3]{CH_3Br}$ XII $\xrightarrow{(1)\ Cl_2,\ H_2O;\ (2)\ NH_3}$ IX

SCHEME 2

shows better penetration into the brain and eye than does acetazolamide. The synthesis of methazolamide is shown in Scheme 2 (p. 56).

Benzylation of 2-amino-1,3,4-thiadiazole-5-thiol yielded compound X which was then acetylated to form XI. Methylation of XI with methyl iodide gave rise to the *N*-methyl derivative XII which was allowed to undergo oxidative chlorination followed by amidation to form methazolamide (IX).

Another compound in this class recently clinically evaluated (16) is 2-(4-chlorobenzenesulfonamido)-1,3,4-thiadiazole-5-sulfonamide (XIII). This drug is approximately five times more potent than acetazolamide as a carbonic anhydrase inhibitor.

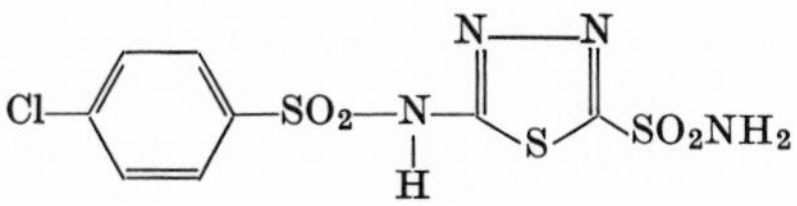

Cl—C6H4—SO_2—NH—(1,3,4-thiadiazole)—SO_2NH_2

XIII

Mode of Action of 1,3,4-Thiadiazolesulfonamides

The 1,3,4-thiadiazolesulfonamides described above have a similar mode of action, and a discussion of acetazolamide will serve to illustrate this action for all compounds in this class.

Acetazolamide. Acetazolamide acts directly in the kidneys by inhibiting the enzyme carbonic anhydrase. A single dose of this drug, intravenously or orally, produces a marked increase in the excretion of sodium, potassium, and bicarbonate ions which in turn leads to the elimination of an osmotic equivalent of water. The effect on chloride ion is minimal. However, the elimination of bicarbonate ion results in metabolic acidosis and as long as the drug is administered consecutively over a period of time, this state of acidosis persists. Under these conditions the diuretic effectiveness of acetazolamide becomes minimized. To overcome this apparent refractoriness, the patient must be taken off the drug for several days until plasma electrolyte balance is restored. In chronic animal studies, Maren *et al.* (17) demonstrated that a hypopotassemia developed and remained as long as administration of the drug was continued. The usefulness of acetazolamide for long-term treatment (e.g., congestive heart failure) has been limited because of the refractoriness resulting from acidosis as well as from the pronounced kaliuretic effect that is obtained initially. This latter side effect is especially undesirable in cases of liver cirrhosis or in the treatment of steroid-induced edema, conditions in which the patients are susceptible to potassium loss. These clinical side effects prompted further research in sulfonamides.

C. Disulfonamides

The benzenedisulfonamides are really the cornerstone of modern diuretic therapy. In this regard the elegant experimental work and far-reaching conclusions of Krebs (8) must be reconsidered (see Table I). His data showed clearly that optimum inhibition of carbonic anhydrase was achieved with aromatic compounds in which the unsubstituted sulfamyl group was attached to carbon of the aromatic ring. Substitution of other polar groups on the aromatic ring also influenced enzyme inhibition. One of the substances reported by Krebs to show significantly high carbonic anhydrase inhibition was *p*-carboxybenzenesulfonamide. Very little was done with this published information until 1954 when Beyer (18) demonstrated that this compound was capable of producing an appreciable natriuretic effect and this was accompanied by a small but significant increase in chloride excretion in the dog, an effect which was clinically corroborated by Merrill (19) and shortly thereafter by Lindsay and Brown (20). However, the compound was reported by the latter group to be poorly absorbed upon oral administration and to be relatively weak. On the strength of this slightly encouraging report the team of Sprague (chemistry) and Beyer (renal pharmacology) combined efforts at the Merck, Sharp and Dohme Laboratories to explore this class of compounds in depth. They initially found that *p*-chlorobenzenesulfonamide (XIV) had about the same enzyme inhibitory activity *in vitro* as sulfanilamide and *p*-carboxybenzenesulfonamide (21). Their attention next turned to *m*-benzenedisulfonamides containing a chloro group on the benzene ring. It was found that compound XV substantially increased the excretion of sodium, chloride, and bicarbonate ions when tested in experimental animals (22). Then dichlorphenamide (XVI) was synthesized and this compound had a mode of action quite similar to acetazolamide except for the definite excretion of less bicarbonate and more chloride ions along with sodium ions. Clinical evaluation of this drug has revealed that because of its greater chloruretic effect, XVI causes less acidosis and consequently there is a lesser tendency for refractoriness to develop than with acetazolamide (23).

It is not known how many compounds of the *m*-benzenedisulfonamide class were prepared by Sprague and co-workers prior to the synthesis of 5-chloro-2,4-disulfamylaniline (XVII). It is conceivable that the rationale behind its synthesis was to prepare a compound which would incorporate the structural features associated with sulfanilamide and *p*-chlorobenzenesulfonamide with the amino and

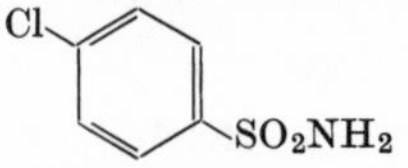

Cl, SO_2NH_2
XIV

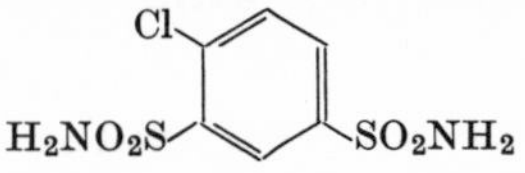

Cl, H_2NO_2S, SO_2NH_2
XV

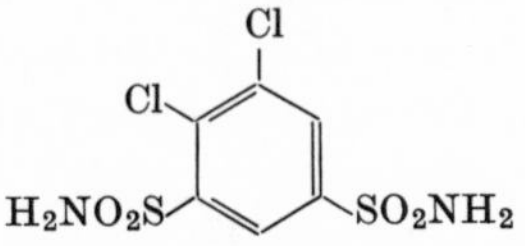

Cl, Cl, H_2NO_2S, SO_2NH_2
XVI
dichlorphenamide

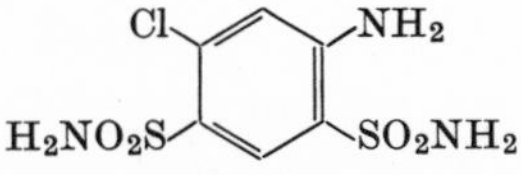

Cl, NH_2, H_2NO_2S, SO_2NH_2
XVII

the chloro groups situated *para* and *ortho*, respectively, to the sulfamyl groups, which is reminiscent of some of the generalizations made by Krebs. Nevertheless, the compound was synthesized and found to produce a pattern of sodium chloride excretion somewhat different from the carbonic anhydrase inhibitors and more like the organomercurials (24). Lund and Størling (25) have confirmed this saluretic response in man. The importance of XVII, however, resides in the central and dominating role it plays in the synthesis of benzothiadiazine-1,1-dioxides. This subject will be covered in detail in Chapter VI. Presently, it is appropriate (a) to present the various synthetic pathways leading to preparation of *m*-benzenedisulfonamides, then (b) to indicate the synthesis of structurally modified *m*-benzenedisulfonamides, and finally (c) to outline the developments in heterocyclic mono- and disulfonamides. The structure–activity relationships of each of the classes of compounds will be discussed accordingly in each section. The diuretic activity of those compounds prepared in the CIBA Laboratories have been determined in dogs according to the method described in Chapter I.

1. Synthesis and Biological Activities of *m*-Benzenedisulfonamides

The general synthesis of *m*-benzenedisulfonamides is illustrated in Scheme 3. The compounds prepared by this procedure are listed in Table IV.

Chlorosulfonation of aniline leads to an aminobenzene mono- or trisulfonamide. To obtain an aminobenzenedisulfonamide it is necessary to block one of the positions *ortho* or *meta* to an amino group with an *ortho* directing group, e.g., chlorine, methyl, methoxyl. The most direct method for the preparation of these compounds is that of Lustig and Katscher (26) and consists of heating the substituted aniline ($R_1 = H$) with chlorosulfonic acid and sodium chloride,

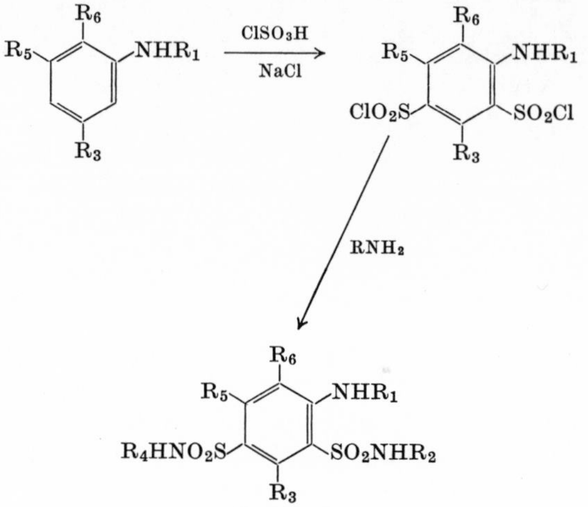

R_6, R_5, NHR_1, R_3 $\xrightarrow[NaCl]{ClSO_3H}$ R_6, R_5, NHR_1, ClO_2S, SO_2Cl, R_3

$\xrightarrow{RNH_2}$

R_6, R_5, NHR_1, R_4HNO_2S, SO_2NHR_2, R_3

SCHEME 3

followed by amidation of the resulting disulfonylchloride with ammonia or a primary amine. Novello *et al.* (22) reported that the various halodisulfamylanilines formed by this procedure provided a convenient route to the isomeric disulfamylanilines which are not readily accessible by other synthetic routes (e.g., direct sulfonation of aniline). Catalytic dechlorination of both 5-chloro- and 6-chloro-2,4-disulfamylaniline using palladium–charcoal catalyst gave 2,4-disulfamylaniline. 4-Bromo-2,6-disulfamylaniline, prepared from *p*-bromoaniline, upon catalytic debromination, yielded 2,6-disulfamylaniline. The 4-chloro-2,4-disulfamylaniline yielded 2,5-disulfamylaniline similarly.

The 5,6-dichloro-2,4-disulfamylaniline was prepared as outlined in Scheme 3 from 2,3-dichloroaniline. Also, Close *et al.* (27) and Short and Biermacher (28) prepared 5-chloro-6-bromo- and 5-chloro-6-nitro-2,4-disulfamylanilines by this procedure. A large number of aminobenzenedisulfonamides have been synthesized for evaluation as diuretics and some of these are outlined in Table IV. These have been

TABLE IV

2, 4-DISULFAMYLANILINES

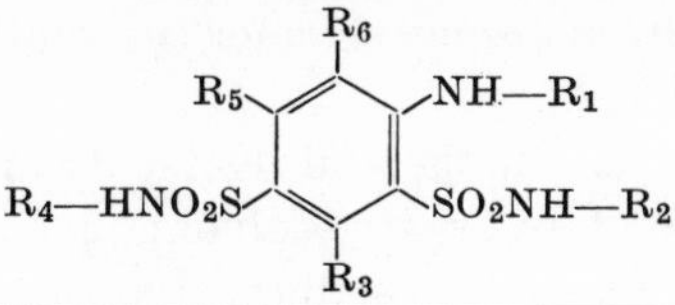

$$R_4\text{—}HNO_2S\text{-}C_6(R_3)(R_5)(R_6)\text{-}NH\text{—}R_1,\ SO_2NH\text{—}R_2$$

R_1	R_2	R_3	R_4	R_5	R_6	Ref.
H	H	H	H	Cl	H	22
H	H	H	H	H	Cl	22
H	H	H	H	Br	Cl	22, 31
H	H	H	H	F	Cl	22, 31
H	H	H	H	CH_3	Cl	22, 31
H	H	H	H	OCH_3	Cl	22
H	H	H	H	NO_2	Cl	22
CH_3	H	H	H	Cl	Cl	22
H	H	H	H	Cl	Cl	27
H	H	H	H	Cl	I	27
H	H	H	H	Cl	Br	27
H	H	H	H	CF_3	H	22, 31, 34
H	H	H	H	Cl	CH_3	31
H	H	H	H	NH_2	H	46
H	H	H	H	H	CH_3	31
H	H	H	H	H	SO_2NH_2	38
H	H	H	H	SCH_3	H	38
H	H	H	H	$SOCH_3$	H	38
H	H	H	H	$SCH_2C_6H_5$	H	38
H	H	H	H	Cl	NO_2	27
H	H	H	H	H	F	27
H	H	H	H	H	SO_2CH_3	27
H	H	CH_3	H	H	CH_3	27
H	H	Cl	H	H	CH_3	27
CH_3	H	Cl	H	Cl	CH_3	22
CH_2CH_2OH	H	Cl	H	CH_3	CH_3	46
NH_2	H	Cl	H	Cl	CH_3	45a
CH_2CH_2OH	H	Cl	H	C_3H_7	CH_3	46
CH_2CH_2OH	H	Cl	H	Cl	CH_3	46
H	CH_3	H	H	Cl	H	27, 31
H	CH_3	H	CH_3	Cl	H	31
CHO	CH_3	H	CH_3	Cl	H	38
H	C_2H_5	H	C_2H_5	Cl	H	38a
H	$CH_2CH{=}CH_2$	H	$CH_2CH{=}CH_2$	Cl	H	38
H	CH_2COOH	H	$CH_2CH{=}CH_2$	CF_3	H	29
H	H	H	H	$NHNH_2$	H	25
H	$(CH_2)_3N(CH_3)_2$	H	$(CH_2)_3N(CH_3)_2$	Cl	H	38
H	NH_2	H	NH_2	Cl	H	38

prepared by Novello *et al.* (22), Lund and Kobinger (29), Close *et al.* (27), Petrow *et al.* (30), and Werner *et al.* (31). The major effort here has been to devise alternate methods for the synthesis of 5-chloro-2,4-disulfamylaniline (XVII).

Modifications of the Lustig and Katscher procedure have been studied; e.g., the use of an organic solvent such as tetrachloroethane as a diluent, and replacement of sodium chloride with thionyl chloride. Logemann and co-workers (32) have shown that the use of a large excess of chlorosulfonic acid alone may suffice to introduce two sulfonyl chloride groups. Other synthetic approaches to XVII also have been developed by Novello (33). These are shown in Schemes 4–6.

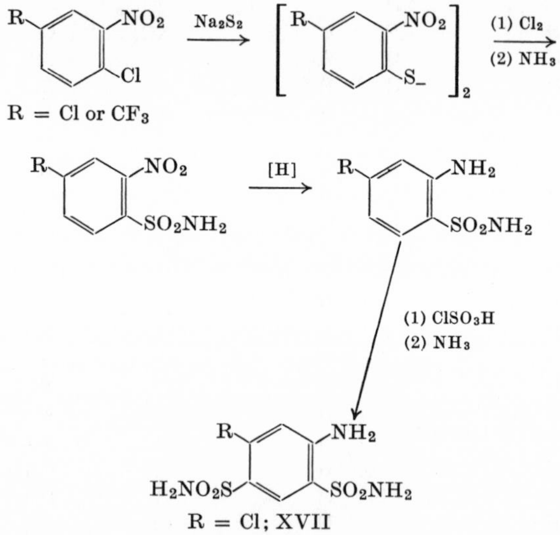

R, NO_2, Cl; Na_2S_2; [R, NO_2, S–]$_2$; (1) Cl_2 (2) NH_3

R = Cl or CF_3

R, NO_2, SO_2NH_2; [H]; R, NH_2, SO_2NH_2; (1) $ClSO_3H$ (2) NH_3

R, NH_2, H_2NO_2S, SO_2NH_2

R = Cl; XVII

R = CF_3; XVIII

SCHEME 4

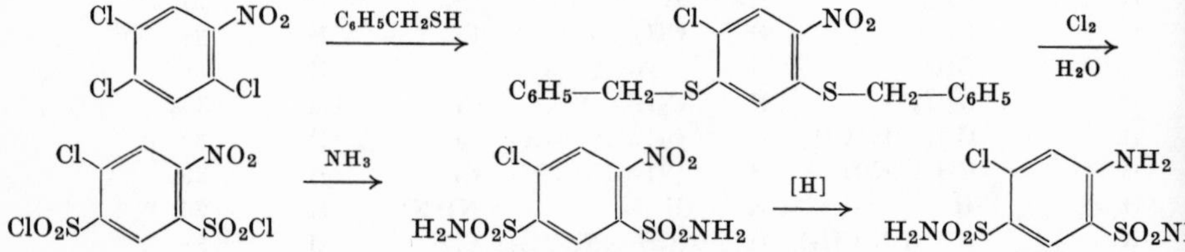

Cl, NO_2, Cl, Cl; $C_6H_5CH_2SH$; Cl, NO_2, C_6H_5—CH_2—S, S—CH_2—C_6H_5; Cl_2 / H_2O

Cl, NO_2, ClO_2S, SO_2Cl; NH_3; Cl, NO_2, H_2NO_2S, SO_2NH_2; [H]; Cl, NH_2, H_2NO_2S, SO_2NH_2

XVII

SCHEME 5

Scheme 4 involves the preparation of a nitrobenzenedisulfide which is oxidatively chlorinated and amidated to the monosulfonamide. Catalytic reduction of the nitro group followed by chlorosulfonation and amidation gave rise to compound XVII. Its trifluoromethyl analog was prepared by a similar sequence of reactions by Holdrege *et al.* (34).

The methods in Schemes 5 and 6 were also developed by Novello. Although these sequences also lead to the synthesis of XVII, they are laborious and the over-all yield of the desired product is inferior to the Lustig and Katscher method.

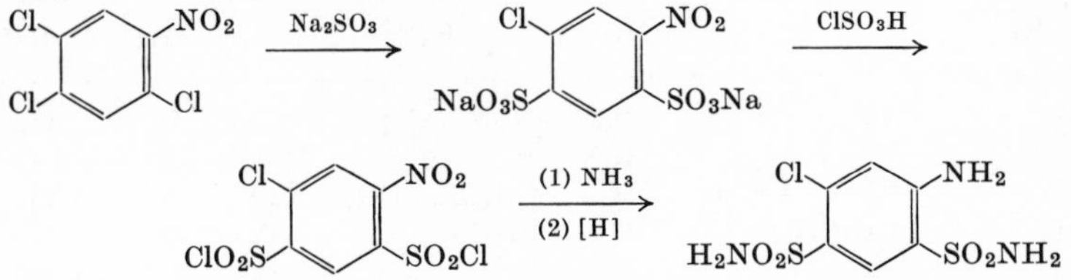

Cl, NO_2, Cl, Cl $\xrightarrow{Na_2SO_3}$ Cl, NO_2, NaO_3S, SO_3Na $\xrightarrow{ClSO_3H}$

Cl, NO_2, ClO_2S, SO_2Cl $\xrightarrow[(2)\ [H]]{(1)\ NH_3}$ Cl, NH_2, H_2NO_2S, SO_2NH_2

XVII

SCHEME 6

The procedure presented in Scheme 3 usually gives good yields of the desired benzenedisulfonyl chlorides. However, when applied to *m*-trifluoromethylaniline low yields are obtained (35). Two procedures for the preparation of 5α,α,α-trifluoromethyl-2,4-disulfamylaniline (XVIII) have been reported, the one using the corresponding trifluoromethyl compound as starting material follows Scheme 4 (36) whereas the other is outlined in Scheme 7 according to the method of Novello *et al.* (22).

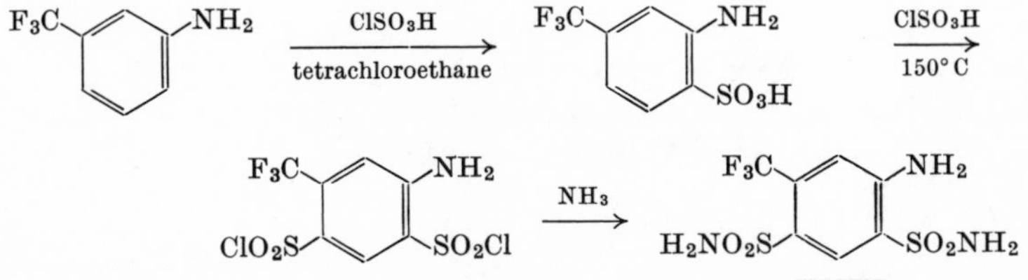

F_3C, NH_2 $\xrightarrow[\text{tetrachloroethane}]{ClSO_3H}$ F_3C, NH_2, SO_3H $\xrightarrow[150°C]{ClSO_3H}$

F_3C, NH_2, ClO_2S, SO_2Cl $\xrightarrow{NH_3}$ F_3C, NH_2, H_2NO_2S, SO_2NH_2

XVIII

SCHEME 7

The methods herein outlined have also proved useful in the preparation of benzenedisulfonamides in which the amino group has been replaced with other functional groups. For example, *m*-chlorotoluene and *m*-chloroanisole have been transformed to the corresponding *m*-benzenedisulfonamides. Some of these compounds are listed in Table V.

TABLE V

DISULFAMYLANILINES

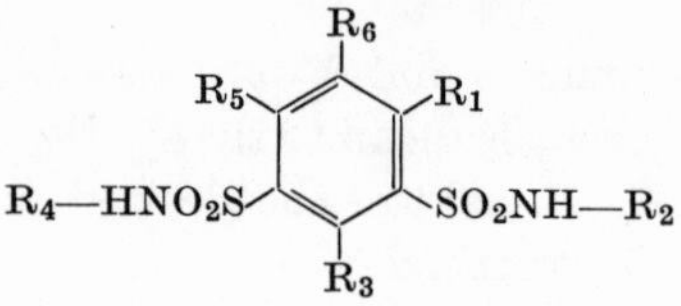

$$R_4{-}HNO_2S{-}C_6(R_1)(R_3)(R_5)(R_6){-}SO_2NH{-}R_2$$

R_1	R_2	R_3	R_4	R_5	R_6	Ref.
CH_3	H	H	H	Cl	H	45, 46
OCH_3	H	H	H	Cl	H	38
CH_3	$CH_2CH{=}CH_2$	H	$CH_2CH{=}CH_2$	Cl	H	45
CH_3	$CH(CH_3)_2$	H	$CH(CH_3)_2$	Cl	H	45
OH	H	H	H	Cl	H	38
COOH	H	H	H	Cl	H	46
$COOC_4H_9$	H	H	H	Cl	H	46
H	H	H	H	OH	Cl	29
H	H	H	H	Cl	Cl	37
Cl	H	H	H	Cl	H	44
Cl	H	H	H	Cl	CH_3	44
Cl	CH_3	H	CH_3	Cl	H	44
Cl	H	H	H	Cl	Cl	44

Dichlorophenamide (XVI) was prepared by Schultz (37) in an indirect manner as shown in Scheme 8. *o*-Chlorophenol was allowed to

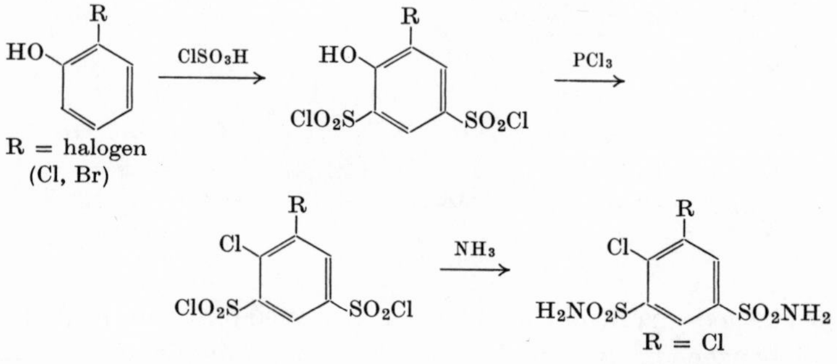

$$\text{HO-}C_6H_4\text{-R} \xrightarrow{ClSO_3H} \text{HO-}C_6H_2(R)(SO_2Cl)_2 \xrightarrow{PCl_3}$$

R = halogen (Cl, Br)

$$\text{Cl-}C_6H_2(R)(SO_2Cl)_2 \xrightarrow{NH_3} \text{Cl-}C_6H_2(R)(SO_2NH_2)_2$$

R = Cl

XVI
dichlorophenamide

SCHEME 8

react with excess chlorosulfonic acid to form the disulfonyl chloride which was then chlorinated with phosphorous trichloride. The resulting dichlorosulfonyl chloride was in turn allowed to react with ammonia to form XVI.

The structure–activity relationships of the following two groups of *m*-benzenedisulfonamides, examples of which are shown in Tables IV and V, have been extensively studied.

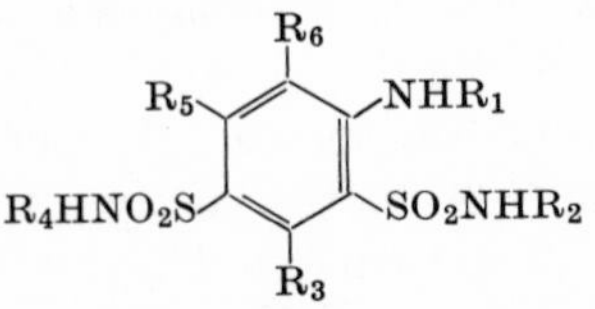

R_6, R_5, NHR_1, R_4HNO_2S, SO_2NHR_2, R_3

A

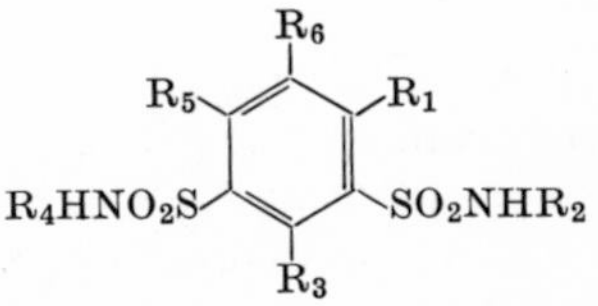

R_6, R_5, R_1, R_4HNO_2S, SO_2NHR_2, R_3

B

In compounds of group A maximum diuretic activity is obtained when R_5 is chlorine, bromine, trifluoromethyl, or nitro and R_1–R_4 and R_6 are hydrogen. Diminished activity is observed with compounds with 5-fluoro, amino, methyl, hydrazino, methoxy, methyl mercapto, and methyl sulfoxide substitution (21, 31). Surprisingly when R_1 to R_6 is equivalent to hydrogen, there results an inactive compound. This is also true when R_6 is —SO_2NH_2 and R_1 to R_5 is hydrogen. The introduction of alkyl substituents (CH_3, —CH_2CH_2—OH) at R_1 with R_5 equal to chlorine and the other R substituents equivalent to hydrogen, gave compounds which are active when given intravenously but are less active when given orally (22, 24, 30, 31). However, it was emphasized by Sprague that the *N*-acyl (CH_3CO to *n*-$C_5H_{11}CO$) derivatives of XVII (5-chloro-2,4-disulfamylaniline) were more active than the parent compound, the diuretic activity increasing from CH_3 to C_5H_{11} (*n*-amyl). With the possible exception of XVII, the above described compounds have not achieved notable clinical importance. However, it is of interest that the substitution of the sulfonamide nitrogens in group A compounds, e.g. R_2 and R_4 equal to methyl or ethyl, R_5 equal to chlorine or trifluoromethyl, and R_3 and R_6 equal to hydrogen, does not lead to substances with lower diuretic activity (38, 39). Cheney and Holdrege (40) have claimed compound XIX to be a more potent natriuretic than the corresponding *N*,*N*′-dimethyl

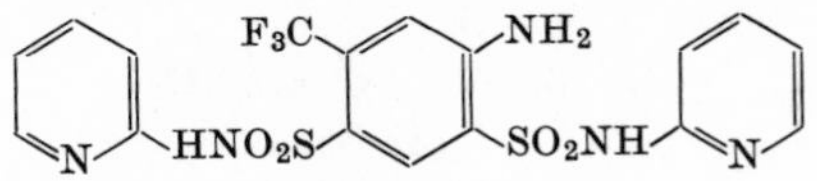

F_3C, NH_2, HNO_2S, SO_2NH, N, N

XIX

analog. Logemann, Giraldi, and Parenti (41) prepared XX, and the diuretic activity of this compound is purported to be equal to hydro-

Cl NH_2
CH_3HNO_2S SO_2NHCH_3
XX

chlorothiazide (see Chapter VI) without causing any inhibition of carbonic anhydrase. They also state that the diuresis brought about by XX is milder and more prolonged than hydrochlorothiazide. These claims have not been clinically supported. Werner and deStevens (38a) have observed that the *N*,*N′*-diethyl derivative (see Table IV) is more potent than XX. It has also been found by deStevens and Werner (38) that the *N*-formyl derivative of XX is slightly more active than XX.

A number of active preparations also have been obtained from group B type compounds. Outstanding among these is dichlorophenamide (XVI). However, this drug is a potent carbonic anhydrase inhibitor with an activity of at least five times that of acetazolamide. Therefore, it is less suitable as a diuretic; its main application is in the treatment of glaucoma (42).

The monochloro compound XV has been clinically evaluated and has found some use as an oral diuretic. Kabisch (43) has indicated it may also find some use in overcoming mild hypertension.

Bourdais and Meyer (44) have prepared a number of substituted 1,3-dichloro-2,4-benzenedisulfonamides (see Table IV) and have compared their carbonic anhydrase inhibitory effects with acetazolamide. The trichloro derivative XXI was reported to be twice as

Cl
Cl Cl
H_2NO_2S SO_2NH_2
XXI

active as acetazolamide. Disulfamide (XXII) has approximately one-tenth the diuretic activity of hydrochlorothiazide with a recom-

Cl CH_3
H_2NO_2S SO_2NH_2
XXII
disulfamide

mended daily dosage of 200–300 mg. Conversion of the methyl group to a carboxyl by oxidation gave a relatively inactive compound (45), but Jackman *et al.* (46) have reported that the *n*-butyl ester of this acid has a diuretic potency comparable to disulfamide. These compounds have more than five times the carbonic anhydrase inhibitory activity of acetazolamide. deStevens and collaborators (45) also found that bismonoalkylation of the sulfamyl nitrogens of XXII yielded compounds with decreased diuretic and carbonic anhydrase inhibitory activities.

2. Synthesis and Biological Activities of Modified Benzenesulfonamides

The structure–activity relationship study initially developed by Novello *et al.* (22) and later confirmed and expanded upon by many investigators established primarily that maximum diuretic activity in the benzene disulfonamides was obtained in those compounds in which the sulfamyl groups were *meta* to each other. Consequently, vigorous efforts were made in a number of laboratories to modify at least one of these groups and then determine the diuretic effect of such compounds in experimental animals. In addition, these substances were used as intermediates in the preparation of quinazolinone and benzotriazine heterocycles related to benzothiadiazine-1,1-dioxides (see Chapter VI).

The obvious change, of course, consisted in replacing one of the sulfamyl groups with a carboxamide group. Novello (47) and then Cohen *et al.* (48) prepared 2-amino-4-chloro-5-sulfamylbenzamide (XXIII) as shown in Scheme 9. The initial step in this synthesis

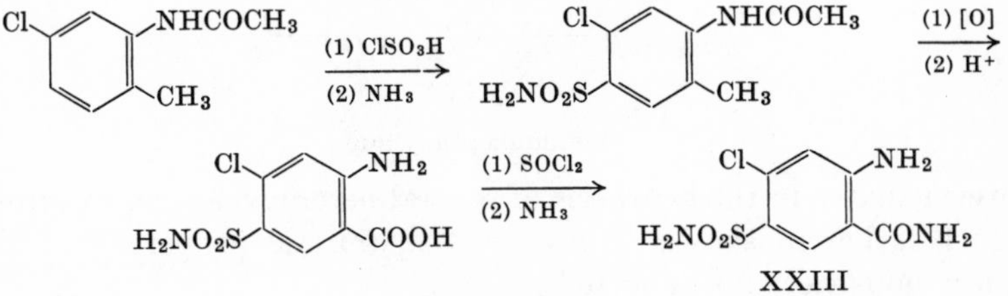

Cl, $NHCOCH_3$, CH_3 benzene $\xrightarrow{(1)\ ClSO_3H;\ (2)\ NH_3}$ Cl, $NHCOCH_3$, H_2NO_2S, CH_3 benzene $\xrightarrow{(1)\ [O];\ (2)\ H^+}$

Cl, NH_2, H_2NO_2S, COOH benzene $\xrightarrow{(1)\ SOCl_2;\ (2)\ NH_3}$ Cl, NH_2, H_2NO_2S, $CONH_2$ benzene (XXIII)

Scheme 9

proceeds smoothly to form the sulfonamide derivative which in turn was oxidized with permanganate and the resulting carboxylic acid was converted to the carboxamide XXIII by the usual method.

Compound XXIII did show some diuretic activity but it was definitely weaker than 5-chloro-2,4-disulfamylaniline (XVII).

Further modifications of XXIII were made by Sturm and coworkers (49). These investigators treated 3-sulfamyl-4,6-dichlorobenzoic acid with various arylmethylamines.

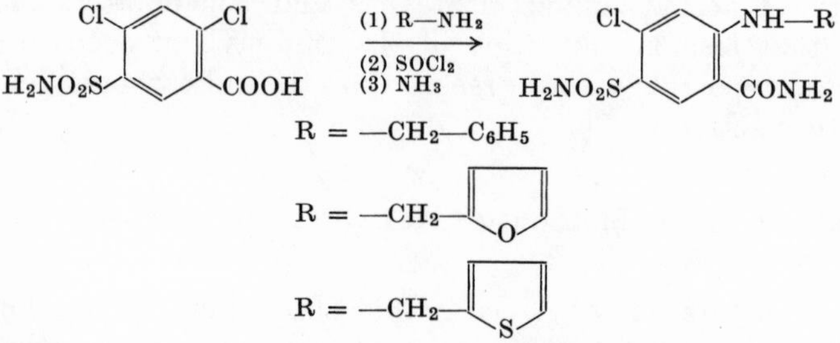

Cl, Cl, H_2NO_2S, COOH —(1) R—NH_2 (2) $SOCl_2$ (3) NH_3→ Cl, NH—R, H_2NO_2S, $CONH_2$

R = —CH_2—C_6H_5

R = —CH_2—(2-furyl)

R = —CH_2—(2-thienyl)

The chloro group *para* to the sulfamyl and *ortho* to the carboxyl groups is activated and is easily replaced by the amine. The carboxylic acid group was converted to the amide. The benzyl and furfuryl derivatives were reported to have diuretic and saluretic effects slightly better than hydrochlorothiazide.

In 1962 Jucker and Lindenmann (50) synthesized a number of 3-sulfamyl-4-chlorobenzamides and benzhydrazides from the acid chloride. Some of the latter compounds are presented in Table VI. Although detailed biological data on all of these compounds have not been forthcoming, it is worthy of note that compound XXIV has been clinically evaluated and has a weaker diuretic effect than hydrochlorothiazide (51). Jucker was also able to use these hydrazides as

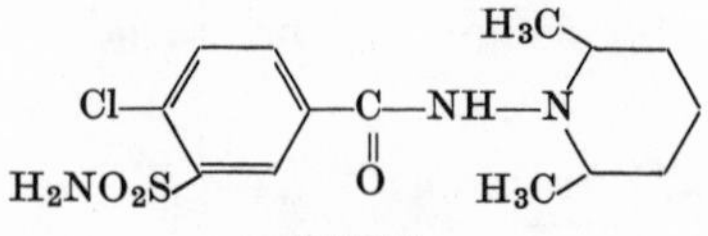

Cl, H_2NO_2S, —C(=O)—NH—N (2,6-dimethylpiperidino; H_3C, H_3C)

XXIV

chlosudimeprimylium

intermediates in the synthesis of several heterocycles, an example of which is herein shown. However, the diuretic properties of these compounds were not reported.

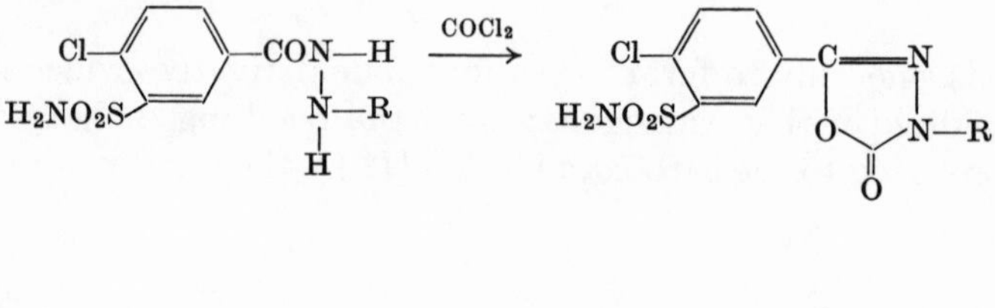

Cl, H_2NO_2S, —CON(H)—N(H)—R —$COCl_2$→ Cl, H_2NO_2S, —C=N—N(R)—C(=O)—O— (ring)

TABLE VI

BENZHYDRAZIDES (50)

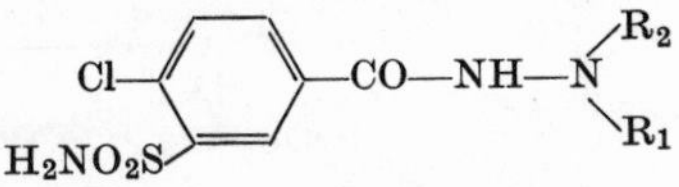

Cl— —CO—NH—N(R_2)(R_1)

H_2NO_2S

R_1	R_2
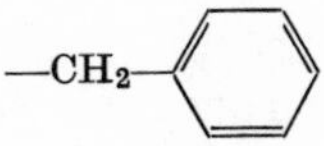 —CH_2—	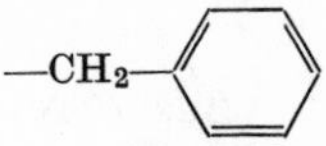 —CH_2—
H	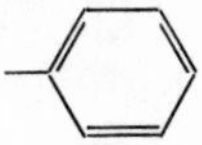
H	—Cl
H	—NO_2
H	—SO_2NH_2
H	SO_2NH_2 —Cl
H	—CH_3
H	N

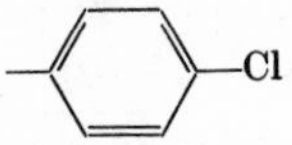

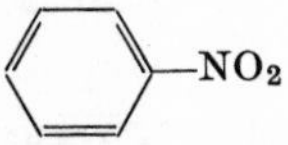

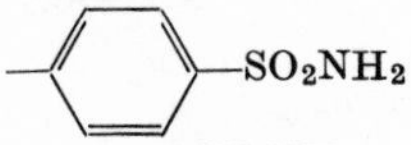

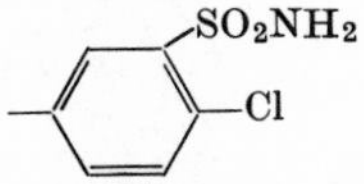

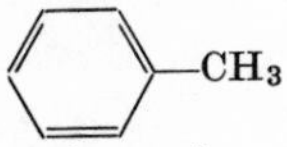

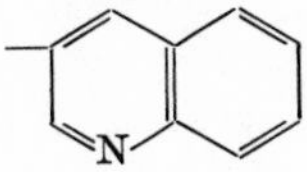

On the other hand the isomeric analog of XXIII was prepared by deStevens and Werner (38) as follows:

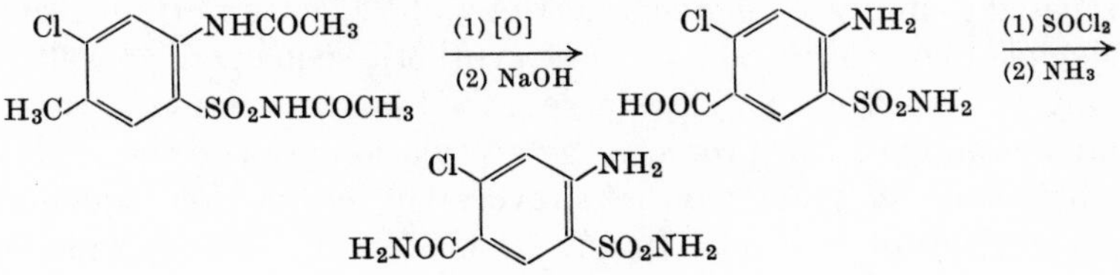

Cl, $NHCOCH_3$, H_3C, $SO_2NHCOCH_3$ $\xrightarrow[\text{(2) NaOH}]{\text{(1) [O]}}$ Cl, NH_2, HOOC, SO_2NH_2 $\xrightarrow[\text{(2) } NH_3]{\text{(1) } SOCl_2}$ Cl, NH_2, H_2NOC, SO_2NH_2

XXV

Compound XXV was devoid of diuretic activity. Furthermore, the dicarboxamide (XXVI) was also inactive (38).

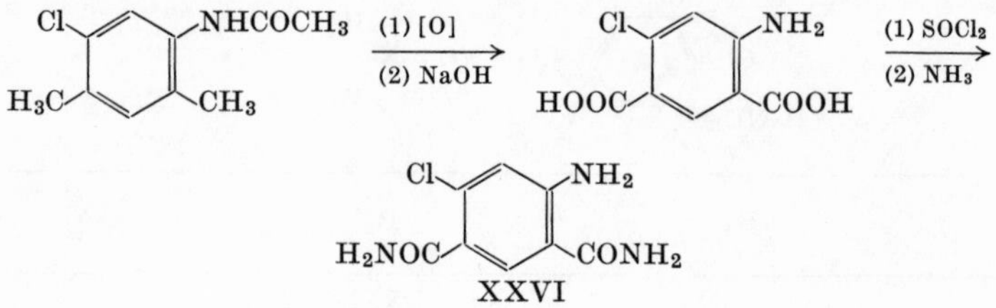

XXVI

Novello *et al.* studied the effect of replacing one of the sulfamyl groups in the parent disulfonamide (XVII) with a methylsulfonyl group. The two isomeric methylsulfonyl analogs (XXVII and XXVIII) were

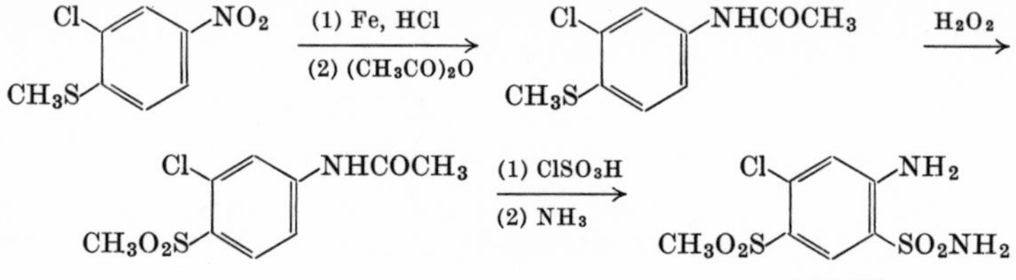

XXVII

SCHEME 10A

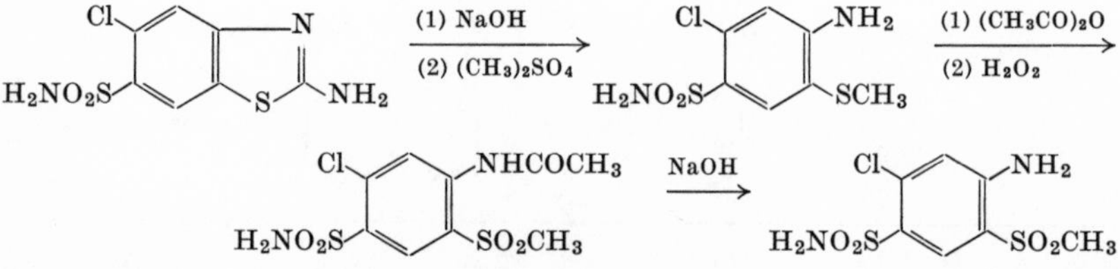

XXVIII

SCHEME 10B

prepared as indicated in Schemes 10A and B. The important reaction principle involved in each of these synthetic sequences, as well as in many of the others previously described in this section is that the amino group must be protected by acetylation prior to the oxidation step. Cohen *et al.* indicated that a reversal of the reaction sequence led to a mixture of products. In any event, Novello has reported compounds XXVII and XXVIII to be only weakly active.

The benzenesulfonamides heretofore described have been characterized by having the two sulfamyl groups or the sulfamyl and carboxamide group on the same benzene ring. The group headed by Petrow (52) at British Drug Houses Ltd., has evaluated a variety of sulfonamides containing bicyclic aromatic structures for their carbonic anhydrase inhibitory action. The outstanding compounds in this series were diphenyl-4-sulfonamide (XXIX), diphenyl-4,4′-disulfonamide (XXX), and diphenylsulfide-4,4′-disulfonamide (XXXI), their *in vitro* inhibitory effect in rats being 360, 690, and 515 times that of sulfanilamide, respectively. Unfortunately, these compounds were totally inactive as diuretic agents upon oral administration. The introduction of a —CH_2 group between the aromatic rings produces a compound, diphenylmethane-4,4′-disulfonamide (XXXII),

$C_6H_5—C_6H_4—SO_2NH_2$

XXIX

$H_2NO_2S—C_6H_4—C_6H_4—SO_2NH_2$

XXX

$H_2NO_2S—C_6H_4—S—C_6H_4—SO_2NH_2$

XXXI

$H_2NO_2S—C_6H_4—CH_2—C_6H_4—SO_2NH_2$

XXXII

which is considered to be several times more active than acetazolamide as a carbonic anhydrase inhibitor in man (53). It is also claimed to be clinically active as a natriuretic agent (54).

An interesting variation of the diphenylsulfonamides has been made by Graf *et al.* working with Stoll at the Geigy Laboratories (55). Their compounds incorporate sulfamyl and carboxamide groups in each benzene ring of the benzophenone system and their mode of synthesis is illustrated in Scheme 11. The more direct route involves amidation of the benzophenonesulfonyl chloride derivative although Graf and co-workers reported that oxidation of the diphenylmethanesulfonamide intermediate gives good yields of the desired benzophenone product. The most active member of this group is 3-(4-chloro-3-sulfamylphenyl)-3-hydroxy-1-oxo-isoindoline (chlorthalidone) (XXXIII), which exists primarily in the tautomeric lactam form.

Two related compounds, 4′-chloro-3,4′-disulfamylbenzophenone and 4′-chloro-3′-sulfamylbenzophenone-2-carboxylic acid were found to be more potent carbonic anhydrase inhibitors than XXXIII, but they had a lower diuretic potency. Moreover, their diuretic effect in dogs ceased in approximately 4 hours whereas the action of an equivalent dose of chlorthalidone lasted for more than 13 hours. Stenger *et al.* (56) has indicated that the pronounced increase in urine

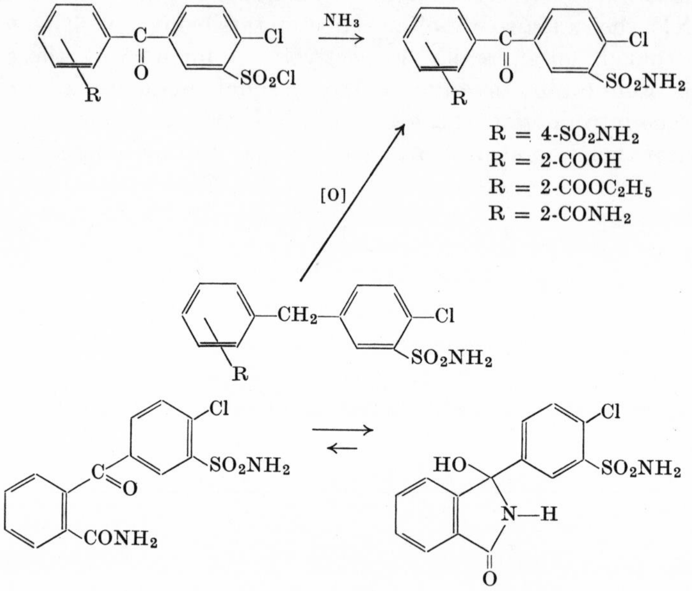

NH_3

[O]

R = 4-SO_2NH_2
R = 2-COOH
R = 2-$COOC_2H_5$
R = 2-$CONH_2$

XXXIII
chlorthalidone

SCHEME 11

flow in dogs caused by chlorthalidone is accompanied by increases in sodium and chloride excretion but the excretion of potassium is not greatly raised. The carbonic anhydrase inhibitory activity was seventeen times as great as that of sulfanilamide by *in vitro* assay. The diuretic effect was not influenced by experimentally induced acidosis or alkalosis. Chronic oral administration to dogs led to only moderate changes in serum electrolytes with serum potassium concentration slightly decreased. Veyrat, Arnold, and Duckert (57) studied chlorthalidone in over one hundred patients with cardiac and cirrhotic edema and found that a single dose of 100–200 mg raised urine flow output and sodium chloride excretion for 24 to 48 hours.

Supplements of potassium citrate were given daily to counteract renal potassium loss. Thus, pharmacologically and clinically, chlorthalidone behaves quite similarly to the thiazides and hydrothiazides (see Chapter VI) with the exception that its duration of action can be as much as 48 hours. Chlorthalidone has been a worthy addition to the armamentarium of nonmercurial orally effective diuretic drugs now in use.

3. Heterocyclic Mono- and Disulfonamides

This section deals only with compounds in which the sulfamyl group or groups are linked directly to a heterocycle. The basic heterocyclic systems along with their *benzo*hetero systems which have been studied extensively are the thiophenes (benzothiophenes), thiazoles (benzothiazoles), and pyridines (quinolines). These heterocyclic mono- and disulfonamides have been prepared for the most part by methods previously described; i.e., chlorosulfonation followed by amidation. Consequently, the discussion here will concern itself with the diuretic effects of these compounds.

(*a*) *Thiophene and Benzothiophene Sulfonamides.* Research on thiophene disulfonamides has been carried out primarily in the Hoechst (58) and CIBA Laboratories (45). The compounds prepared in this series are listed in Table VII. The first of these to be synthesized was 5-acetamido-2,4-disulfamylthiophene—a compound structurally related to acetazolamide. This compound was found to exhibit only slight diuretic activity when tested in rats. In each case these substances have been diuretically compared with hydrochlorothiazide.

On the other hand, 5-chloro-2,4-disulfamylthiophene had one-tenth the diuretic activity of hydrochlorothiazide. Surprisingly, the corresponding 5-bromo derivative had weaker diuretic activity. However, the 5-alkyl-2,4-disulfamylthiophenes showed significant effects. Outstanding in this group is 5-ethyl-2,4-disulfamylthiophene which elicited one-fifth the diuretic effect of hydrochlorothiazide.

deStevens *et al.* (45) then extended this study to determine the effect of the 3-alkyl-2,5-disulfamylthiophenes. However chlorosulfonation followed by amidation of 3-methylthiophene yielded two isomers which were shown by ultraviolet absorption measurements to be compounds XXXIV and XXXV. The latter substance was one-fifth as active as hydrochlorothiazide, whereas XXXIV was only weakly active.

TABLE VII

THIOPHENE DISULFONAMIDES (45)

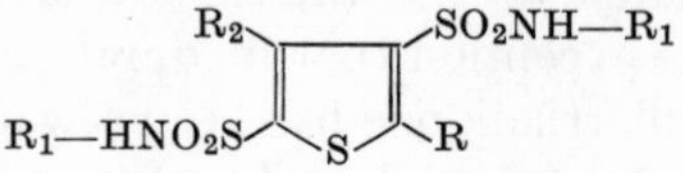

R	R_1	R_2	Diuretic activity (hydrochlorothiazide = 1)
$NHCOCH_3$	H	H	weak
Cl	H	H	0.1
Br	H	H	weak
CH_3	H	H	0.1
C_2H_5	H	H	0.20
C_3H_7(iso)	H	H	0.1
C_3H_7(*n*)	H	H	0.1
C_2H_5	H	CH_3	weak

The above data indicated that the 3-methyl and the 5-ethyl derivatives were the most effective diuretic agents in the thiophene series when tested in experimental animals. Consequently, a compound incorporating both of these groups at the 3- and 5-positions of the thiophene molecule was synthesized (last compound in Table VII). 5-Ethyl-3-methyl-2,4-disulfamylthiophene was tested for its diuretic properties but was found to be only weakly active.

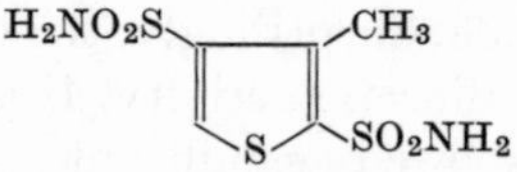

XXXIV 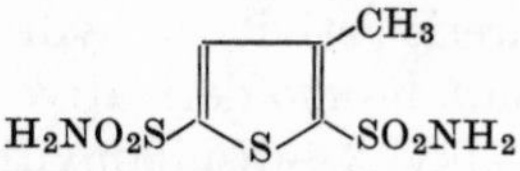 XXXV

Finally, it is noteworthy that all of the active compounds in this series not only increased sodium excretion but also raised the output of potassium substantially. This is an indication of their potent carbonic anhydrase inhibitory action. This side effect makes this type of compound less desirable as a diuretic.

Two isomeric benzothiophene disulfonamides were prepared in the CIBA Laboratories (38) but both of these were inactive. The position of substitution of the sulfamyl group on the benzene ring was not determined.

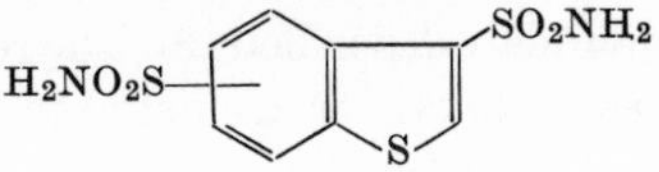

H_2NO_2S— [benzothiophene ring] —SO_2NH_2

Isomer I: mp 305–307° C
Isomer II: mp 235° C

(*b*) *Thiazole and Benzothiazole Sulfonamides*. In the thiazole class, two groups of compounds have been prepared, the 2-amino-5-sulfamylthiazoles and 2-sulfamyl-4-substituted thiazoles. The former compounds were synthesized by Ziegler, Kuhl, and Sprague (59) from the 2-acetamidothiazoles according to known methods. The 2-(*p*-carboxybenzenesulfonylamino)-5-sulfamylthiazole was prepared by allowing 2-amino-5-sulfamylthiazole to react with *p*-carboxybenzenesulfonylchloride. Table VIII contains some of the compounds prepared and their diuretic effects (60).

TABLE VIII

THIAZOLE SULFONAMIDES (60)

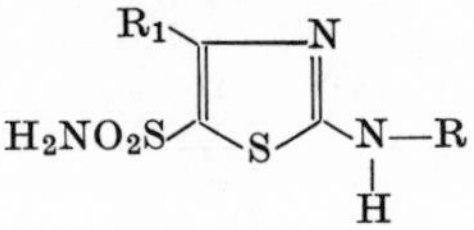

R_1, N, H_2NO_2S, S, N—R, H

R	R_1	Dose (intravenous)
 HOOC—C_6H_4—SO_2—	H	1/4
 HOOC—C_6H_4—SO_2—	CH_3	1/10
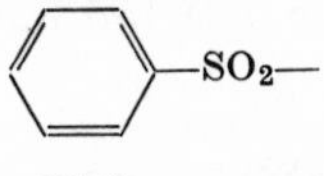 C_6H_5—SO_2—	CH_3	1/2
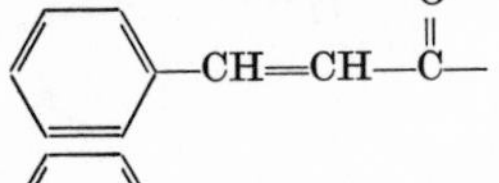 C_6H_5—CH=CH—C(=O)—	CH_3	1/2
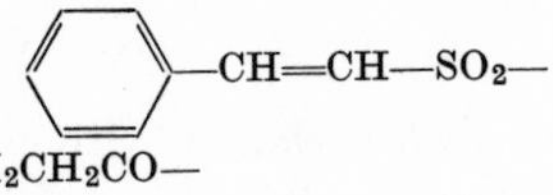 C_6H_5—CH=CH—SO_2—	CH_3	1/4
$CH_3CH_2CH_2CO$—	CH_3	1/10

The alternate isomer, 2-sulfamyl-4-substituted thiazole, was synthesized *via* the 2-mercapto derivative according to the chlorine oxidation method previously described (9). The results of the biological testing of some of these substances are listed in Table IX (61). In the activity tests reported in Tables VIII and IX, the fractions express that part of a full dose at which the compound is active. A full dose is conventionally and arbitrarily set as an initial priming dose of 25 mg/kg of body weight, followed by an infusion of 30 mg/kg per hour. These tests were run in dogs. Although these animal results seem quite impressive, it is difficult to determine how these substances would behave clinically.

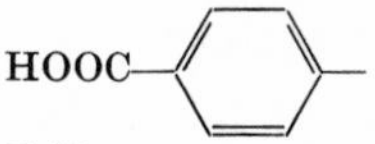

TABLE IX

THIAZOLE SULFONAMIDES (61)

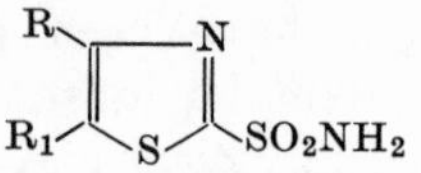

R	R_1	Dose (intravenous)
COOH	H	1/4
CH_3	COOH	1/4
HOOC–C_6H_4–	H	1/4
HOOC–C_6H_4–	Cl	1/10
C_6H_5	H	1/4

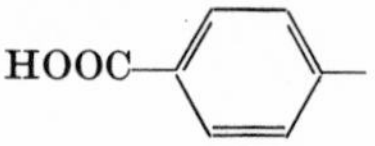

In the benzothiazole series, two compounds (XXXVI and XXXVII) were prepared by Werner and deStevens (38), but both were devoid of diuretic effects.

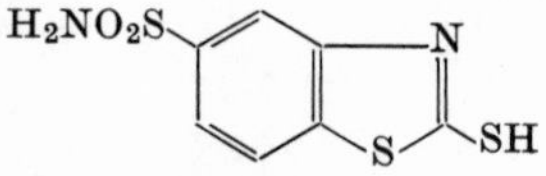

XXXVI 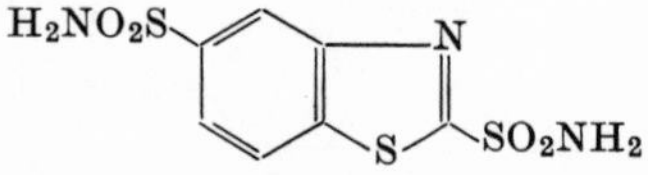 XXXVII

(c) *Pyridine and Quinoline Sulfonamides.* Investigations in 2-aminopyridinedisulfonamides were initially carried out in the CIBA

Laboratories (45a, 62) and shortly thereafter reports were forthcoming from the Sprague (63) group at Merck, Sharp and Dohme and from Yale (64) and co-workers at Squibb.

At the time this work was commenced, 3,5-pyridinedisulfonic acid (65, 66) was the only disulfonated pyridine described in the literature. An attempt to prepare 3,5-disulfamylpyridine was not too successful. However, an amino group in the 2-position of the pyridine ring greatly facilitated the sulfonation and consequently several 2-amino-3,5-disulfamylpyridines with and without substituents at position 6 have been prepared. 2-Amino-3,5-disulfamylpyridine (R = H) and 2,6-diamino-3,5-disulfamylpyridine (R = NH_2) were found to be very

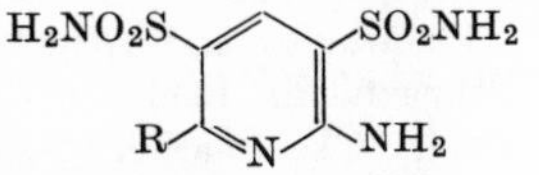

H_2NO_2S SO_2NH_2
R N NH_2

R = H, CH_3, NH_2 (62–64)
R = OH, Cl (64)

weakly active as diuretics; 2-amino-6-methyl-3,5-disulfamylpyridine (R = CH_3) showed greater diuretic activity but was still less active than a similar analog in the benzene series (compound XXII, disulfamide). The biological properties of the 6-hydroxy- and 6-chloro-3,5-disulfamylpyridines have not been reported.

The Merck group also converted 4-aminopeyridine to 4-amino-3,5-disulfamylpyridine (XXXVIII) for use as an intermediate in the synthesis of pyrido[4,3-*e*]-1,2,4-thiadiazine-1,1-dioxides (to be discussed in Chapter VI). However, no biological data were presented on this substance.

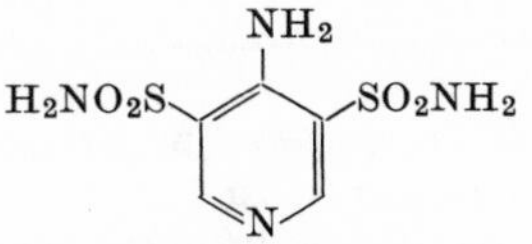

NH_2
H_2NO_2S SO_2NH_2
N

XXXVIII

In the quinoline series (formally, this ring system can be considered a benzopyridine), a patent has been issued to Meyer (67) for the preparation of 7-chloro-4-hydroxy-6-sulfamylquinoline (XXXIX).

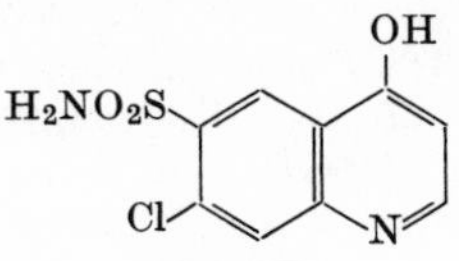

OH
H_2NO_2S
Cl N

XXXIX

This substance is described as a diuretic agent of high activity producing a marked increase in sodium and chloride excretion as well as in urine volume. It is also orally effective. No clinical data are available on this compound.

References

1. G. Domagk, *Deut. Med. Wochschr.* **61**, 250 (1935).
2. J. Trefouël, Mme. J. Trefouël, F. Nitti, and D. Bovet, *Compt. Rend. Soc. Biol.* **120**, 756 (1935).
3. T. Mann and D. Keilin, *Nature* **146**, 164 (1940).
4. R. F. Pitts and R. S. Alexander, *Am. J. Physiol.* **144**, 239 (1945).
5. E. Goldberger, "Water, Electrolyte and Acid-Base Syndromes." Lea and Febiger, Philadelphia, Pennsylvania, 1959.
6. L. Goodman and A. Gilman, "The Pharmacological Basis of Therapeutics," p. 839. Macmillan, New York, 1960.
7. W. B. Schwartz, *New Engl. J. Med.* **240**, 173 (1949).
8. H. A. Krebs, *Biochem. J.* **43**, 525 (1948).
9. R. O. Roblin, Jr., and J. W. Clapp, *J. Am. Chem. Soc.* **72**, 4890 (1950).
10. W. H. Miller, A. M. Dessert, and R. O. Roblin, Jr., *J. Am. Chem. Soc.* **72**, 4893 (1950).
11. J. W. Clapp, *J. Biol. Chem.* **223**, 207 (1956).
12. J. Korman, U.S. Pat. 2,868,800 (Jan. 13, 1959).
13. R. V. Ford, *G. P., J. Am. Acad. Gen. Pract.* **14**, 118 (1956).
14. J. Vaughan, Jr., J. A. Eichler, and G. W. Anderson, *J. Org. Chem.* **21**, 700 (1956).
15. R. W. Young, K. H. Wood, J. A. Eichler, J. R. Vaughan, Jr., and G. W. Anderson, *J. Am. Chem. Soc.* **78**, 4649 (1956).
16. G. Kühn, E. Göres, F. Jung, and G. Hilgetag, *Acta Biol. Med. Ger.* **3**, 574 (1959).
17. T. H. Maren, E. Mayer, and B. C. Wadsworth, *Bull. Johns Hopkins Hosp.* **95**, 199 (1954).
18. K. H. Beyer, *Arch. Intern. Pharmacodyn.* **98**, 97 (1954).
19. J. P. Merrill, *Am. J. Med.* **14**, 519 (1953).
20. A. E. Lindsay and H. Brown, *J. Lab. Clin. Med.* **43**, 839 (1954).
21. K. H. Beyer and J. E. Baer, *Pharmacol. Rev.* **13**, 517 (1961).
22. F. C. Novello, S. C. Bell, E. L. A. Abrams, C. Ziegler, and J. M. Sprague, *J. Org. Chem.* **25**, 965 (1960).
23. H. F. Russo, K. H. Beyer, J. E. Baer, and A. S. Haimbach, *Federation Proc.* **17**, 407 (1958).
24. J. M. Sprague, *Ann. N.Y. Acad. Sci.* **71**, 328 (1957).
25. A. Lund and K. Størling, *Acta Pharmacol. Toxicol.* **15**, 300 (1959).
26. O. Lustig and E. Katscher, *Monatsh. Chem.* **48**, 87 (1927).
27. W. J. Close, L. R. Swett, L. E. Brady, J. H. Short, and M. Vernsten, *J. Am. Chem. Soc.* **82**, 1132 (1960).
28. J. H. Short and U. Biermacher, *J. Am. Chem. Soc.* **82**, 1135 (1960).

29. F. J. Lund and W. Kobinger, *Acta Pharmacol. Toxicol.* **16**, 297 (1960).
30. B. G. Boggiano, V. Petrow, O. Stephenson, and A. M. Wild, *J. Pharm. Pharmacol.* **12**, 497 (1960); V. Petrow, O. Stephenson, and A. M. Wild, *J. Pharm. Pharmacol.* **12**, 705 (1960).
31. L. H. Werner, A. Halamandaris, S. Ricca, Jr., L. Dorfman, and G. deStevens, *J. Am. Chem. Soc.* **82**, 1161 (1960).
32. W. Logemann, P. Giraldi, and S. Galimberti, *Ann. Chem.* **623**, 157 (1959).
33. F. C. Novello, U.S. Pat. 2,910,475 (Oct. 27, 1959); U.S. Pat. 2,965,656 (Dec. 20, (1960).
34. C. T. Holdredge, R. B. Babel, and L. C. Cheney, *J. Am. Chem. Soc.* **81**, 4807 (1959).
35. R. Selleri and O. Caldini, *Ann. Chim.* (*Rome*) **50**, 170 (1960).
36. H. Kracker and F. Herrlein, U.S. Pat. 2,119,882 (June 6, 1938).
37. E. M. Schultz, U.S. Pat. 2,835,702 (May 20, 1958).
38. G. deStevens and L. H. Werner, unpublished results from the CIBA, Summit Laboratories.
38a. L. H. Werner and G. deStevens, U.S. Pat. 2,970,154 (Jan. 31, 1961).
39. E. Schlittler, G. deStevens, and L. H. Werner, *Angew. Chem. Intern. Ed. Engl.* [I], **5**, 235 (1962).
40. L. C. Cheney and C. T. Holdrege, U.S. Pat. 2,947,742 (Aug. 2, 1960).
41. W. Logemann, P. N. Giraldi, and M. A. Parenti, *Nature* **182**, 1510 (1958).
42. J. E. Harris, O. Beaudreau, and G. Hoskinon, *Am. J. Ophthalmol.* **45**, 120 (1958).
43. G. Kabisch, *Die Med.*, p. 2179 (1959).
44. J. Bourdais and F. Meyer, *Bull. Soc. Chim. France*, p. 550 (1961).
45. G. deStevens, A. Halamandaris, S. Ricca, Jr., and L. H. Werner, *J. Med. Pharm. Chem.* **1**, 565 (1959).
45a. L. H. Werner, S. Ricca, Jr., A. Halamandaris, and G. deStevens, Meeting-in-Miniature, *Am. Chem. Soc. North Jersey Sect.* (Feb., 1960).
46. G. B. Jackman, V. Petrow, O. Stephenson, and A. M. Wild, *J. Pharm. Pharmacol.* **12**, 648 (1960).
47. F. C. Novello, U.S. Pat. 2,910,488 (Oct. 27, 1959).
48. E. Cohen, B. Klarberg, and J. R. Vaughan, Jr., *J. Am. Chem. Soc.* **82**, 2731 (1960).
49. K. Sturm, W. Siedel, and R. Weyer, U.S. Pat. 3,058,882 (Oct. 16, 1962).
50. E. Jucker and A. Lindenmann, *Helv. Chim. Acta* **45**, 2316 (1962).
51. E. Jucker, *Intern. Congr. Pharm. Chem., Florence, Italy* (Sept., 1962).
52. Y. M. Beasley, B. G. Overell, V. Petrow, and O. Stephenson, *J. Pharm. Pharmacol.* **10**, 696 (1958).
53. W. Modell, *Am. J. Med. Sci.* **231**, 564 (1956).
54. F. Meythaler and E. Hofer, *Ger. Med. Monthly* **3**, 146 (1958).
55. W. Graf, E. Girod, E. Schmid, and W. G. Stoll, *Helv. Chim. Acta* **42**, 1085 (1959).
56. E. G. Stenger, H. Wirz, and R. Pulver, *Schweiz. Med. Wochschr.* **89**, 1126, 1130 (1959).
57. R. Veyrat, E. F. Arnold, and A. Duckert, *Schweiz. Med. Wochschr.* **89**, 1133 (1959).
58. Hoechst Company, West Germany, South African Pat. 3495A-58 (Feb. 1, 1959).
59. C. Ziegler, E. K. Kuhl, and J. M. Sprague, *J. Org. Chem.* **25**, 1454 (1960).
60. J. M. Sprague and C. Ziegler, U.S. Pat. 2,994,702 (Aug. 1, 1961).
61. J. M. Sprague and C. Ziegler, U.S. Pat. 2,994,701 (Aug. 1, 1961).
62. CIBA Ltd., South African Pats. 594,079 and 594,080 (Oct. 15, 1959); Indian Pat. 66,425 (Aug. 14, 1960); Australian Pats. 53,925 and 53,926 (Oct. 22, 1959).

63. E. J. Cragoe, Jr., J. A. Nicholson, and J. M. Sprague, *J. Med. Pharm. Chem.* **4**, 369 (1961).
64. H. L. Yale, K. Losse, and J. Bernstein, *J. Am. Chem. Soc.* **82**, 2042 (1960).
65. L. Hoffmann and W. Koenigs, *Ber. Deut. Chem. Ges.* **16**, 727 (1883).
66. W. Koenigs and R. Geigg, *Ber. Deut. Chem. Ges.* **17**, 589 (1884).
67. R. F. Meyer, U.S. Pat. 3,057,869 (Oct. 9, 1962).

CHAPTER VI

Thiazides and Hydrothiazides

A. Chlorothiazide and Hydrochlorothiazide

The *m*-benzenedisulfonamides studied initially by Sprague *et al.* were shown by Beyer and his group to possess diuretic properties of considerable interest. For example, 5-chloro-2,4-disulfamylaniline (I) (Scheme 1) showed a significant sodium and chloride excretion pattern somewhat similar to the organomercurials and unlike the carbonic anhydrase inhibitor, acetazolamide. As noted previously in these pages, the *N*-acyl (CH_3CO to $C_5H_{11}CO$) derivatives of this compound were more active than the parent substance, the diuretic activity increasing from CH_3 to C_5H_{11} (*n*-amyl). However, these compounds were effective clinically only at relatively high doses and it was uncertain whether or not acidosis could be avoided.

Then a most important development took place. Following an old publication of Ekbom (1) on the condensation of orthanilamide with formic acid, Novello and Sprague (2) treated compound I with this acid. The formylamino intermediate appears to have only transitory existence since the product isolated was the cyclic derivative, 6-chloro-7-sulfamyl-2*H*-1,2,4-benzothiadiazine-1,1-dioxide (chlorothiazide*) (II). The 3-alkyl substituted benzothiadiazine-1,1-dioxides could be prepared readily from the acyl derivatives. Ring closure occurs readily when the sulfamyl group *ortho* to the acylamino group is unsubstituted. The 3-oxo compound (III) was obtained from I by reaction with urea (3).

Chlorothiazide had the most potent diuretic effect of these

* The term "thiazide" is restricted to compounds of the 2*H*-1,2,4-benzothiadiazine-1,1-dioxide series related to chlorothiazide.

compounds. Its outstanding saluretic effect in animals (4) prompted immediate clinical evaluation.

Chlorothiazide showed an unusually high degree of diuretic activity with low toxicity when tested orally in humans. The daily oral dose was found to be from 500 to 2000 mg. Moreover, unlike carbonic anhydrase inhibitors this compound resembled the mercurial diuretics in its action, i.e., approximately equivalent amounts of sodium and chloride ions are excreted. Continued administration did not lead to acidosis and full effectiveness was maintained. More detailed biological

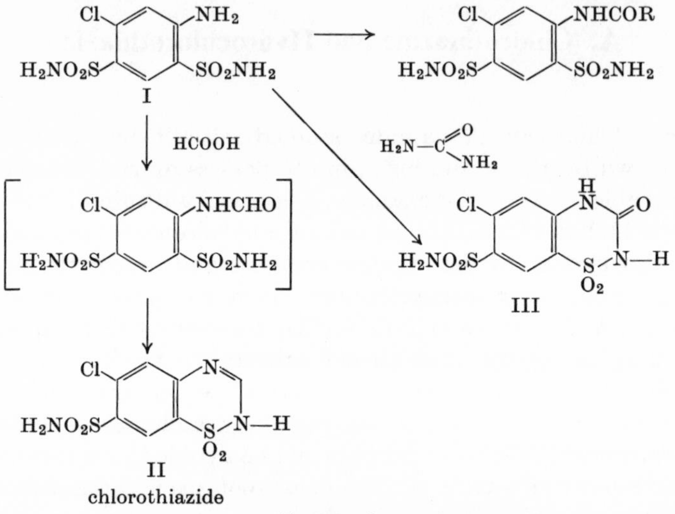

Cl, NH_2, H_2NO_2S, SO_2NH_2 — I → Cl, NHCOR, H_2NO_2S, SO_2NH_2

I —HCOOH→ [Cl, NHCHO, H_2NO_2S, SO_2NH_2] → II chlorothiazide (Cl, H_2NO_2S, N, S, O_2, N—H)

I —$H_2N—C(=O)NH_2$→ III (Cl, H_2NO_2S, H, N, O, S, O_2, N—H)

SCHEME 1

data will be presented later in this chapter. Suffice it to say that chlorothiazide marks the great breakthrough in the search for potent nonmercurial diuretics. But like all breakthroughs, the subsequent directions to be taken were diverse and marked with greater gains and disappointments.

In the course of studies carried out in the CIBA Laboratories on the chemotherapeutic properties of sulfonamides, it became of interest to determine the nature of products derived from the condensation of sulfonamides with aldehydes. The literature (5–7) abounds with examples in which such condensations lead to polymeric materials.

However, in 1951 Freeman and Wagner (8) reported that substituted *o*-aminobenzenesulfonamides react with formaldehyde in alkaline solution to yield *N*-(2)-substituted 3,4-dihydro-1,2,4-benzothiadiazine-1,1-dioxides.

$$\text{o-}C_6H_4(NH_2)(SO_2NHR) \xrightarrow[OH^-]{CH_2O} \text{3,4-dihydro-2-R-1,2,4-benzothiadiazine-1,1-dioxide}$$

R = phenyl or substituted phenyl

This reaction was carried out by deStevens *et al.* (9) on unsubstituted *o*-aminobenzenesulfonamide and various aldehydes in nonpolar solvents with catalytic amounts of hydrogen chloride, and analogous compounds were obtained. Since interest in these heterocycles was influenced primarily by the reported diuretic effects of disulfonamides and related substances, attention was turned to the condensation of 5-chloro-2,4-disulfamylaniline (I) with various aldehydes. On the basis of previous experience, the possible formation of a polymer could not be discounted.

One of the first reactions explored was condensation of formaldehyde with I under acidic conditions (see Scheme II). In spite of the second sulfamyl group, only cyclization occurred to give an excellent yield of 6-chloro-3,4-dihydro-7-sulfamyl-2*H*-1,2,4-benzothiadiazine-1,1-dioxide (VI). This structure of VI was confirmed by sodium borohydride reduction of chlorothiazide (II) to VI. It is also possible to reconvert VI to II in good yield via permanganate oxidation. Compound VI (hydrochlorothiazide*) proved to be from ten to fifteen times more potent than chlorothiazide as a diuretic agent when tested in laboratory animals and humans. The daily oral dose in humans is from 25 to 150 mg. This observation of the increased activity of the dihydro compounds was confirmed later in many hundreds of compounds prepared in this series for diuretic evaluation. It was one of the major findings in this field after the initial investigations of Novello and Sprague since it resulted in a flood tide of work in which chemically and biologically interesting heterocycles emerged from test tubes in profusion.

Before going into a detailed discussion of the structure–activity relationships of chlorothiazide and hydrochlorothiazide and the many compounds prepared in each series, it is of interest to outline some of the chemical transformations and physical properties of these two compounds.

* The term "hydrothiazide" is restricted to compounds of the 3,4-dihydro-(2*H*)-1,2,4-benzothiadiazine-1,1-dioxide series related to hydrochlorothiazide.

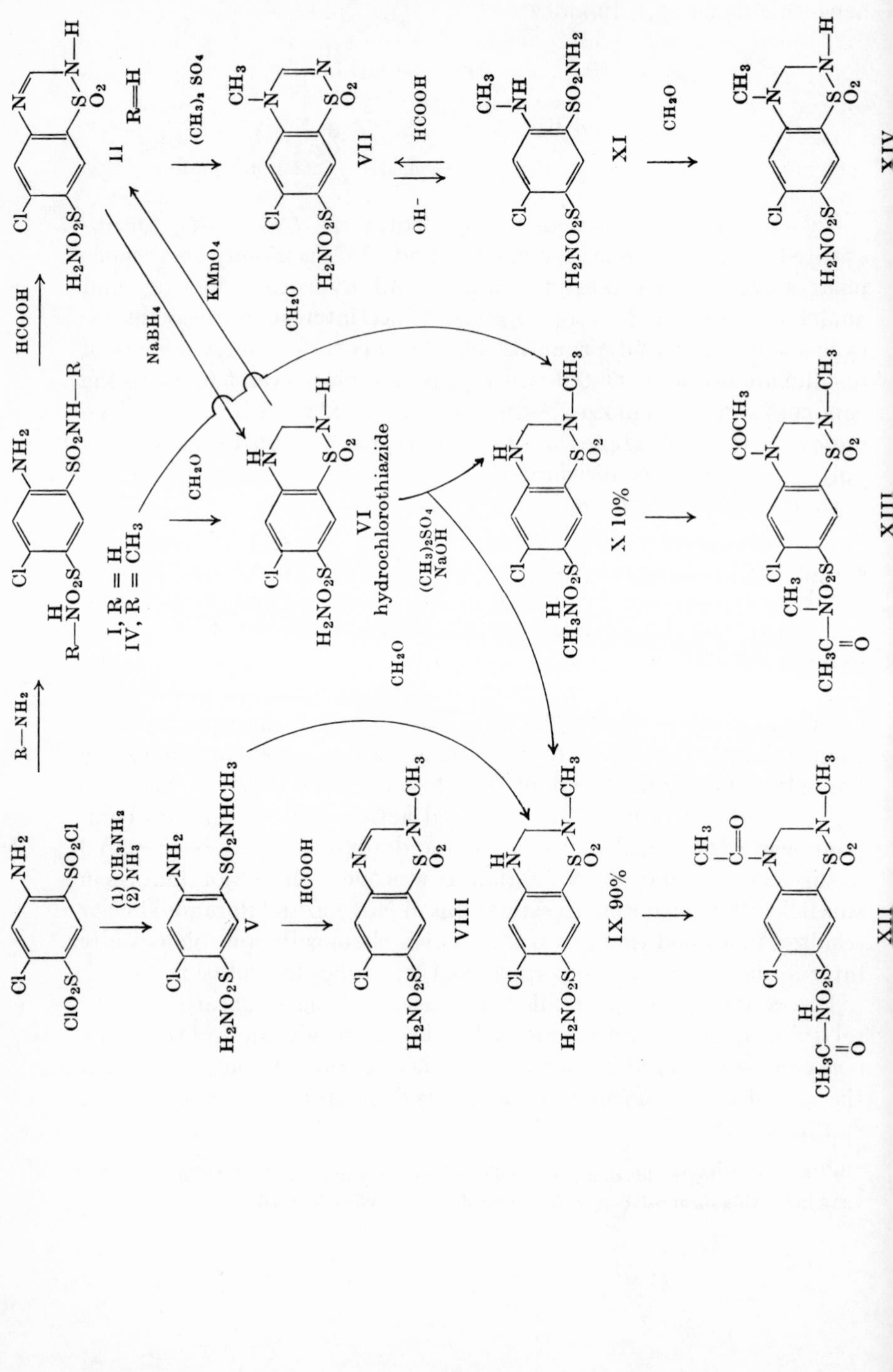

$R{-}NH_2$ → I, R = H; IV, R = CH_3 —HCOOH→ II (R=H)

I, IV —CH_2O→ VI hydrochlorothiazide

II —$NaBH_4$→ VI; VI —$KMnO_4$→ II

II —$(CH_3)_2SO_4$→ VII; VII ⇌ XI (OH⁻ / HCOOH); VII —CH_2O→ (from IV)

XI —CH_2O→ XIV

(1) CH_3NH_2 (2) NH_3 → V —HCOOH→ VIII

V —CH_2O→ IX

VI —$(CH_3)_2SO_4$, NaOH→ X 10% + IX 90%

IX 90% → XII

X 10% → XIII

B. Alkylation Studies

Alkylation and arylalkylation studies were carried out on the parent heterocycles and some interesting differences in the chemical reactivity of these two compounds were noticed. The methylation studies as outlined in Scheme 2 will serve to illustrate these differences.

The methylation of VI (10) with dimethyl sulfate yielded a monomethyl (90%) and a dimethyl derivative (10%). The latter was found to be identical with X which was obtained by condensing the *N*,*N'*-dimethyl-*m*-benzenedisulfonamide (IV) with formaldehyde. In accordance with the proposed structure, the infrared spectrum of this compound did not show NH_2 bands and its diacetyl derivative (XIII) was devoid of NH bands.

In contrast, the infrared spectrum of the monomethyl derivative did exhibit bands characteristic of NH_2 absorption suggesting either structure IX or XIV. However, on the basis of infrared spectra alone, also a 7-methylsulfamyl derivative could not be disregarded. The 4-methyl derivative (XIV) was finally discounted since this compound was synthesized by Novello *et al.* (11) directly from XI and found to be different from the methylation product. To ascertain unequivocally whether the methyl group was in the 2- or 7-position, the elegant diagnostic method of duVigneaud (12) was used. The monomethyl compound was cleaved reductively with sodium in liquid ammonia.

Cl, H_2NO_2S, H, N, S, O_2, N—CH_3, IX $\xrightarrow[NH_3]{Na}$

Cl, NaO_2S, NH—CH_2, N—CH_3, H, SO_2Na $\xrightarrow{(1)\ H^+ \quad (2)\ OH^-}$ CH_3NH_2 ↑

It should be stressed that methylamine is obtained only after the reduction product has been subsequently treated with dilute acid followed by alkali. Contrary to this, a 7-methyl group is already split off as methylamine during sodium liquid ammonia reduction step and is evaporated together with ammonia when working up the reaction mixture. With compound IX methylamine was obtained only after acid and alkali treatment thus indicating a 2-methyl group. The amine was identified by vapor phase chromatography and as its hydrochloride salt. Although trace amounts of ammonia (from incomplete evaporation of the liquid ammonia) are always obtained in this reaction, the isolation of a significant amount of methylamine is critical. It is also worth mentioning that cleavage cannot be obtained by subjecting the 2-methyl compound (IX) solely to the hydrolytic steps of the degradation. As an additional check, 5-chloro-2,4,*N*,*N'*-dimethylsulfamylaniline (IV) was also submitted to the cleavage and hydrolytic procedure, but methylamine was not obtained. Compound IX was obtained alternatively by treating 4-amino-6-chloro-benzene-disulfonylchloride first with 2 molar equivalents of methylamine, and then with ammonia to give V, followed by ring closure with formaldehyde. Condensation of V with formic acid gave rise to 2-methyl-6-chloro-7-sulfamyl-1,2,4-benzothiadiazine-1,1-dioxide (VIII) (11).

Close and co-workers (13) have developed a method for obtaining only the 2-alkyl-substituted dihydrobenzothiadiazine-1,1-dioxides from 6-chloro-3-oxo-7-sulfamyl-3,4-dihydro-1,2,4-benzothiadiazine-1,1-dioxide (III) (Scheme 3). Since the cyclic sulfonamide grouping is

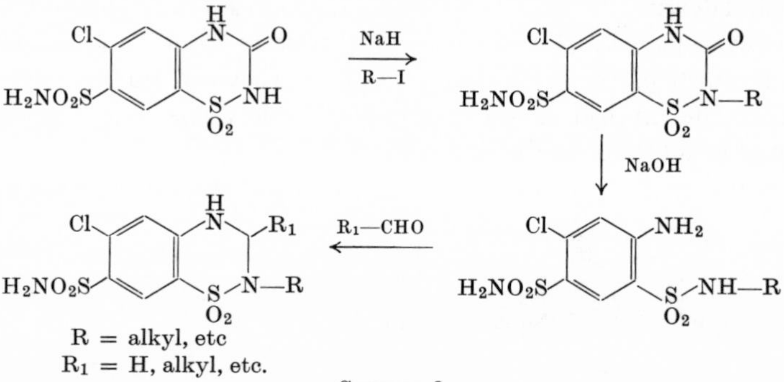

NaH, R—I; NaOH; R_1—CHO

R = alkyl, etc
R_1 = H, alkyl, etc.

SCHEME 3

a stronger acid than the 7-sulfamyl group, alkylation resulted only in the formation of the 2-substituted derivative, which was hydrolyzed and recyclized with the appropriate aldehyde to form the 2-monosubstituted or the 2,3-disubstituted dihydrobenzothiadiazine-1,1-dioxides. The over-all yield of 2-substituted compounds by this procedure is not better than that obtained by the direct alkylation of hydrochlorothiazide.

The well-known conversion of a sulfamyl group to the sulfonyl chloride by the action of chlorosulfonic acid was found by Novello *et al.* (11) to prove useful in transformations in the benzothiadiazine-1,1-dioxide series (see Scheme 4). Thus, the 7-sulfamyl group was converted to the sulfonyl chloride without attack upon the sulfamyl group that is a part of the thiadiazine ring. However, the nature of the final sulfonyl chloride which was obtained varied with the substituent on the nitrogen in the 2-position. When this position was unsubstituted

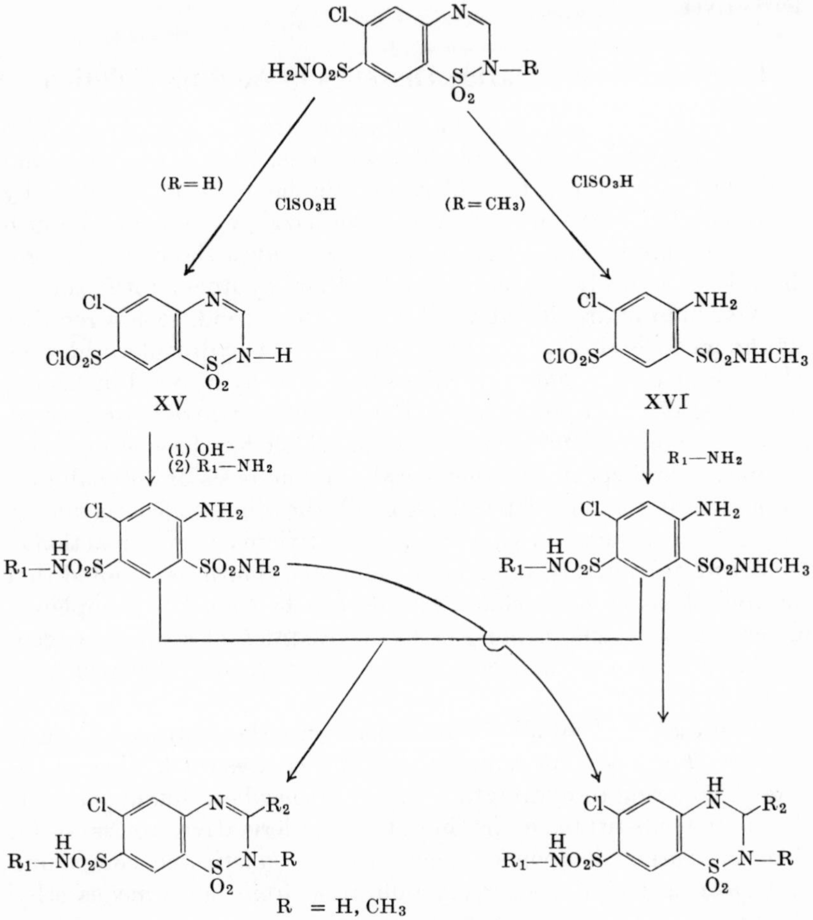

(R = H) $ClSO_3H$ → XV; ($R = CH_3$) $ClSO_3H$ → XVI

XV: (1) OH^- (2) $R_1—NH_2$

XVI: $R_1—NH_2$

R = H, CH_3
$R_1 = R_2$ = lower alkyl, etc.

SCHEME 4

(R = H), the heterocyclic ring remained intact and the sulfonyl chloride derivative (XV) was obtained in 96% yield. However, a substituent in the 2-position labilizes the heterocyclic ring toward hydrolytic cleavage. Thus, when $R = CH_3$, the product of the chlorosulfonic acid reaction was the corresponding 2-methylsulfamyl-5-chloroaniline-4-sulfonyl chloride (XVI) (60%) resulting from such ring opening. The sulfonyl chlorides, XV and XVI, reacted with ammonia or various amines providing useful disulfonamide intermediates for conversion to chlorothiazide and hydrochlorothiazide derivatives.

C. Stability of Thiazide Diuretics in Aqueous Solution

Chlorothiazide and hydrochlorothiazide are slowly hydrolyzed in aqueous, neutral, acid or alkaline solutions. Stability studies and analytical procedures for chlorothiazide have been reported by Charnicki *et al.* (14) and for hydrochlorothiazide by Rehm and Smith (15). The kinetic data compiled in these studies show that chlorothiazide is hydrolyzed more rapidly than hydrochlorothiazide in 0.1 *N* sodium hydroxide at 25° C. Under these conditions it requires 300 hours to hydrolyze approximately 1% of hydrochlorothiazide, whereas the same amount of chlorothiazide is hydrolyzed in 1 hour. Of course, at higher temperatures (70–90° C) the rate of hydrolysis by alkali is much greater. This reaction, which has been established chemically and spectrophotometrically, is the basis of an analytical method (16) for the determination of the diuretic compound in biological specimens through the quantitative diazo color reaction of 5-chloro-2,4-disulfamylaniline (I). Rehm and Smith have noted that the hydrolysis of hydrochlorothiazide can be forced to completion under relatively mild conditions by the addition of a suitable agent (e.g., hydroxylamine hydrochloride) to react with the formaldehyde as it is formed.

The presence of an alkyl substituent on either nitrogen atom in positions 2 or 4 of chlorothiazide greatly increases the lability of the heterocyclic ring to hydrolytic cleavage. It has been found generally that 2- or 3-substituted hydrochlorothiazide derivatives are less stable than the parent compound. Some of these substituted compounds undergo ring fission upon recrystallization from hot aqueous ethyl alcohol.

D. Spectral Properties

1. Ultraviolet Absorption Spectra

The thiadiazine ring of chlorothiazide and its 3-substituted derivatives is undoubtedly a tautomeric system (A $\rightleftharpoons$ B). The double bond may occupy either the 2,3- or the 3,4-position and the anion would be expected to be a resonance hybrid. In an elegant study Novello *et al.* (11) have used ultraviolet absorption data to elucidate which form predominates in solution.

A $\rightleftharpoons$ B

In ethyl alcohol solution, the spectra of compounds having an unsubstituted nitrogen bear a close resemblance to the spectra of those compounds which have the double bond fixed in the 2,3-position (i.e., 4-substituted compounds such as VII in Scheme 2). They show absorption maxima of similar intensity in the region of 265–280 mμ. The presence of chlorine in the benzenoid ring at position 6 produces a strong band at 220–230 mμ, and all compounds have a detectable shoulder at 290–310 mμ. In aqueous sodium hydroxide solution, the spectra of the 2- and 4-unsubstituted compounds show a shift of the 265–280 mμ band to higher wavelengths by 8–17 mμ; the 220–230 mμ band is unaffected and the shoulder at 290–310 mμ becomes more pronounced. In the 2-methyl derivatives which have the double bond fixed at the 3,4-position, a distinct band now appears at 295–310 mμ where only a shoulder exists in all other compounds.

These comparative data indicate that in ethyl alcohol solutions, chlorothiazide and derivatives which are unsubstituted at positions 2 and 4 exist predominantly in the form B with the double bond at the 2,3-position. In aqueous alkali, however, tautomer A with the double bond at the 3,4-position predominates.

The ultraviolet absorption spectra of hydrochlorothiazide and derivatives have three distinct maxima of decreasing intensity at 224–226, 264–273, and 302–325 mμ, comparable to the spectra of the aniline 2,4-disulfonamides.

2. Infrared Absorption Spectra

The infrared absorption spectrum of the 3,4-dihydro-1,2,4-benzothiadiazine-1,1-dioxide (hydrochlorothiazide) will be discussed and compared with that of 1,2,4-benzothiadiazine-1,1-dioxide (chlorothiazide) (10). Because of the insolubility of these compounds in the usual solvents the infrared curves described were run as Nujol mulls.

It was observed that where the benzene ring of the heterocycles was unsubstituted, the N—H bands appeared at approximately 3360 and 3250 cm^{-1}, with the latter band being the stronger of the two. The 1,2,4-benzothiadiazine type compounds always exhibit a strong band at 1625 cm^{-1} which is due in part to the influence of the C=N group adjacent to an aromatic nucleus. In addition, a strong band is present at 1600 cm^{-1} which is caused by the —N—H deformation absorption superimposed on the —C=C— stretching vibrations of the aromatic system. The strength of this band is also associated with the presence of electronegative groups on the benzene ring. On the other hand, the 3,4-dihydro-1,2,4-benzothiadiazine-1,1-dioxides contain only one strong band at 1600 cm^{-1}, as is expected.

The two antisymmetric SO_2 bands appear at approximately 1340 and 1325 cm^{-1} with the latter band sometimes appearing as an inflection and may be associated with the ring $>SO_2$ group. The symmetric $>SO_2$ band absorbs in the region of 1170 cm^{-1}. In the 1,2,4-benzothiadiazine-1,1-dioxides an additional medium-to-strong band appears at 1120 cm^{-1} which is probably characteristic of the SO_2 moiety in the ring. With variously 2,3- and 4-substituted compounds the above described bands are shifted accordingly.

E. Mode of Action of Thiazides and Hydrothiazides

Beyer (4) first observed that chlorothiazide differed from previously known nonmercurial diuretics in that it inhibited renal tubular reabsorption of sodium and chloride in nearly equimolar amounts when administered orally to dogs. The elimination of sodium chloride in turn led to the elimination of an osmotic equivalent of water. However, at high dosages, it was found that potassium and bicarbonate excretion also was increased along with an increase in chloride excretion. This latter effect is in contrast to acetazolamide which causes a marked increase in potassium and bicarbonate secretion with minimum chloride elimination. The diuretic activity of chlorothiazide still persists even at high doses in which excess bicarbonate and potassium have been excreted, whereas under these conditions acetazolamide is rendered ineffective. Hydrochlorothiazide appears to have even a lesser tendency to cause excretion of bicarbonate (17–19). Barrett and co-workers (17) and later Beyer (20) have shown that hydrochlorothiazide is approximately one-tenth as active as chlorothiazide and one-hundredth as active as acetazolamide as a carbonic anhydrase inhibitor. In addition, Plummer *et al.* also presented a detailed comparative evaluation of the diuretic and saluretic effects of chlorothiazide and hydrochlorothiazide when administered orally to the dog. The results of this study are presented in Table I. Hydrochlorothiazide was found to be 6.3 times as potent as chlorothiazide with respect to urine excretion, 5.0 times as potent in terms of sodium output, 4.4 times as potent in terms of potassium excretion, and 9.4 times as potent with respect to chloride elimination. The potassium excretion values, however, are variable and are somewhat dependent on dosage. A comparative study of the absolute potencies (milligrams per milligram effect to obtain a similar diuretic response) of the two compounds in dogs revealed the dihydro compound to be at least 10 times more potent, although each produced its diuretic action within 30 to 60 minutes after oral administration.

TABLE I

A Comparison of the Relative Potencies of Hydrochlorothiazide and Chlorothiazide as Diuretic Drugs in Dogs (17)

Parameter	Relative potency $\frac{\text{Hydrochlorothiazide}}{\text{Chlorothiazide}}$	Confidence limits at $p = 0.05$
Water excretion	6.3	2.7–10.9
Na excretion	5.0	1.9–16.3
K excretion	4.4	1.6–13.3
Cl excretion	9.4	5.8–18.8

To compare the duration of action, the water, sodium, potassium, and chloride excretion values of these two compounds were calculated by Plummer and his associates for three successive 2-hour periods. These results are presented in Figs. 1–4. Examination of these graphs indicates that hydrochlorothiazide is not only more potent than chlorothiazide but possesses a greater duration of action as well. At the 0.08 mg/kg dose level, chlorothiazide failed to evoke a diuretic response at any of the 2-hour intervals. As the dose was increased, the longer duration of action of hydrochlorothiazide resulted in a marked diuretic effect even at the third 2-hour (4–6 hours) interval. Chlorothiazide regularly showed a reduction in diuretic activity at the 2–4

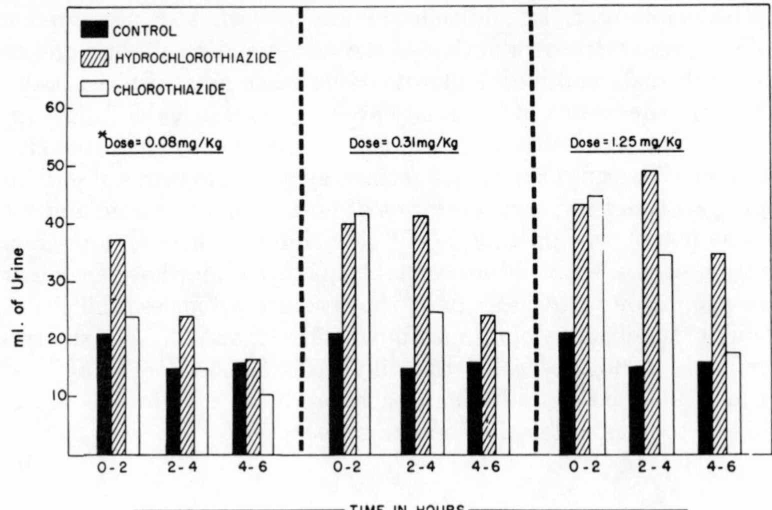

FIG. 1. Comparison of the duration of the diuretic effect in dogs of hydrochlorothiazide and chlorothiazide after oral doses of 0.08, 0.31, and 1.25 mg/kg. Each column represents the average total urine excreted per dog for three successive 2-hour intervals.

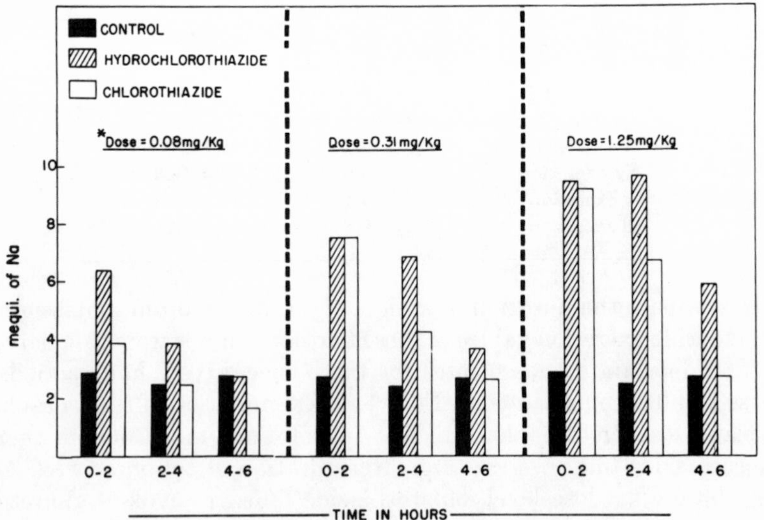

FIG. 2. Comparison of the duration of the natriuretic effect in dogs of hydrochlorothiazide and chlorothiazide after oral doses of 0.08, 0.31, and 1.25 mg/kg. Each column represents the average total milliequivalents of sodium excreted per dog for three successive 2-hour intervals.

hour interval, compared with the 0–2 hour interval, and failed to exhibit any diuretic effect at the 4–6 hour period with the doses employed. A comparison of the urinary excretions of sodium, potassium, and chloride after the administration of the two drugs revealed the same general excretory pattern as was observed for water excretion, with hydrochlorothiazide exhibiting the greater duration of action when both drugs were administered at the same dose level.

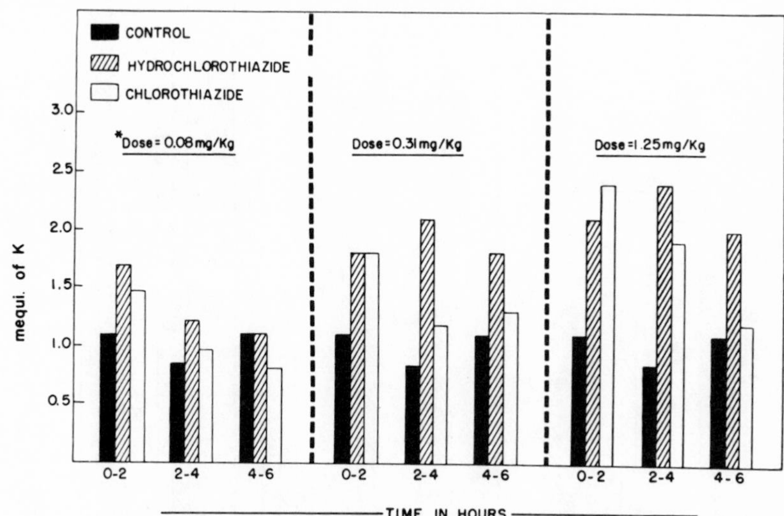

FIG. 3. Comparison of the duration of the kaliuretic effect in dogs of hydrochlorothiazide and chlorothiazide after oral doses of 0.08, 0.31, and 1.25 mg/kg. Each column represents the average total milliequivalents of potassium excreted per dog for three successive 2-hour intervals.

Finally one of the striking differences in action between these two compounds observed by Plummer and his group is the significantly greater urinary excretion of chloride following the oral administration of hydrochlorothiazide (Fig. 4). In fact, the major anion excreted is the chloride ion. With an increase in the oral dosage, they were able to show that the duration of the increased urinary excretion of the chloride ion also increased. This increased chloride excretion was further reflected in the fact that the urinary pH became far less alkaline than with chlorothiazide.

The conventional extrarenal pharmacologic attributes of chlorothiazide have been reported by Preziosi *et al.* (21) and of hydrochlorothiazide by Barrett and colleagues (17). In general they report similar effects. Neither compound produced significant antihistaminic, adrenergic blocking, atropine-like or ganglionic blocking

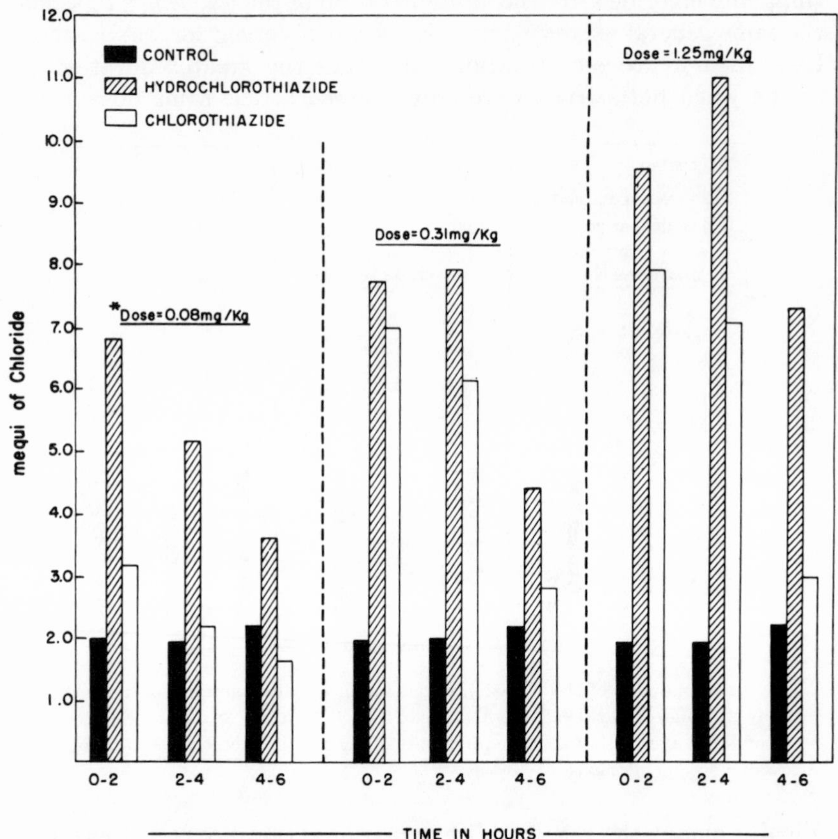

FIG. 4. Comparison of the chloruretic effect in dogs of hydrochlorothiazide and chlorothiazide after oral doses of 0.08, 0.31, and 1.25 mg/kg. Each column represents the total milliequivalents of chloride excreted per dog for three successive 2-hour intervals.

activity, nor did they have analgesic properties. These compounds also did not produce hypotension in normal animals.

The fact that hydrochlorothiazide potentiated the hypotensive effect of hydralazine, evoked a hypotensive response per se after the administration of nonhypotensive doses of hydralazine, and potentiated the cardiovascular depressor response to intravenously administered histamine, suggested that it may increase the responsiveness of the dog to endogenous histamine. This activity may account for its augmentative effect with hydralazine. The increased responsiveness to endogenous histamine may be secondary to electrolyte alterations brought about by hydrochlorothiazide. These cardiovascular interactions with hydralazine prompted Plummer and collaborators to suggest that hydrochlorothiazide could have important clinical applications in the treatment of hypertension. This has been amply demonstrated in extensive clinical studies.

Toxicity is usually low with all compounds in this heterocyclic class. Suspensions of chlorothiazide or hydrochlorothiazide at oral doses of 10,000 mg/kg did not produce death in mice. These substances have been administered daily in oral doses of 1000 mg/kg to dogs for several months, and at 500 mg/kg per day intravenously for weeks without adverse effects. The intravenous LD_{50} of the sodium salt of both compounds exceeded 800 mg/kg in mice. These large doses have produced no adverse effects on renal function nor have they caused any lesions of organs (22, 23).

Characteristically, chlorothiazide and hydrochlorothiazide are limited in their distribution in the body to essentially extracellular fluid space, there being little, if any, concentration of these drugs in erythrocytes or in other tissues over that in plasma except in the kidney. The concentration of the drugs in the kidney reflects in a measure their rapid secretion by the renal tubules in addition to glomerular filtration. Thus, the clearance of these compounds substantially exceeds that of glomerular filtration rate. They are eliminated in the urine of normal dogs to a large extent within a few hours (2 to 4) after intravenous administration, whereas a 30–60% of an oral dose was eliminated only after 24 hours (24, 25). Consequently, their duration of action is more protracted when administered orally than when injected intravenously.

Beyer (20) has reported that the site of action of chlorothiazide is, for the most part, in the proximal convoluted tubules, and this has been substantiated by the stop-flow experiments of Vander and his associates (26) and Kessler *et al.* (27). The latter investigators also indicated that some action occurs at the distal convoluted tubules. Darmady *et al.* (28) have studied the localization of tritium-labeled hydrochlorothiazide (tritium in the 3-position) within the kidney of the rat. They were able to show the distribution of radioactivity was remarkably constant in all nephrons examined. Little or no activity was seen over the glomerulus. The radioactivity was localized in the central portion of the proximal convoluted tubule and throughout the distal convoluted tubule. Radioactivity was not apparent over the collecting tubules.

F. Clinical Utility

The introduction of chlorothiazide followed shortly thereafter by hydrochlorothiazide is undoubtedly the most significant advance in clinical diuretic therapy since the discovery of organic mercurials, in as much as they are well tolerated and potent when given by mouth. They are effective in metabolic acidosis (acetazolamide is ineffective) and alkalosis (in which the mercurials become ineffective). They have been found most useful in controlling edema, especially in the patient with chronic congestive heart failure. Such patients can now be maintained free of edema with these drugs. They have found excellent use in the treatment of nephrotic syndromes, regardless of cause, without adverse effects on damaged kidneys. They are also useful in alleviating premenstrual edema, toxemia of pregnancy, and edema from adrenal cortical therapy. In hepatic cirrhosis with ascites and edema the diuretic response may not be good since such patients appear particularly prone to severe losses of potassium.

A major use of chlorothiazide from the beginning has been in the treatment of hypertension. Hydrochlorothiazide, at a dosage level reduced by a factor of 10, has also found wide use in the management of hypertension. Alone, and in combination with reserpine and hydralazine, chlorothiazide and hydrochlorothiazide are effective in lowering blood pressure. Hydrochlorothiazide is particularly useful in combination with guanethidine in reducing resistant hypertension (29). This subject will be discussed in greater detail in Chapter IX.

The most notable undesirable side effect of these compounds is hypopotassemia (excess loss of potassium), leading to muscular weakness. This has been overcome to some extent with a potassium supplement in the diet. However, with cirrhotic patients this side effect is somewhat pronounced. The chronic use of these compounds also can lead to some potassium depletion. Thus, much research has been carried out in numerous laboratories to develop a compound causing less hypokalemia. From this work has evolved a structure–activity relationship which in some aspects has provided useful generalizations but in other respects is replete with inconsistencies.

G. Structure–Activity Relationships of Thiazides and Hydrothiazides

To the chemist working in medicinal chemistry, a study of structure–activity relationships of a series of biologically interesting compounds becomes an intriguing exercise. Sometimes such an investigation may be limited due to the unique and specific structural features responsible for the activity. This has been observed in many instances, especially in chemotherapy. In certain cases the presence or absence of a methyl group at a certain position in the molecule is responsible for activity or the total lack of it (e.g., Bayer 205).

The same situation can also apply to pharmacologically active compounds. For instance, reserpine is an effective hypotensive drug whereas isoreserpine is totally inactive. The only difference between the two compounds is the configuration of the hydrogen at the 3-position of each molecule. Thus, not only particular groups but also spatial orientation can be a factor for biological activity. Still another factor for activity, and undoubtedly a decisive one, is the general structural features of the class of compounds considered. This usually means that a uniformity of structure is responsible for the biological activity. Under these circumstances, certain generalizations can be made from which a structure–activity rationale is developed. The thiazides which were the first group of benzothiadiazine-1,1-dioxides to be studied represent such a series of compounds. As will be noted, a reasonable structure–activity rationale has evolved from a study of these substances simply because the requirements for activity were quite specific. In addition, some of the generalizations developed thereof were of use as a basis for structure–activity relationship studies in the hydrothiazide series. However, unlike the thiazides, the structural requirements for activity with hydrothiazides were unusually broad and, although hundreds of compounds have been prepared in this series, only a few additional generalizations have evolved. Since structure–activity relationships show some difference in the thiazide and hydrothiazide groups, the two will now be considered separately. Diuretic activities relative to chlorothiazide and hydrochlorothiazide will be dealt with in each section.

1. Thiazides

As shown earlier, 6-chloro-7-sulfamyl-1,2,4-benzothiadiazine-1,1-dioxide (chlorothiazide, III) exists in two tautomeric forms. It is possible to introduce substituents at the 2,3- or 3,4-positions. Substitution in the benzene ring is possible at positions 5, 6, 7, and 8.

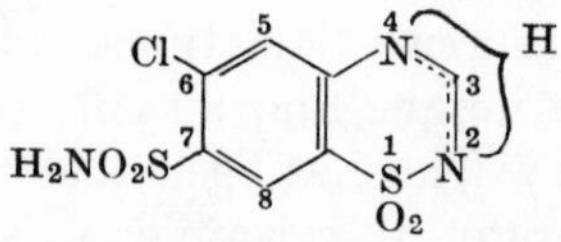

III

Novello and Sprague (3, 11) made the above substitutions from which evolved several important generalizations. A free sulfamyl group at position 7 or a substituted one capable of being metabolized to the free sulfamyl group is essential for high diuretic and saluretic effects. This was illustrated by Beyer and Baer (30) with the 7-caproyl ($C_5H_{11}CO$) derivative of chlorothiazide. In this instance, the carbonic anhydrase inhibitory activity of the urine indicated that 59% of the excreted drug was present as chlorothiazide. However, in those cases where the alkyl or acyl group attached to the sulfamyl group cannot be readily removed, generally a compound of lower activity is obtained. This generalization does not follow conclusively in the hydrothiazide series (*vide infra*). For maximum activity in the thiazide series, an additional substituent must be present at position 6 (see Table II). Thus, when this position was unsubstituted, the compound was virtually inactive. Compounds with chlorine, bromine, nitro, and trifluoromethyl groups in this position are highly active. The trifluoromethyl derivative has been introduced as flumethiazide and it is as active as chlorothiazide. Methyl, methoxy, amino, and fluoro are less effective as augmenting substituents. Introduction of a chloro or a methyl group in position 5 in addition to the chlorine in the 6-position lowers the activity. A chloro or a methyl group in position 5 without any substituent in position 6 gives rise to an inactive compound. The 6-sulfamyl-7-chloro analog of chlorothiazide is practically inactive. A sulfamyl group in position 5 also offers no advantage. Finally, replacement of the 7-sulfamyl group by a methylsulfonyl group produces some change in the biological properties of the original sulfonamide. These analogs are exceedingly weak carbonic anhydrase inhibitors and do not promote electrolyte excretion in the dog.

TABLE II

COMPARATIVE EFFECT UPON ELECTROLYTE EXCRETION (3)

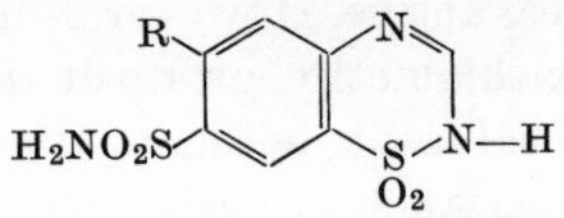

R		Oral (dog)	
	Na^+	Cl^-	K^+
H	−	−	−
Cl	++++	++++	+
Br	++++	++++	+
CH_3	+	+	±
OCH_3	++	++	±
NO_2	+++	+++	±
NH_2	−	−	−
Chlormerodrin	+++	+++	±

TABLE III

COMPARATIVE EFFECT UPON ELECTROLYTE EXCRETION (3)

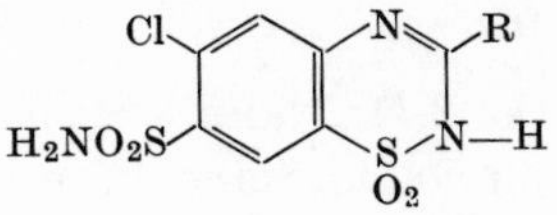

R		Oral (dog)	
	Na^+	Cl^-	K^+
H	++++	++++	−
CH_3	+++	+++	±
n-C_3H_7	+++	+++	±
n-C_5H_{11}	+++	+++	±
C_6H_5	±	±	±

Methylation of either nitrogen atom in the heterocyclic ring gives rise to compounds with lower activity. The 3-oxo derivative (III) was weakly active. In Table III are shown the activities of some 3-alkyl-

and 3-aryl-substituted chlorothiazides. Compounds with an alkyl group in the 3-position retain a high order of activity, whereas the 3-phenyl derivative is less active. However, it has been found that the introduction of a benzylthiomethyl group at the 3-position of chlorothiazide increases the saluretic potency approximately ten times. Benzthiazide (XVII) has an unusually high order of carbonic an-

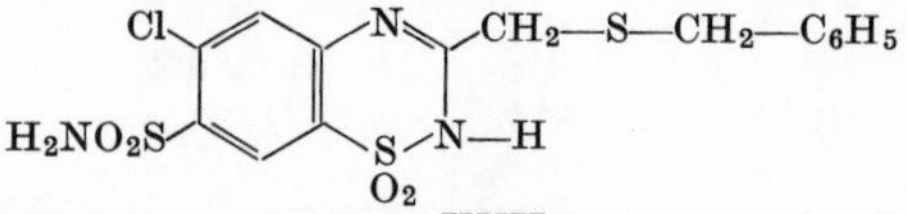

Cl, N, CH_2—S—CH_2—C_6H_5, H_2NO_2S, S, N—H, O_2

XVII
benzthiazide

hydrase inhibitory activity for a thiazide (3.6×10^{-7} compared to 1.7×10^{-6} for chlorothiazide) (30).

The 3-chloromethyl derivative (Su-5969*) was about two-thirds as active as the parent compound whereas the dichloromethyl analog (Su-7898) had ten times the activity of chlorothiazide. The 3-cyclopentylmethyl compound (Su-8819) was approximately twenty times as active as chlorothiazide when tested in experimental animals (31). Whitehead and Traverso (32) have also reported on cyclopentylmethyl

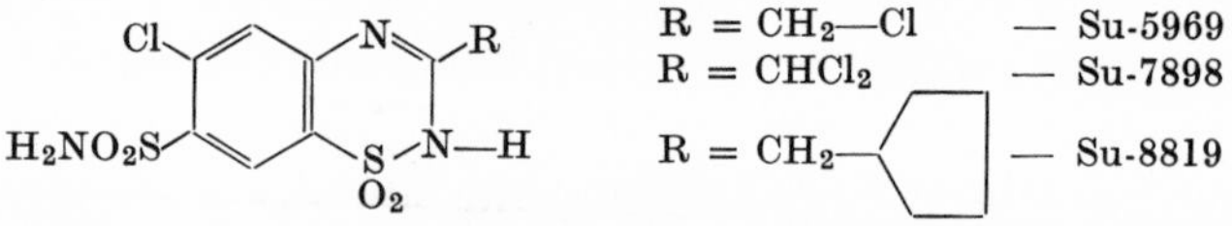

Cl, N, R, H_2NO_2S, S, N—H, O_2

R = CH_2—Cl — Su-5969
R = $CHCl_2$ — Su-7898
R = CH_2—(cyclopentyl) — Su-8819

derivatives as well as the 3-(1,2- and 3-cyclohexenyl) derivatives of chlorothiazide. These compounds have diuretic activities comparable to Su-8819.

2. Hydrothiazides

Previously it had been stated that hydrogenation of the 3,4-double bond of chlorothiazide led to a 10–20-fold increase in saluretic activity. This saturation also reduced its carbonic anhydrase inhibitory activity (2.3×10^{-5}) as compared with chlorothiazide in the dog (17, 19) and in man (33). However, the most important feature of this saturation other than increased diuretic activity is that the hydrogenated ring system allows for more possibilities for substitution. Contrary to the unsaturated heterocycle, the discovery of

* The prefix Su- refers to compounds prepared at CIBA Laboratories, Summit, New Jersey.

the hydrothiazides led to the ready synthesis of 2,3- and 4-monosubstituted, 2,3-, 2,4-, 3,4-, 3,7-, or 2,7-disubstituted, 2,3,7-trisubstituted, and 2,3,4,7-tetrasubstituted dihydrobenzothiadiazine-1,1-dioxides. As a consequence, the structure–activity relationships have been studied more extensively with compounds related to hydrochlorothiazide. Most of the compounds cited in this section were prepared and evaluated in the CIBA Laboratories and hence will be referred to by their Su-numbers.

The effects of the substitution of the benzene ring run parallel with those already described in the chlorothiazide series and do not necessitate further elaboration with the exception of the trifluoromethyl-substituted derivative. This compound whose trifluoromethyl

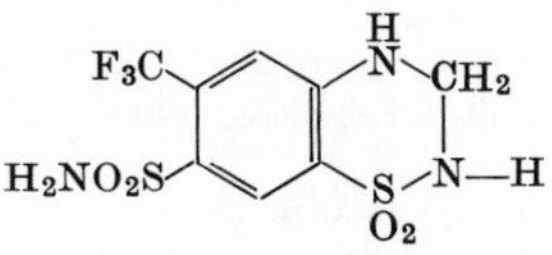

hydroflumethiazide

group has been referred to as a pseudohalogen (20) has been introduced as hydroflumethiazide. Its whole spectrum of biological activity runs parallel to hydrochlorothiazide. Thus, with some few exceptions, the structure–activity relationships determined for chloro-substituted compounds also apply to its trifluoromethyl analogs.

Presently, the effect of substituents at positions 2, 3, 4, or 7 or combinations thereof will be considered in detail. At the end of each section the structure of representative members and their activity compared to hydrochlorothiazide are given (HCT = hydrochlorothiazide). The activities given represent diuretic and saluretic effects in dogs.

(*a*) *Substitution in Position 3.* Position 3 has received the most attention in the hydrothiazide series. Several reasons are responsible for this. First, as emphasized in Section A of this chapter, the method of synthesis of the hydrothiazides allows for a wide variety of substituents in position 3. In fact, the number of available aldehydes and ketones is so great that virtually no limitations to the nature of the substituent at 3 was imposed. Unlike the thiazides, in many cases substitution in position 3 in the hydrothiazides led to compounds more active than the parent substance.

Straight-chain alkyl groups. Substitution with a methyl group in the

3-position gave a compound which was slightly less active than hydrochlorothiazide. However, lengthening the straight-chain alkyl groups gives rise to a substance with increased activity. The maximum activity is obtained with the 3-*n*-butyl derivative which is approximately from five to ten times more active than the parent substance. This activity then steadily diminishes from the *n*-amyl to the *n*-heptyl derivative. The latter compound has about the same order of activity as hydrochlorothiazide. The 3-allyl derivative (Su-7344) was also prepared and found to have the same order of activity.

Cl, H, N, CH—$C_4H_9(n)$, H_2NO_2S, S, N—H, O_2

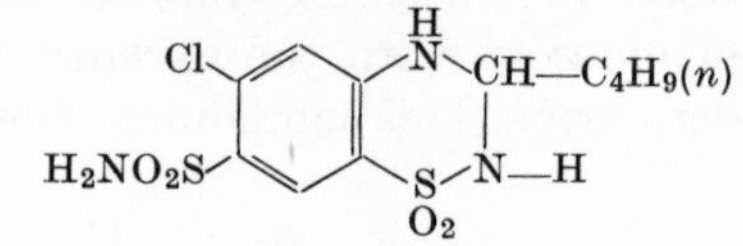

Su-6254
3-*n*-butyl derivative, 5–10 × HCT

Branched-chain alkyl groups. The lowest member of this group, the 3-isopropyl derivative, is less active than hydrochlorothiazide. The 3-isobutyl and the 3-(1-methylpropyl) derivatives are approximately twenty times as potent as hydrochlorothiazide, whereas the 3-(1-methylbutyl), the 3-(1-ethylpropyl), and the 3-(1-ethylpentyl) derivatives are less active than the parent substance. The 3-(1-ethylvinyl) derivative was less active than Su-6187. A tertiary butyl group at position 3 gave rise to a weakly active compound (34). Thus, in this group, branching at the α-carbon of the side chain results in compounds with lower activity than the unbranched ones. Thiabutazide (Su-6187) is the only member of this group which has been introduced.

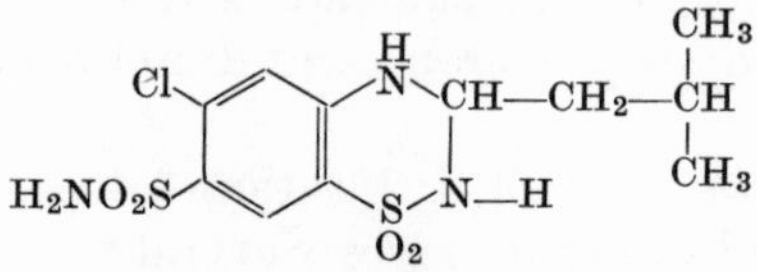

Cl, H, N, CH—CH_2—CH(CH_3)(CH_3), H_2NO_2S, S, N—H, O_2

Su-6187
thiabutazide, 20 × HCT

Alkyl ethers. The substitution of methoxy or ethoxymethyl group has not led to compounds with outstanding activity. However, the ethoxyethyl derivative was almost as active as hydrochlorothiazide. The ethylthioethyl substituent yielded a compound which was approximately five times more potent than hydrochlorothiazide. As in the case of benzthiazide, a sulfur-containing group in the side chain enhances biological activity. Surprisingly, the dihydro derivative of benzthiazide is only as active as benzthiazide.

Cl, H_2NO_2S, H, N, $CH—CH_2CH_2—S—C_2H_5$, S, O_2, N—H

Su-7307, 5 × HCT

Halogenalkyl groups. Halogenalkyl groups in the 3-position also increased the diuretic activity. The 3-bromomethyl derivative was twice as active as hydrochlorothiazide and the 3-chloromethyl analog was approximately seven times as active. The 3-iodomethyl derivative was almost as active as the parent compound. The 3-dichloromethyl derivative was about twenty times more active than hydrochlorothiazide (35, 36). This compound has been assigned the generic name trichloromethiazide and is clinically available. The difluoromethyl and dibromomethyl compounds were less active (34). On the other hand, the 3-trichloromethyl and the 3-(1,2-dichloroethyl) analogs are only as active as hydrochlorothiazide. The 3-(2-chloroethyl) and the 3-(1,1,2-trichloroethyl) derivatives are five times as active as hydrochlorothiazide. However, the 3-(1,1-dichloroethyl) compound was less active than hydrochlorothiazide (34). A clearly defined structure–activity relationship cannot be drawn from this group of compounds. It can only be concluded that maximum activity is obtained with those compounds which have two chlorine groups on the α-carbon.

Cl, H_2NO_2S, H, N, CH—R, S, O_2, N—H

R = $CHCl_2$ — Su-7057—trichloromethiazide, 20 × HCT
R = CH_2CH_2Cl — Su-7596, 5 × HCT
R = $CCl_2—CH_2Cl$ — Su-7470, 5 × HCT

Aminoalkyl groups. Because hydrochlorothiazide is only slightly soluble in water, it was thought of interest to add water-solubilizing groups to this molecule. One approach was to prepare compounds with an aminoalkyl substituent in position 3. Such compounds were synthesized and isolated as their hydrochloride salts which were water soluble. However, substitution with aminoalkyl groups resulted generally in compounds with no increase in activity. Some of the 3-aminoalkyl substituents investigated are listed here.

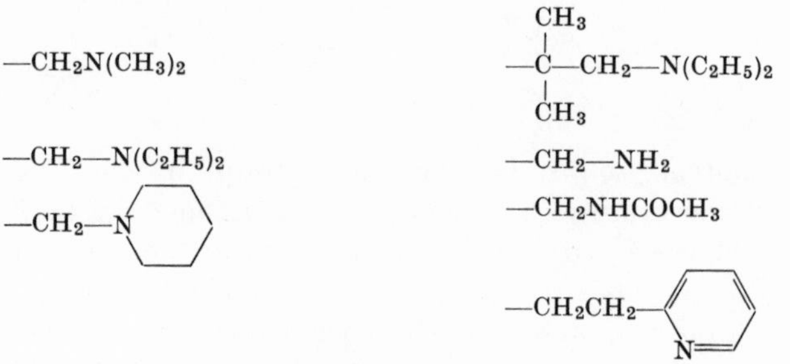

$—CH_2N(CH_3)_2$

$—C(CH_3)_2—CH_2—N(C_2H_5)_2$

$—CH_2—N(C_2H_5)_2$

$—CH_2—NH_2$

$—CH_2—N$ (piperidino)

$—CH_2NHCOCH_3$

$—CH_2CH_2—$ (2-pyridyl)

3-aminoalkyl substituents

Aralkyl groups. The introduction of aralkyl groups in the 3-position had a favorable influence on diuretic activity. For instance, the 3-benzyl derivative (Su-6227) was approximately twenty times as active as hydrochlorothiazide. The 6-trifluoromethyl-3-benzyl analog shown below has been introduced as benzhydroflumethiazide. Lund and Kobinger (37) have reported that Su-6227 was only one-twentieth as potent as benzhydroflumethiazide when administered in the form of tablets orally to man, suggesting that solubility or stability may be responsible for this marked difference in activity. Notwithstanding these comments, clinical evaluation of Su-6227 by CIBA has shown this compound to have the same order of activity in man as shown in dogs.

Substitution on the phenyl ring of the benzyl group with chlorine, bromine, methyl, methoxy, and nitro group did not yield more active compounds. The 3-phenethyl derivative had the same order of activity as Su-6227. However, branching of the side chain, as in the 3-(α-methylbenzyl) derivative, Su-7078, resulted in still higher activity. Su-7078 is approximately 100 times more active than hydrochlorothiazide. This order of activity has been borne out in man. The corresponding 3-(α-ethylbenzyl) compound (Su-8633) was less active. The introduction of two methyl groups on the α-carbon yielded a compound which was less active than hydrochlorothiazide. Replacement of the side-chain methyl group with a hydroxyl group again gave a less active compound. A 3-phenylpropyl side chain also did not give a more potent compound. Recently, the 3-(2-thienyl)-

methyl derivative has been reported to be highly active. The activity of this substance should correspond to that of Su-6227.

X = Cl; R = H — Su-6227, 20 × HCT
X = Cl; R = CH_3 — Su-7078, 100 × HCT
X = Cl; R = C_2H_5 — Su-8633, 50 × HCT
X = CF_3; R = H — benzhydroflumethiazide, 20 × HCT

Phenyl and substituted phenyl groups. In contrast to the aralkyl groups, the introduction of phenyl or substituted phenyl groups in the 3-position has not yielded compounds with high order of activity. Some of the substituents investigated include: phenyl, *o*- and *m*-tolyl, *m*- and *o*-fluorophenyl, *o*-carboxyphenyl, *m*-hydroxyphenyl, *o*-, *m*-, *p*-chlorophenyl. Heterocyclic groups such as 2-thienyl, 2-furfuryl, and 4-pyridyl in the 3-position have similar effects. In general, this series has not yielded advantageously active substances, and the structure–activity relationship is negative.

Cycloalkyl groups. This group has afforded several of the most potent compounds in the hydrothiazide series. Among the many substances prepared in this series, the 3-cyclopentyl (Su-7526) derivative was found to be five times more potent than hydrochlorothiazide. More significantly, this substance was also observed to cause a minimum amount of potassium excretion when tested in laboratory animals. Consequently, the 3-cyclohexyl, 3-cycloheptyl, and 3-cyclooctyl analogs were prepared. The diuretic activity of these substances was twenty, ten, and five times more than that of hydrochlorothiazide, respectively. Substituents on the cyclohexyl ring (e.g., methyl, carbethoxy) were not advantageous. However, the unsaturated 3-Δ^3-cyclohexenyl derivative was somewhat more potent, being about forty times as active as hydrochlorothiazide.

The introduction of a methylene group between the heterocyclic ring and the cycloalkyl group led to additional compounds with potent diuretic effects. The 3-cyclopropylmethyl and 3-cyclobutylmethyl derivatives are twenty times more active than hydrochlorothiazide. A very marked increase in activity then followed with the 3-cyclopentylmethyl-6-chloro-7-sulfamyl-3,4-dihydro-1,2,4-benzothiadiazine-1,1-dioxide (Su-8341). This compound is the most potent of the 3-substituted hydrochlorothiazide derivatives. Rutledge, Barrett, and

Plummer (38) studied this substance in dogs and found it to be *166 times as potent a diuretic agent as hydrochlorothiazide*, its chloruretic and natriuretic ratios to hydrochlorothiazide being 88 and 141, respectively. Its effect on potassium excretion is minimal and it also is a relatively weak carbonic anhydrase inhibitor (1.3×10^{-5}) (30). This drug has been introduced under the generic name, *cyclopenthiazide*.

Further modifications of cyclopenthiazide revealed that the 3-cyclohexylmethyl derivative (Su-8395) is less active and that a further decrease in activity was observed with the 3-cycloheptylmethyl and 3-cyclooctylmethyl compounds. The 3-(2-cyclopentylethyl) compound (Su-8740) was found to be only twenty times more active than hydrochlorothiazide, whereas the 3-(1-cyclopentylethyl) derivative (Su-8734) was fifty times as active as the parent substance. Whitehead *et al.* (39) have reported on the preparation of similar compounds, one of which being recently introduced as cyclothiazide. This substance is the 3-(5-norbornylenyl) derivative of hydrochlorothiazide and is approximately 75–100 times more active than the parent substance.

Thus, it is apparent that the structural requirements for maximum activity in the monocycloalkyl series are quite specific with regard to the cycloalkyl group and to its distance from the benzothiadiazine ring. Moreover, substitution on the methylene group (Su-8734) led to a less active compound. This is in contrast to the findings in the aralkyl group in which such substitution led to a marked increase in diuretic potency (compare Su-6227 with Su-7078). Finally, it is interesting that the diuretic activities of the 3-cycloalkylhydroflumethiazide derivatives do not correspond to those found with the above described substances when tested in laboratory animals. For example, the 6-trifluoromethyl analog of Su-8341 is about one-fourth as potent as cyclopenthiazide. The same is true for the cyclohexylmethyl derivative (31).

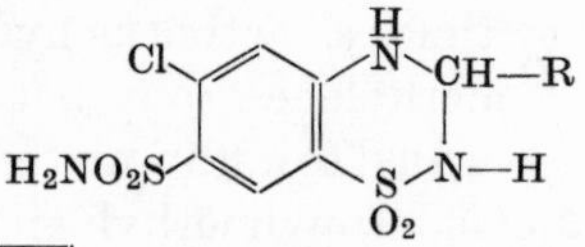

R = 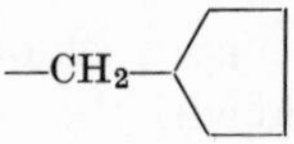

— Su-8341—cyclopenthiazide, 166 × HCT

R = 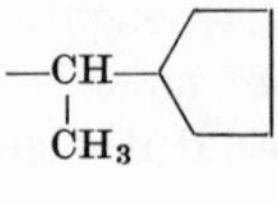

— Su-8734, 50 × HCT

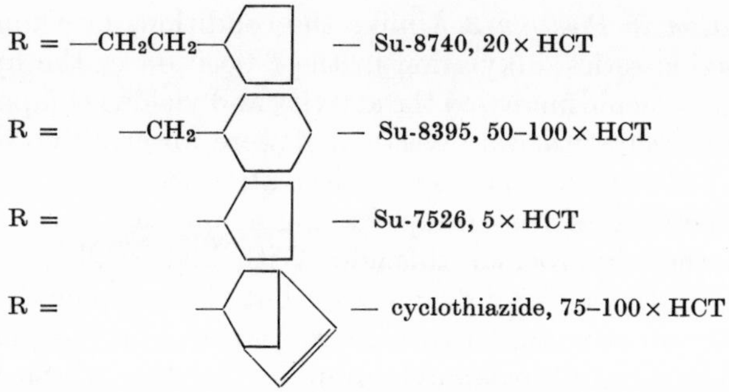

R = —CH_2CH_2—(cyclopentyl) — Su-8740, 20 × HCT

R = —CH_2—(cyclohexyl) — Su-8395, 50–100 × HCT

R = —(cyclopentyl) — Su-7526, 5 × HCT

R = —(bicycloheptenyl) — cyclothiazide, 75–100 × HCT

3,3-Disubstituted groups. The condensation of 5-chloro-2,4-disulfamylaniline with a ketone was found to yield 3,3-disubstituted hydrothiazides.

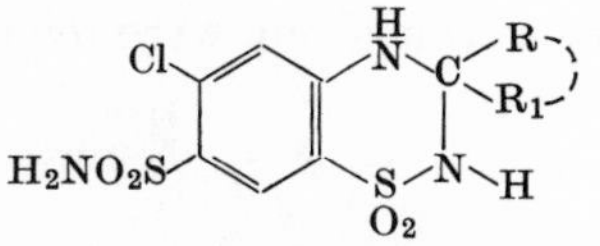

The 3,3-disubstituted derivatives can be divided into two types: (*1*) those in which the R and R_1 are separate substituents and (*2*) the spiro compounds where R and R_1 are part of a ring. In general, the ring compounds (spiro group) were found to exhibit significant diuretic activity. As the cycloalkane ring size was increased from 4 to 7 atoms, optimum activity was found with the 6-membered ring (Su-7329), an activity comparable to hydrochlorothiazide being attained. Substitution of a methyl group in the 3-position of the cyclohexane ring of Su-7329 had little effect on activity, whereas substitution of a methyl group at the 4-position of the 6-membered ring gave a compound which was over ten times as potent as hydrochlorothiazide. However, as increasingly larger alkyl or cycloalkyl groups were introduced into the 4-position, the potency gradually diminished. Cragoe *et al.* (40) have attributed the comparable activity relationship (3 × HCT) of the 4-methoxy- and 4-ethyl-substituted compounds to their similar molecular size. The replacement of the methylene group in the 4-position of the 6-membered spiro ring with a hetero atom, e.g., oxygen or sulfur, produced little change in activity.

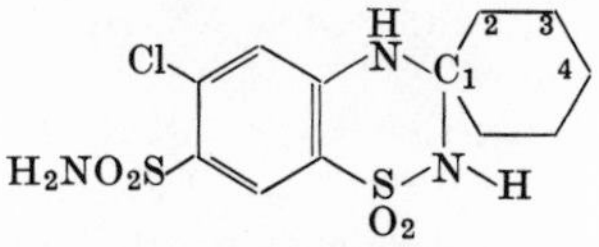

Su-7329, 1–2 × HCT

(*b*) *Substitution in Position 2.* Unlike the conditions prevailing in the chlorothiazide series, alkylation in the 2-position of the hydrochlorothiazide molecule increased the activity and yielded compounds of high potency. Substituents investigated were lower alkyl, cyclopentyl, allyl, and benzyl. The 2-ethyl derivative (Su-6835) was the most potent member of this group, having a diuretic activity 100 times greater than hydrochlorothiazide. With higher alkyl groups and with benzyl, the activity dropped off but the compounds were considerably more active than hydrochlorothiazide. Surprisingly, the compound with a butylcarbamoyl group in position 2 (Su-8124) caused marked diuresis in dogs. This compound was devoid of hypoglycemic activity. The 2-(2-pyranyl) derivative was also twenty times as active as hydrochlorothiazide. The structural requirements for maximum activity in this group were relatively unspecific.

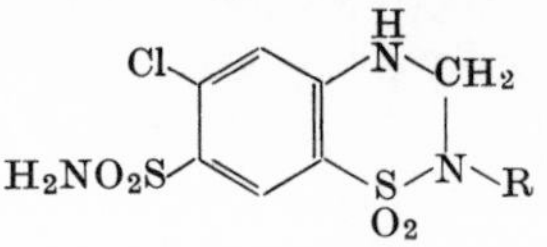

[Structure: Cl, H_2NO_2S benzene ring fused to ring with N(H)—CH_2—N—R—$S(O_2)$]

R = $—CH_3$	Su-6441, 3 × HCT
R = $—C_2H_5$	Su-6835, 100 × HCT
R = $—CH_2—CH{=}CH_2$	Su-6991, 50–75 × HCT
R = $—CH_2CH_2CH_3$	Su-8305, 65 × HCT
R = $—CH_2—C_6H_5$	Su-8066, 20 × HCT
R = $—C(=O)—N(H)—C_4H_9$	Su-8124, 20 × HCT

(*c*) *Substitution in Position 4.* Methylation in the 4-position of hydrochlorothiazide decreased the activity considerably. Alkyl groups in this position do not appear to be very fruitful and no reports of highly active compounds of this type have appeared. 6-Chloro-4-methyl-7-sulfamyl-3,4-dihydro-1,2,4-benzothiadiazine-1,1-dioxide (Su-6247) is less effective than hydrochlorothiazide. Substitution of a basic group at 4 appeared to have an ameliorating effect. Siedel and Sturm (41) have reported the 4-anilino derivative to be more potent than hydrochlorothiazide with a higher sodium–potassium quotient.

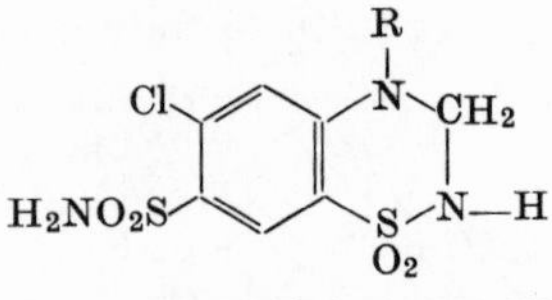

[Structure: Cl, H_2NO_2S benzene ring fused to ring with N(R)—CH_2—N—H—$S(O_2)$]

R = CH_3	Su-6247, less than HCT
R = NHC_6H_5	Hoechst, greater than HCT

(*d*) *Simultaneous Substitutions in Positions 2 and 3.* Since the 2- and the 3-substituted hydrothiazides gave very potent diuretic compounds, it was next of interest to prepare 2,3-disubstituted derivatives, the supposition being that an additive effect might be forthcoming. Indeed, a number of highly potent compounds were obtained in this series, but with little additive relationship to the monosubstituted compounds.

It is remarkable that the introduction of a bulky group such as a benzyl in the 2-position in addition to the chloromethyl group in position 3 as in Su-8293 does not lower the activity but actually increases it. On the other hand, Su-8134 and Su-8015, both of which incorporate the dichloromethyl group in position 3 and the benzyl and ethyl group, respectively, in position 2, were not more active than Su-7057 (see Section G, 2, a). 2,3-Disubstituted compounds with the allyl group in position 2 have also been prepared and found to be active.

Methychlothiazide (42) and polythiazide (43, 44) are the only compounds from this group to be introduced to date. A broad and undefined structural activity relationship exists in this group. In general, the results obtained from the monosubstituted compounds cannot be extrapolated to this series.

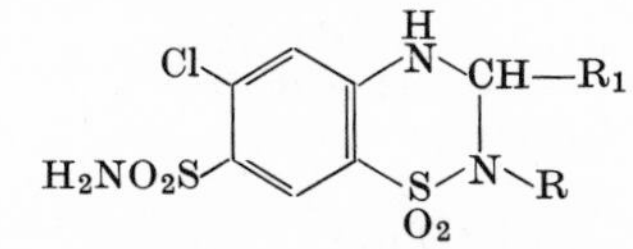

Cl; H; N; $CH—R_1$; H_2NO_2S; S; N; R; O_2

$R = R_1 = CH_3$,	equal to HCT
$R = CH_3$; $R_1 = CH_2Cl$	methyclothiazide, 10 × HCT
$R = CH_3$; $R_1 = CH_2S—CH_2—CF_3$	polythiazide, 50 × HCT
$R = CH_2—C_6H_5$; $R_1 = CH_2Cl$	Su-8293, 20 × HCT
$R = CH_2—C_6H_5$; $R_1 = CHCl_2$	Su-8134, 20 × HCT
$R = C_2H_5$; $R_1 = CHCl_2$	Su-8015, 30 × HCT

(*e*) *Substitutions in the 2,7- and the 2,3,7-Positions.* It has already been noted that substitution on the 7-sulfonamido terminal nitrogen with a group which cannot be metabolically cleaved affords only weakly active compounds. These conclusions are based on the work of Beyer and Baer using 7-caproylchlorothiazide and the report of Lund and Kobinger (37) who determined that 5-chloro-2,4-dimethylsulfamylaniline was inactive of itself, but was demethylated in the body to the active compound. However, certain discrepancies have been observed in the hydrothiazide series and the evaluation of additional compounds will be necessary before this generalization can be finalized.

Su-12,012 was found to be more active than hydrochlorothiazide whereas Su-6442 was almost as active as the unmethylated parent substance. Logemann and Giraldi (45) have confirmed this activity in humans and were not able to detect the appearance of the demethylated product in the urine. Accordingly, this study indicated the relative unimportance of carbonic anhydrase inhibition in the diuretic action of this class of heterocycles. However, 7-methylhydrochlorothiazide (Su-6635) was only as active as chlorothiazide. Metabolic cleavage of the methyl group should yield, according to Beyer, hydrochlorothiazide. Recently, the 7-methoxy analog (46) was reported to have activity in the range of hydrochlorothiazide. Feit (47) has reported on a variety of mono- and disubstituted 7-sulfamyl derivatives of hydroflumethiazide as well as 3,7-disubstituted derivatives. The following compounds were more active than hydroflumethiazide when administered orally to rats:

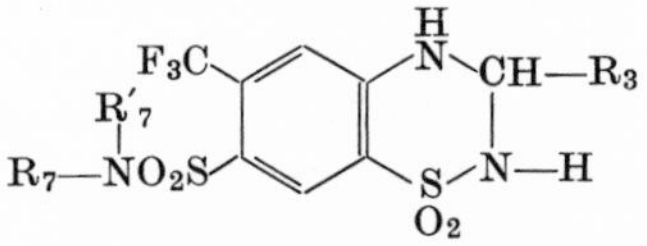

$R_3 = n\text{-}C_5H_{11}$; $R_7 = CH_2—C_6H_5$; $R'_7 = H$
$R_3 = CH_2—C_6H_5$; $R_7 = R'_7 = n\text{-}C_4H_9$
$R_3 = CH_2—C_6H_5$; $R_7 = CH_3$; $R'_7 = H$

Finally, simultaneous substitution in the 2,3- and 7-positions gave compounds with varying activities. For instance, Su-6706 was one-half as active as hydrochlorothiazide whereas Su-8244 was forty times more potent than the standard.

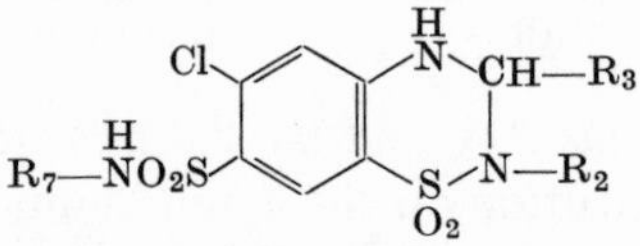

$R_3 = H$; $R_2 = C_2H_5$; $R_7 = C(=O)—NH—C_4H_9$	Su-12,012, 20 × HCT
$R_3 = R_2 = H$; $R_7 = CH_3$	Su-6635, weak
$R_3 = H$; $R_2 = R_7 = CH_3$	Su-6442, equal to HCT
$R_3 = R_2 = R_7 = CH_3$	Su-6706, one-half HCT
$R_3 = R_2 = H$; $R_7 = OCH_3$	Hoffmann-La Roche, equal to HCT
$R_3 = CH_2Cl$; $R_2 = R_7 = C(=O)—NH—C_4H_9$	Su-8244, 40 × HCT

(*f*) *Substitutions in the 3,4- and the 2,3,4,7-Positions.* Several compounds in this group were prepared but, in accordance with previous findings, the substitution of a methyl group at position 4 generally led to substances with diminished activity. Because of this, synthetic efforts in this direction have received little attention.

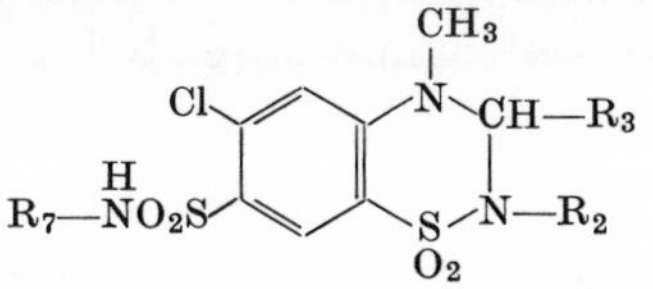

CH_3 | Cl | N | CH—R_3 | H | R_7—NO_2S | S | N—R_2 | O_2

$R_2 = R_7 = H; R_3 = CH_3$ Su-7174, weakly active
$R_2 = R_7 = R_3 = CH_3$ Su-7144, one-half HCT
$R_2 = R_7 = CH_3; R_3 = (CH_2)_2C_6H_5$ Su-7148, one-tenth HCT

3. Thiazides and Hydrothiazides with a Heterocyclic Aromatic Ring

Extensive work has also been carried out on the synthesis of "aza" analogs of chlorothiazide (CT) and hydrochlorothiazide; i.e., compounds in which the benzene nucleus has been replaced by pyridine. Several of these substances are outlined below but none have been found to be qualitatively or quantitatively superior to the thiazides or hydrothiazides. The members of the (2,3-*e*) series (e.g., Su-6857) were consistently more active than those of the (4,3-*e*) series. This is not surprising, since in the 1,2,4-benzothiadiazine-1,1-dioxide series, the location of the sulfamyl group in the 7-position is critical for optimum activity. In the [4,3-*e*] series, the location of this essential sulfamyl group in the 7-position is not possible, since a nitrogen atom occupies that position (48). These compounds have received little clinical attention.

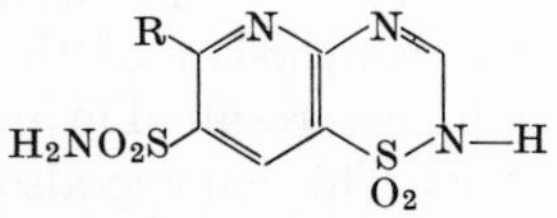

R | N | N | H_2NO_2S | S | N—H | O_2

R = H Su-5938, inactive
R = CH_3 Su-5939, equal to CT
R = Cl Merck, equal to CT

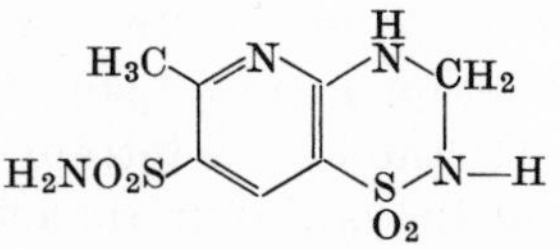

H_3C | N | H | N | CH_2 | H_2NO_2S | S | N—H | O_2

Su-6857, equal to HCT

[2, 3-*e*] series

H_2NO_2S | H | N | CH_2 | N | S | N—H | O_2

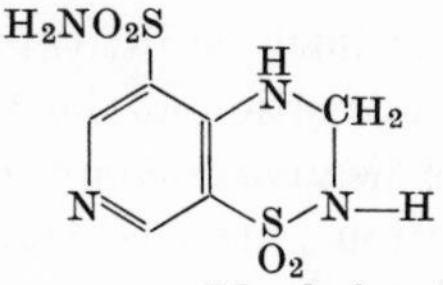

[4, 3-*e*] series

Merck, less than HCT

4. Quinazolinone Sulfonamides and Related Compounds

The synthesis of 4-chloro-5-sulfamylanthranilic acid (XVIII) and its amide (XIX) by Novello (49) and also Cohen *et al.* (50) have already been outlined (see Chapter V, C, 2). These substances have been allowed to react with acid amides, acid chlorides, and aldehydes to form quinazoline sulfonamides related to chlorothiazide (see Scheme 5).

XVIII → XIX

XVIII —$RCONH_2$→ quinazolinone —$NaBH_4$→ tetrahydroquinazolinone

XIX —RCHO→ tetrahydroquinazolinone

Scheme 5

These compounds with R = H, which may be considered as analogs of the benzothiadiazine-1,1-dioxides in which the cyclic >SO_2 group is replaced by >C=O, showed an activity equal to that of the corresponding compounds in the benzothiadiazine series. In general, minor variations in R from H to lower alkyl had very little effect on the over-all activity but Cohen *et al.* have indicated that this change did affect the dose–response curves as well as the sodium, chloride, and potassium excretion ratios. Like the thiazides, conversion of the quinazolinones to the 1,2,3,4-tetrahydroquinazolinones resulted in an enhancement of the oral diuretic activity in dogs. This change also reduced the potassium excretion as compared to the chloride excretion. Compounds in the tetrahydro series in which R is equal to benzyl or cyclopentylmethyl gave rise to potent diuretics (51). However, this potency was not comparable to similarly substituted compounds in the hydrochlorothiazide series. Substitution at the 3-position with an alkyl group, however, proved to be disadvantageous in that it reversed the chloride and potassium excretion patterns. Quinethazone is the only member of this group to be introduced.

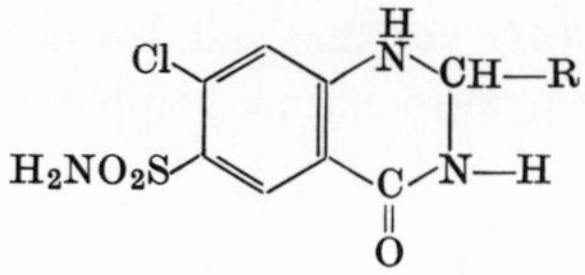

$R = C_2H_5$ quinethazone, equal to HCT
$R = CH_2C_6H_5$ Su-8427, equal to HCT

The diazotization of compound XIX and its substituted carboxamide derivatives by Gadekar and Frederick (52) yielded 1,2,3-benzotriazine-4(3*H*)-ones. Childress (53) was also able to prepare 1,2,3,4-benzothiatriazine-1,1-dioxides by treating 5-chloro-2,4-disulfamylaniline (I) and its derivatives with nitrous acid. In both cases, diuretically active compounds were obtained but their quantitative comparison with the standard compounds was not reported.

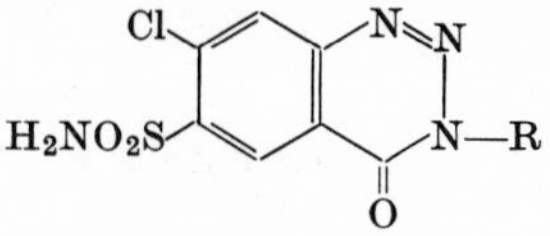

1,2,3-benzotriazine-4(3*H*)-ones 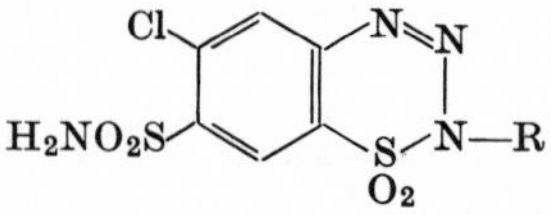 1,2,3,4-benzothiatriazine-1,1-dioxides
R = H, lower alkyls

H. Miscellaneous Heterocycles Related to Benzothiadiazines

Several 5- and 7-membered ring heterocycles related to chlorothiazide and hydrochlorothiazide were prepared for evaluation as diuretics. Su-5923 and Su-6264 were synthesized in the CIBA Laboratories but proved to be inactive.

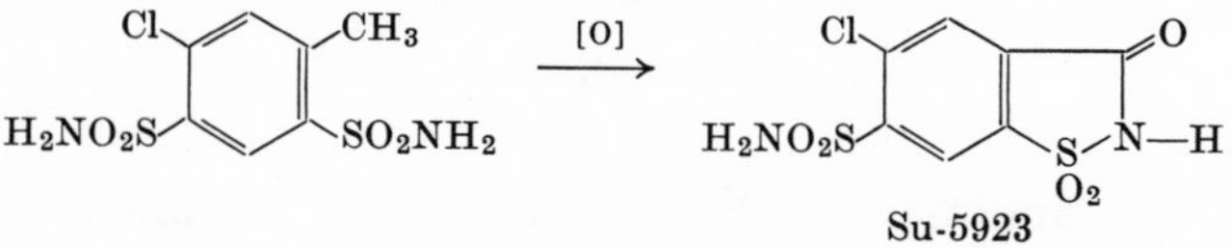

[O]

Su-5923

(1) $ClCOCH_2Cl$
(2) NaH

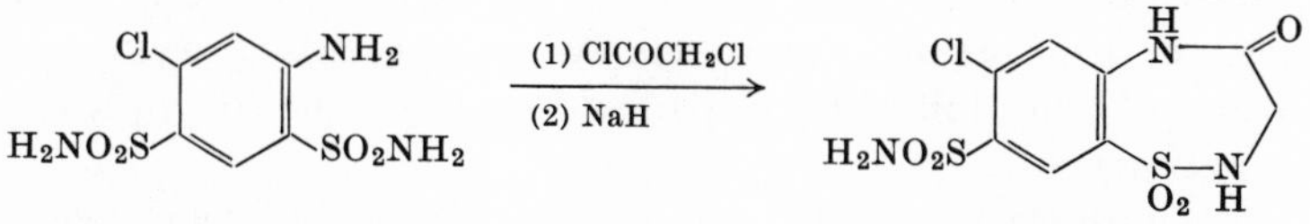

Su-6264

Gadekar and Frederick (52) also prepared 5-chloro-6-sulfamylbenzimidazolone (XX) which was reported to be devoid of diuretic activity, and Novello (54) synthesized several 5-substituted 6-sulfamylphthalimides which were claimed to have some activity.

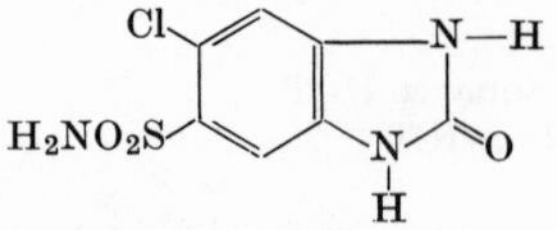

Cl, H_2NO_2S, N—H, N, H, O

XX

Cl, H_2NO_2S, O, N—R, O

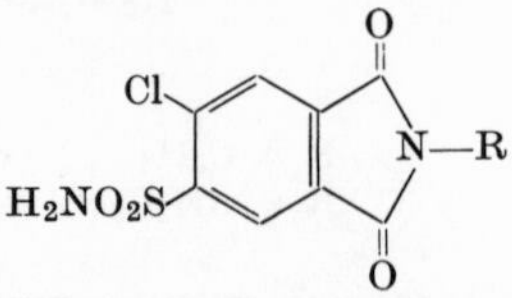

R = lower alkyl, aralkyl, etc.

Another interesting variation of chlorothiazide and hydrochlorothiazide is the 4,5-dihydrobenzothiadiazepine (XXI) prepared by Whitehead and Traverso (54a)

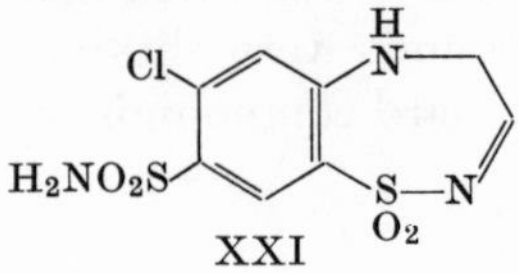

H, N, Cl, H_2NO_2S, S—N, O_2

XXI

However, these authors have not reported on the biological effects of this substance.

Finally, the unsubstituted and the 8-bromo-1,3-dihydro-2,3,5-benzothiadiazepine-2,2-dioxides were prepared by Teotino and Cignarella (55). These substances are supposed to be very effective diuretics. They can be administered in doses ranging between 100 and 500 mg three to four times daily. No clinical reports have been published on these compounds.

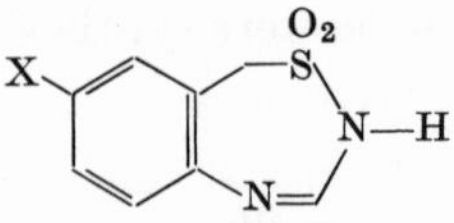

O_2, S, X, N—H, N=

X = H, Br

I. Summary of Structure–Activity Studies

The above described structure–activity relationship study of the thiazides, hydrothiazides, and related compounds permits the summation of the following broad generalizations for optimum diuretic activity:

(*1*) With both classes of compounds (thiazides and hydrothiazides) the benzene ring must have a sulfamyl group, preferably unsubstituted, at position 7 and a halogen group (chlorine, bromine, or so-called pseudohalogen trifluoromethyl) at position 6.

(*2*) The saturation at the 3,4-positions of 1,2,4-benzothiadiazine-1,1-dioxide generally leads to an increase in activity.

(*3*) Substitution at position 3 affords compounds with diverse activity, a maximum effect being attained with the cyclopentylmethyl group. With the exception of one compound, Su-7470 (Section G, 2, a), it appears that a hydrogen atom on the α-carbon of a substituent at the 3-position is very important.

(*4*) A lower alkyl group at position 2 is useful and the 2,3-disubstituted compounds also are effective.

(*5*) Position 1 of the heterocyclic ring can be either $\rangle SO_2$ or $\rangle C{=}O$. Maximum activity, however, is usually obtained with the $\rangle SO_2$ compounds.

J. Comparative Evaluation of Benzothiadiazine Diuretics

After the introduction of chlorothiazide and hydrochlorothiazide, much of the research carried out in this area was directed toward the preparation of derivatives which might cause less potassium depletion. Of the hundreds of compounds prepared, the twelve drugs outlined in Table IV have been introduced in clinical practice. With the introduction of each of these drugs, the major advantage stressed, other than increased potency, has been the more favorable ratio of sodium to potassium they produce in the urine. Certainly this can be shown to be the case with some of these compounds in carefully controlled experiments in animals. In fact, the same can be shown in humans when these drugs are taken for a period of time limited to a few days. Over an extended period of time, however, the pronounced saluretic effect of the thiazides leads to electrolyte imbalance. Sodium and potassium deficiency-producing metabolic syndromes, such as hyponatremia and hypokalemia with or without alkalosis, are then primarily a result of the pharmacologic activity of the drug and not a toxic effect. These metabolic deficiencies can be prevented by careful observation of the patient and replacement therapy (potassium salt supplement).

The differences between chlorothiazide and flumethiazide are not marked. However, hydrochlorothiazide behaves in some respects pharmacologically different. In addition to the change in effective dose, there is a change in the electrolyte excretion pattern of this drug as compared to chlorothiazide since its chloride excretion effect is now greater than its sodium excretion effect. Potassium excretion with hydrochlorothiazide is similar to that of chlorothiazide.

Benzthiazide, trichloromethiazide, and thiabutazide behave similarly. Methyclothiazide and polythiazide are reported to have a longer duration of action (24 versus 18 hours for hydrochlorothiazide).

TABLE IV

THIAZIDES AND HYDROTHIAZIDES

Drug (generic name)	Effective dose range (mg/day)
Chlorothiazide	250–2000
Flumethiazide	250–2000
Benzthiazide	50–200
Hydrochlorothiazide	25–150
Hydroflumethiazide	25–150
Thiabutazide	20–100
Benzhydroflumethiazide	5–20
Trichloromethiazide	5–20
Methychlothiazide	2–10
Polythiazide	1–5
Cyclothiazide	1–2
Cyclopenthiazide	0.25–2

Cyclopenthiazide shows a very pronounced chloride excretion pattern with negligible potassium loss when used in short-term therapy (56, 57).

The general response to all of these drugs has been excellent in the treatment of edema. The sodium excreting effects at their effective dose as well as the weight loss response in heart failure patients has been most gratifying. In fact, the application of the benzothiadiazine diuretics covers a broad spectrum including all of the common clinical edema syndromes, as well as hypertension. The preponderance of evidence indicates that these drugs lower the blood pressure in hypertension primarily as a consequence of the natriuretic action (17, 24). In this respect, therefore, they resemble the long-established efficacy of drastic sodium restriction; the results obtained by either drug or diet are comparable. Both decrease plasma and extracellular fluid volume, total exchangeable body sodium, and cardiac output and increase the responsiveness to other antihypertensive drugs and to sympathectomy. Although these effects accompany the lowering of the blood pressure after the initiation of drug or dietotherapy, subsequent adjustments in the organism occur with restoration of the plasma volume and cardiac output to pretreatment levels despite the maintenance of the decline in blood pressure.

The concomitant simultaneous use of these drugs with other diuretics have been shown to have mutually potentiating effects. Thus, the simultaneous administration of hydrochlorothiazide and mercaptomerin on the first, ninth, and fourteenth days was observed to cause pronounced sodium excretion (58).

The thiazide and hydrothiazide diuretics have gained clinical prominence primarily because they are potent, nontoxic and consistently orally effective and cause a diuretic effect not unlike the organomercurials which must be administered parenterally.

References

1. A. Ekbom, *Bih. Svenska, Vet.-Akad. Handl.* [II], **27**, (No. 1), 22 (1902); *Beilstein, 4th ed.* **27**, 570; **14**, 682 (1918).
2. F. C. Novello and J. M. Sprague, *J. Am. Chem. Soc.* **79**, 2028 (1957); F. C. Novello, U.S. Pat. 2,809,194 (Oct. 8, 1957).
3. J. M. Sprague, *Ann. N.Y. Acad. Sci.* **71**, 4, 328 (1958).
4. K. H. Beyer, *Ann. N.Y. Acad. Sci.* **71**, 4, 363 (1958).
5. E. Hug, *Bull. Soc. Chim. France* **5**, 990 (1934).
6. J. McMaster, *J. Am. Chem. Soc.* **56**, 204 (1934).
7. F. C. Wood and A. E. Battye, *J. Soc. Chem. Ind.* **52**, 346 (1933).
8. J. H. Freeman and E. C. Wagner, *J. Org. Chem.* **16**, 815 (1951).
9. G. deStevens, L. H. Werner, A. Halamandaris, and S. Ricca, Jr., *Experientia* **14**, 463 (1958).
10. L. H. Werner, A. Halamandaris, S. Ricca, Jr., L. Dorfman, and G. deStevens, *J. Am. Chem. Soc.* **82**, 1161 (1960).
11. F. C. Novello, S. C. Bell, E. L. A. Abrams, C. Ziegler, and J. M. Sprague, *J. Org. Chem.* **25**, 970 (1960).
12. V. duVigneaud and O. K. Behrens, *J. Biol. Chem.* **117**, 27 (1937).
13. W. J. Close, L. R. Swett, L. E. Brady, J. H. Short, and M. Vernsten, *J. Am. Chem. Soc.* **82**, 1132 (1960).
14. W. F. Charnicki, F. A. Bacher, S. A. Freeman, and D. H. DeCesare, *J. Am. Pharm. Assoc., Sci. Ed.* **48**, 656 (1959).
15. C. R. Rehm and J. B. Smith, *J. Am. Pharm. Assoc., Sci. Ed.* **49**, 386 (1960).
16. J. E. Baer, H. L. Leidy, A. V. Brooks, and K. H. Beyer, *J. Pharmacol. Exptl. Therap.* **125**, 295 (1959).
17. W. E. Barrett, R. A. Rutledge, H. Sheppard, and A. J. Plummer, *Toxicol. Appl, Pharmacol.* **1**, 333 (1959).

18. R. V. Ford, *Southern Med. J.* **52**, 40 (1959).
19. J. E. Baer, H. F. Russo, and K. H. Beyer, *Proc. Soc. Exptl. Biol. Med.* **100**, 442 (1959).
20. K. H. Beyer, *in* "Edema" (J. H. Moyer and M. Fuchs, eds.), pp. 270–276; Saunders. Philadelphia, Pennsylvania, 1960.
21. P. Preziosi, A. Bianchi, B. Loscalzo, and A. F. De Schaepdryver, *Arch. Intern. Pharmacodyn.* **118**, 467 (1959).
22. H. M. Peck, S. E. McKinney, J. E. Baer, E. C. McManns, and K. H. Beyer, *J. Pharmacol. Exptl. Therap.* **122**, 60A (1958).
23. A. A. Renzi, J. J. Chart, and R. Gaunt, *Toxicol. Appl. Pharmacol.* **1**, 406 (1959).
24. J. E. Baer, H. L. Leidy, and A. V. Brooks, *Federation Proc.* **16**, 278 (1957).
25. H. Sheppard, N. R. Bowen, T. F. Mowles, and A. J. Plummer, *Federation Proc.* **18**, 444 (1959).
26. A. J. Vander, R. L. Malvin, W. S. Wilde, and L. P. Sullivan, *J. Pharmacol. Exptl. Therap.* **125**, 19 (1959).
27. R. H. Kessler, K. Hierholyer, R. S. Gurd, and R. F. Pitts, *Am. J. Physiol.* **196**, 1346 (1959).
28. E. M. Darmady, T. F. Mowles, A. A. Renzi, H. Sheppard, and F. Straneck, *Clin. Sci.* **22** (No. 2), 295 (1962).
29. A. Grollman, *Clin. Pharmacol. Therap.* **1**, 735 (1960).
30. K. H. Beyer and J. E. Baer, *Pharmacol. Rev.* **13**, 517 (1961).
31. G. deStevens and L. H. Werner, unpublished results from the CIBA Laboratories, Summit, New Jersey.
32. C. W. Whitehead and J. J. Traverso, *J. Org. Chem.* **27**, 951 (1962).
33. A. F. Esch, I. M. Wilson, and E. D. Freis. *Med. Ann. District Columbia* **28**, 9 (1959).
34. R. M. Taylor and J. G. Topliss, *J. Med. Pharm. Chem.* **5**, 312 (1962).
35. G. deStevens, L. H. Werner, W. E. Barrett, J. J. Chart, and A. A. Renzi, *Experientia* **16**, 113 (1960).
36. M. H. Sherlock, N. Sperber, and J. G. Topliss, *Experientia* **16**, 184 (1960).
37. F. J. Lund and W. Kobinger, *Acta Pharmacol. Toxicol.* **16**, 297 (1960).
38. R. Rutledge, W. E. Barrett, and A. J. Plummer, *Federation Proc.* **20**, 409 (1961).
39. C. W. Whitehead, J. J. Traverso, H. R. Sullivan, and F. J. Marshall, *J. Org. Chem.* **26**, 2814 (1961).
40. E. J. Cragoe, Jr., O. W. Woltersdorf, Jr., J. E. Baer, and J. M. Sprague, *J. Med. Pharm. Chem.* **5**, 896 (1962).
41. W. Siedel and K. Sturm, DAS (Germ. Pat. Pending) 1,141,992 (Jan. 3, 1963).
42. R. V. Ford, *Current Therap. Res.* **2**, 422, 430 (1960).
43. J. M. McManus, A. Scriabine, and W. M. McLamore, *Federation Proc.* **20**, 411 (1961).
44. R. V. Ford, *Current Therap. Res.* **3**, 320 (1961).
45. W. Logemann and P. N. Giraldi, *Brit. J. Pharmacol.* **18**, 61 (1962).
46. Hoffmann-La Roche, Belgian Pat. 593,790 (Aug. 4, 1960).
47. P. W. Feit, *Acta Chem. Scand.* **16**, 297 (1962).
48. E. J. Cragoe, Jr., J. A. Nicholson, and J. M. Sprague, *J. Med. Pharm. Chem.* **4**, 369 (1961).
49. F. C. Novello, U.S. Pat. 2,952,680 (Sept. 13, 1960).
50. E. Cohen, B. Klarberg, and J. R. Vaughan, Jr., *J. Am. Chem. Soc.* **81**, 5508 (1959); *J. Am. Chem. Soc.* **82**, 273 (1960).

51. L. H. Werner and G. deStevens, U.S. Pat. 3,072,656 (Jan. 8, 1963).
52. S. M. Gadekar and J. L. Frederick, *J. Org. Chem.* **27**, 1383 (1962).
53. S. J. Childress, *J. Pharm. Sci.* **51**, 806 (1962).
54. F. C. Novello, U.S. Pat. 3,064,006 (Nov. 13, 1962).
54a. C. W. Whitehead and J. J. Traverso, *J. Org. Chem.* **28**, 743 (1963).
55. U. Teotino and G. Cignarella, U.S. Pat. 3,067,208 (Dec. 4, 1962).
56. B. Truniger and W. Siegenthaler, *Schweiz. Med. Wochschr.* **91**, 1, (1961).
57. H. J. Schafroth, *Praxis* **10**, 1 (1961).
58. M. Fuchs and S. F. Mallin, *in* "Edema" (J. M. Moyer and M. Fuchs, eds.), pp. 276–284. Saunders, Philadelphia, Pennsylvania, 1960.

CHAPTER VII

Aldosterone: Antagonists and Secretory Inhibitors

A. Mineralocorticoid Function and Diuresis

The first reports concerning the possible presence of a vital mineralocorticoid in the adrenal cortex are attributed to Wintersteiner (1) and Kendall (2). They found that separation from adrenal extracts of the then-known, six active hormones and all related substances left an appreciable amorphous fraction which, on biological examination, proved to have marked sodium-retaining properties. Moreover, this effect was noted to be more pronounced with the amorphous fraction than with the known crystalline 11-deoxycorticosterone (cortexone). Thus, an intensive effort was made, notably on the part of Hartman and Spoor (3) to isolate the active principle from these amorphous fractions. However, it was not until 1951 that Luetscher (4) succeeded in separating, from the urine of patients with edema, a fraction with powerful sodium-retaining properties. Shortly thereafter, Simpson and Tait (5) of the Middlesex Hospital Medical School, London, presented positive evidence for the existence of such a compound. These investigators determined the mineralocorticoid activity of the various extracts from the amorphous fraction by noting the change in the urinary ratio Na^{23}/K^{42} following the administration of the test substance. They eventually isolated from a beef adrenal extract 1 mg of amorphous material with very high sodium-retaining activity. Because of its ability to control electrolyte balance, this fraction was conveniently known as electrocortin. Then, Simpson and Tait in cooperation with Reichstein and co-workers at the University of Basel, and Wettstein (6) and his collaborators at the CIBA Laboratories,

Basel, began the tremendous undertaking of isolating enough pure material for structural elucidation of this life maintenance hormone. The details of this study are reported elsewhere (7), but suffice it to say that within a 2-year period 1000 kg of beef adrenals were processed to afford a *total* of 56 mg of pure substance. Structural elucidation studies carried out on this substance as well as on some less pure material, showed that the new steroid differed from other cortical hormones in having an aldehyde group in position 18 of the pregnane skeleton. This unique structural feature resulted in the choice of the name *aldosterone* (I). Aldosterone is the third genuine hormone of the adrenal cortex, the other two being hydrocortisone and corticosterone.

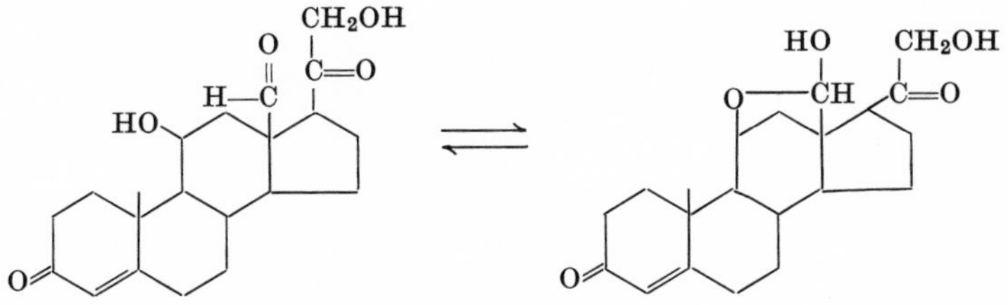

IA $\rightleftharpoons$ IB

Like the latter two substances, aldosterone has an 11β-hydroxyl group, a Δ^4-3-ketone group and a ketol side chain. The 11β-hydroxyl group interacts with the 18-carbonyl group to form a cyclohemiacetal, the forms A and B being in equilibrium.

The elucidation of the constitutional formula was soon followed by the total synthesis of aldosterone by Wettstein (8) and his group. Although *dl*-aldosterone was initially synthesized, a later synthesis by this group gave rise to the *d* (the active isomer) and the *l* forms, the former by stereospecific synthesis and the latter by resolution (9). Barton and Beaton (10) recently have described an ingenious four-step synthesis of *d*-aldosterone from *d*-corticosterone acetate. In this transformation the oxygen at position 18 is elaborated by photochemical means.

Aldosterone is formed in the outer layer of the adrenal cortex, the *zona glomerulosa* (see Fig. 1, Chapter I). It seems probable that it is produced via deoxycorticosterone and corticosterone. However, the enzymic process of the decisive step in the biosynthesis, i.e., the hydroxylation of corticosterone at position 18, has not been determined. Nevertheless, it has been possible to show in man that injected corticosterone is transformed into aldosterone. The average production of aldosterone in man is from 0.1 to 0.2 mg per 24 hours (11). The amount secreted is dependent on several factors, both physiological and pathological; e.g., reduction in extracellular volume (12), salt restriction (13), or potassium excretion (14). Endogenous overproduction of aldosterone occurs either in the form of *primary* hyperaldosteronism (15, 15a) which is characterized by hypertension, polyuria, and potassium loss, and *no* edema, or a *secondary* hyperaldosteronism which results from an increase in salt (sodium chloride) and water

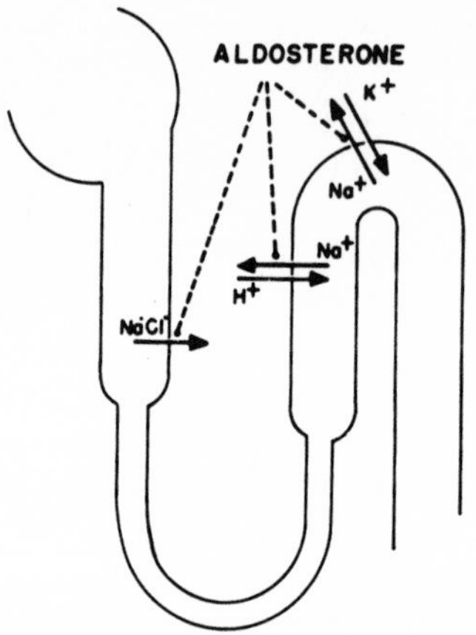

FIG. 1. Schematic outline of site of action of aldosterone in the nephron.

retention (edema) arising from cirrhosis, nephrosis, congestive heart failure, or hypertension. However, it should be emphasized that, although aldosterone is responsible for sodium retention, the adrenals play only a small but very important part in maintaining the sodium level in the organism. The adrenalectomized animal reabsorbs in the kidney 98% of the sodium filtered in the primary urine instead of 99.9% as under normal conditions. Thus, aldosterone is responsible for about 2% of the sodium retained in the kidney. Laragh (16) has presented evidence which suggests that the site of action (sodium reabsorption) of aldosterone in the nephron is in the distal renal tubules (see Fig. 1).

Considerable work has been carried out recently in a number of laboratories to design drugs which (a) could antagonize the action of aldosterone at its site of action or (b) could block the secretion of this mineralocorticoid by inhibiting its biosynthesis, the consequence of which would be sodium diuresis accompanied by water excretion. To date, steroidal and nonsteroidal compounds have been found to antagonize aldosterone, whereas several synthetic substances have been developed which inhibit aldosterone biosynthesis. Each of these will now be considered as described.

B. Aldosterone Antagonists

1. Steroidal Spirolactones

In 1957 Cella and Kagawa (17) of G. D. Searle and Co. reported on their preparation of 3-(3-oxo-17β-hydroxy-4-androstene-17α-yl) propanoic acid lactone [this compound will be referred to as compound VI (see Scheme 1) or SC-5233] which showed aldosterone blocking activity when administered subcutaneously to rats. Since that time Cella and co-workers (18–21) have presented a number of papers on structure–activity relationships in this series. The pharmacological evaluation of these compounds was carried out in an assay which involves determination of the per cent reversal by deoxycorticosterone acetate (DCA) on the urinary sodium and potassium content in adrenalectomized rats (22).

The synthesis of SC-5233 is outlined in Scheme 1 and serves as a model for the preparation of structurally related compounds. The Grignard reagent of 17α-ethynyl-5-androstene-3β,17β-diol was allowed to react with carbon dioxide to yield the acetylenic acid (II). Selective reduction of the acetylenic bond to the olefin was accomplished by catalytic hydrogenation over palladium on calcium carbonate using dioxane and pyridine as solvents. The resulting product on treatment with mineral acid afforded unsaturated lactone (III) which was reduced catalytically to V and then oxidized by an Oppenhauer reaction to VI (SC-5233). Oppenhauer oxidation of III yielded the unsaturated lactone (IV).

SC-5233 was the first steroidal compound prepared by Cella and his colleagues to show an anti-aldosterone effect. Consequently, this series was expanded further, first by preparing the 19-nor derivatives and, second, by preparing the 6-membered lactone analogs of SC-5233 and its 19-nor derivative.

The 19-nor analog (IX) of SC-5233 was prepared from a steroidal nucleus containing an aromatic A ring which was initially allowed to

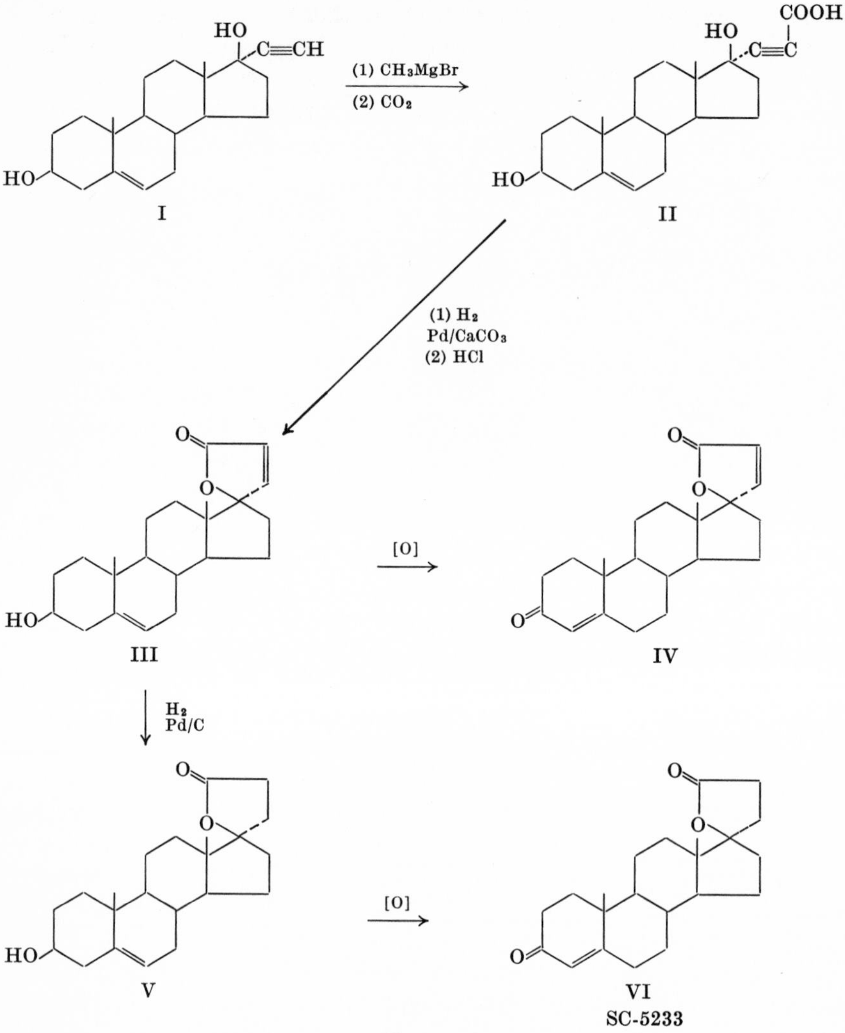

SCHEME 1

undergo a Birch reduction followed by essentially the same series of reactions used in Scheme I. This reaction sequence is shown in Scheme 2.

The 6-membered lactone analogs of VI and IX were prepared from the 17α-propargyl derivatives by a similar sequence of reactions (see Scheme 3).

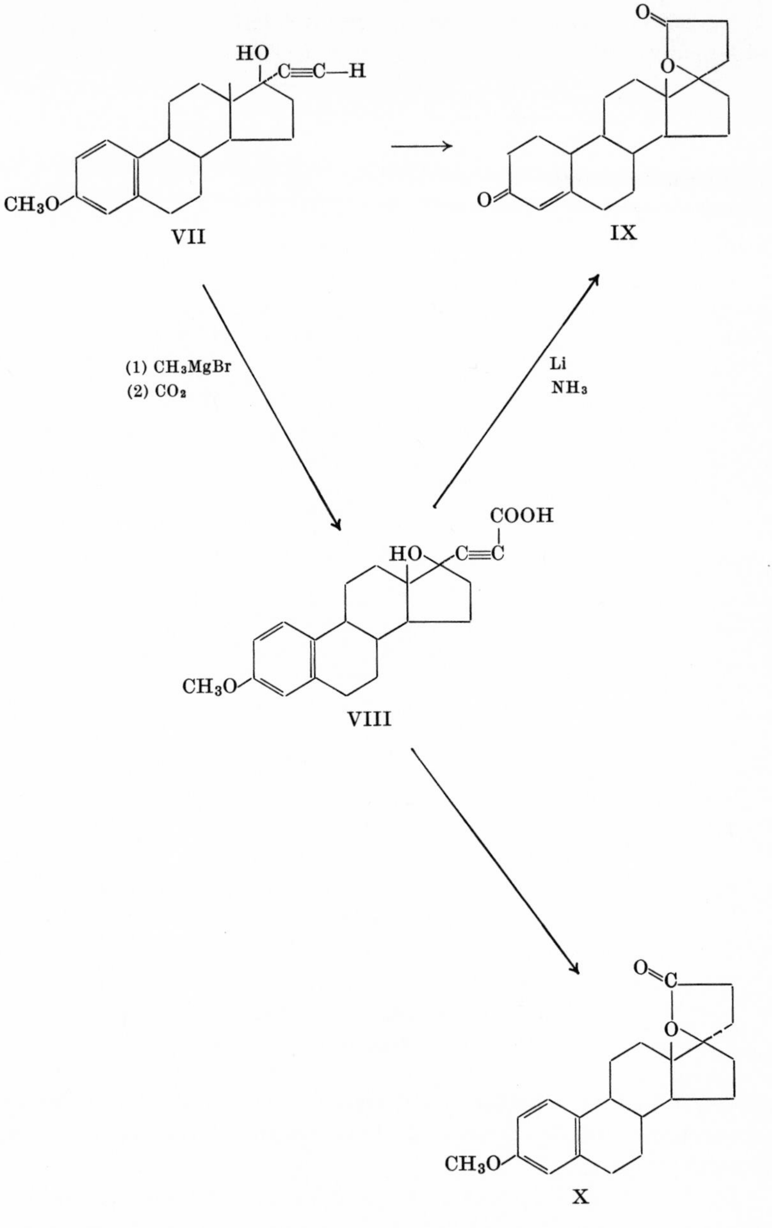

HO
C≡C—H
CH_3O
VII

IX

(1) CH_3MgBr
(2) CO_2

Li
NH_3

COOH
HO C≡C
CH_3O
VIII

CH_3O
X

Scheme 2

Of the compounds heretofore described only VI and IX showed significant aldosterone blocking effects. These initial studies further suggested that a 5-membered spirolactone at position 17 and a 3-ketoΔ^4-arrangement were necessary for activity (reduction of the double bond at C-4,5 to the dihydro compounds, AB *cis* and *trans*, led to virtually inactive substances). It was finally determined that VI and IX showed much better aldosterone blocking activities when administered parenterally than when given orally. Thus, Cella and his collaborators commenced a vigorous attack on the spirolactone steroid systems to find a compound possessing oral activity.

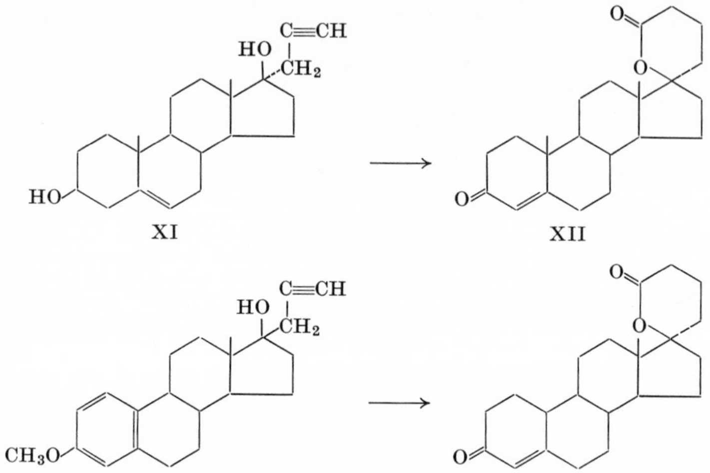

Scheme 3

It was first decided to introduce unsaturation at the C-1 and C-6 centers of VI because of the desirable effects produced by such changes in some biologically active steroids (22) (see Scheme 4).

Dehydrogenation of compound VI with selenium dioxide produced the corresponding $\Delta^{1,4}$-3-oxo derivative (XV) whereas treatment of VI with chloranil yielded the $\Delta^{4,6}$-3-oxospirolactone (XVI). Compound XVI could be converted to the $\Delta^{1,4,6}$-3-oxo steroid (XIX) with selenium dioxide. As anticipated all of these dehydrogenated derivatives possessed enhanced oral activity. The Searle group then observed that the 7α-hydroxy progesterone is more active than the parent compound when administered parenterally. Thus, the alkanethiolic acid adducts of the unsaturated compounds were prepared.

As expected, ethanethiolic acid added readily to either the 1,2 or the 6,7 double bond (23). Molecular rotational data and analogy to known epoxidation studies (24, 24a) suggested the α-configuration for the 1-acetylthio and 7-acetylthio groups. Steric considerations support this since the approach of a thiolic acid molecule to the double bond should occur more readily from the less hindered α-side. Moreover, the evidence further indicates that the acylation is a *trans* diaxial

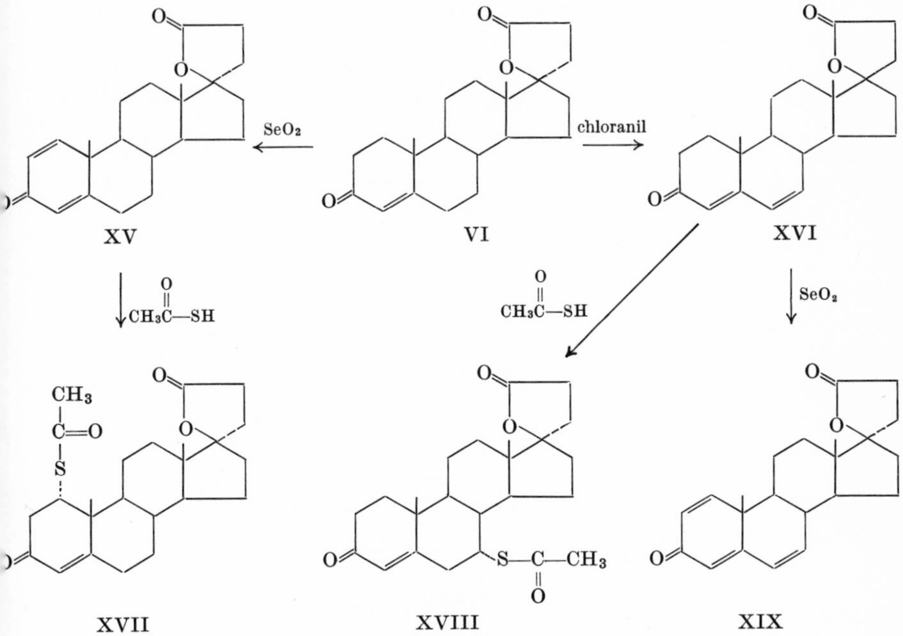

XV ← SeO_2 — VI — chloranil → XVI

XV ↓ $CH_3C(=O)$—SH → XVII

XVI ↙ $CH_3C(=O)$—SH → XVIII

XVI ↓ SeO_2 → XIX

XVII

XVIII
SC-9420—spironolactone

XIX

SCHEME 4

addition to the double bond. Propanethiolic acid addition gave the corresponding 1α-propionylthio and 7α-propionylthio compounds. These compounds were tested for their aldosterone blocking activity and found to be less active than SC-5233 (VI) when administered parenterally. However, the *oral* activity of the acylthio compounds was greatly *increased*, particularly in the case of 3-(3-oxo-7α-acetylthio-17β-hydroxy-4-androsten-17α-yl) propanoic acid lactone, SC-9420 (XVIII).

Over a period of 3 years the Searle chemists (21, 25, 26) prepared a variety of spirolactone-substituted steroid derivatives (e.g., methyl group at 2,4,6,7 or 16; 11-keto, 11-hydroxy, and 9-fluoro-11-hydroxy) by well-defined paths. None of these compounds have been found to be superior to XVIII. As a matter of fact, methylation usually caused a large decrease in potency, both subcutaneously and orally. The Searle group also prepared C-16 spirolactone corresponding to

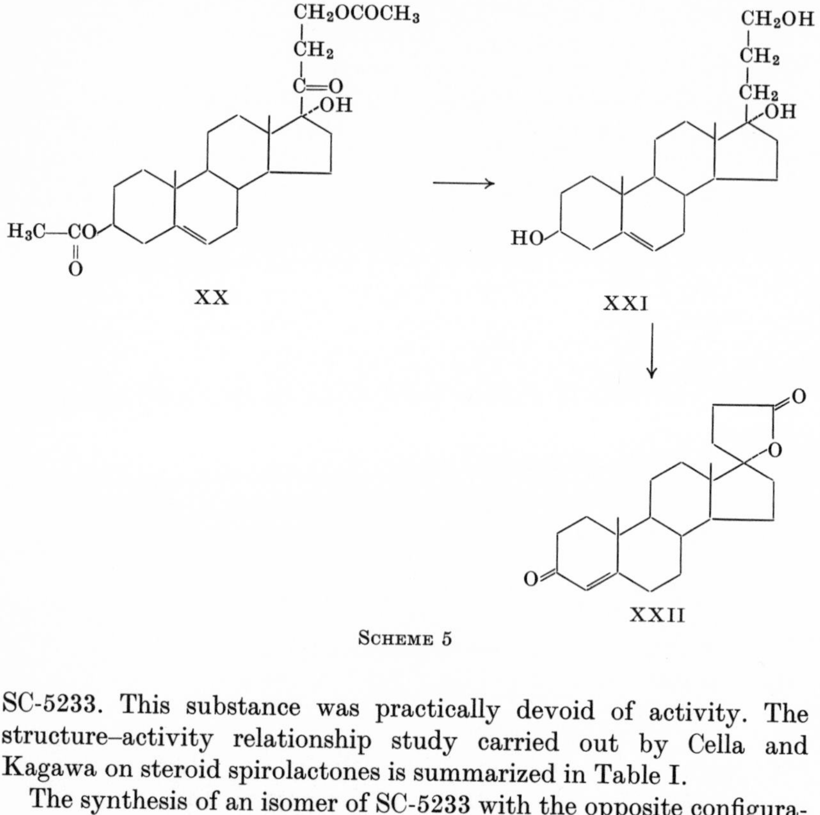

XX → XXI → XXII

SCHEME 5

SC-5233. This substance was practically devoid of activity. The structure–activity relationship study carried out by Cella and Kagawa on steroid spirolactones is summarized in Table I.

The synthesis of an isomer of SC-5233 with the opposite configuration at C-17 was outlined recently by Hess (27) (see Scheme 5). Compound XX was reduced in two steps to the triol (XXI). Protection of the double bond in XXI with bromine permitted simultaneous oxidation of the 3-alcohol and the primary alcohol in the side chain with chromic acid in acetic acid. Elimination of bromine with zinc and isomerization with hydrochloric acid gave the α,β-unsaturated

TABLE I

SPIROLACTONES AND THEIR DCA BLOCKING ACTIVITIES

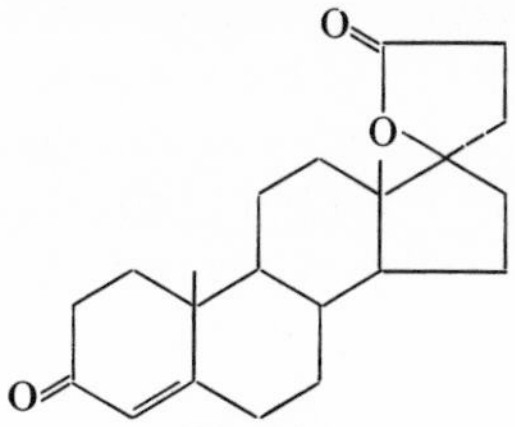

SC-5233

Substitution or modification of SC-5233	DCA blocking activities Subcutaneous	Oral
SC-5233 (VI) (standard)	100	1
IV	<7	—
V	<7	—
IX (19-nor)	190	7
XII	5	<1
XIV	50	<17
XV (Δ^1)	80	9
XVI (Δ^6)	29	17
XIX(Δ^1 and Δ^6)	70	17
XVII (1α-S—C(=O)—CH_3)	18	7
SC-9420 (XVIII) [7α-S—C(=O)—CH_3]	70	42
7β-S—C(=O)—CH_3	<7	<4
2α-CH_3	<13	<13
6α-CH_3	15	21
6β-CH_3	60	12
16α-CH_3	<7	—
6α-CH_3,7α-S—C(=O)—CH_3	~7	~40
11β-OH	15	—
11α-OH	<7	—
2α-CH_3,9α-F, 16β-OH	low	low
Aromatic A ring with 3-OCH_3	<7	—

Note. For purposes of comparison, the DCA blocking activity of SC-5233 is used as a standard and assigned a relative value of 100; 0.16 mg of SC-5233 administered subcutaneously causes a 50% reversal of urinary electrolyte effects of 12 μg of DCA.

ketone. Under these conditions cyclization of the γ-hydroxy acid to the lactone (XXII) occurred readily. Compound XXII did not show any of the electrolyte regulating effects exhibited by SC-5233.

Another modification of the spirolactone consisted in the preparation of the spirolactam corresponding to SC-5233. The original work carried out in this series is attributed to Nysted and Burtner (28) of Searle and Co. These investigators found that the conventional method for converting γ-lactones to γ-lactams by treatment of the lactone with an appropriate amine only resulted in the formation of the corresponding amides. An alternate approach proved more successful (see Scheme 6).

Smilagenin (XXIII) was degraded to 3β-acetoxy-16-pregnen-20-one (XXIV) by the procedure of Mueller (29). The reduced product XXV was converted to oxime (XXVI) which was subjected sequentially to Beckmann rearrangement and saponification to yield 3β-hydroxy-17β-amino-5β-androstane (XXVII). Selective monoacetylation and oxidation afforded the 17-nitro compound (XXVIII) which condensed smoothly with methyl acrylate yielding compound XXIX. The configuration of this Michael adduct is based on the following theoretical considerations and spectral evidence.

(a) Oxidation of the 17β-amino group under acidic conditions produced the kinetically favored product since addition occurs from the less hindered side. Only one adduct could be obtained confirming the stereoselectivity of the reaction. Equilibrium studies on the adduct established that the Michael addition is irreversible.

(b) The optical rotatory dispersion curves are similar for the 17β-nitro compound and the Michael adduct. This would not have been true had inversion occurred during addition.

Catalytic hydrogenation of the adduct XXIX afforded the spirolactam (XXX) which was saponified and oxidized to the ketone (XXXI). Compound XXXI was finally converted by conventional methods (bromination followed by dehydrobromination) to the desired spirolactam (XXXII). In a later paper, Patchett and co-workers (30) of Merck, Sharp and Dohme treated XXXII with chloranil to form the $\Delta^{4,6}$-derivative to which was added transdiaxially thiolacetic acid at C-7 to yield XXXIII. These compounds did not possess significant aldosterone blocking activity (31). Other modifications of the spirolactam (N-methylation or reduction to the spiramine) gave only inactive compounds.

Finally, Chinn, Dryden, and Burtner (32) prepared a des-A analog

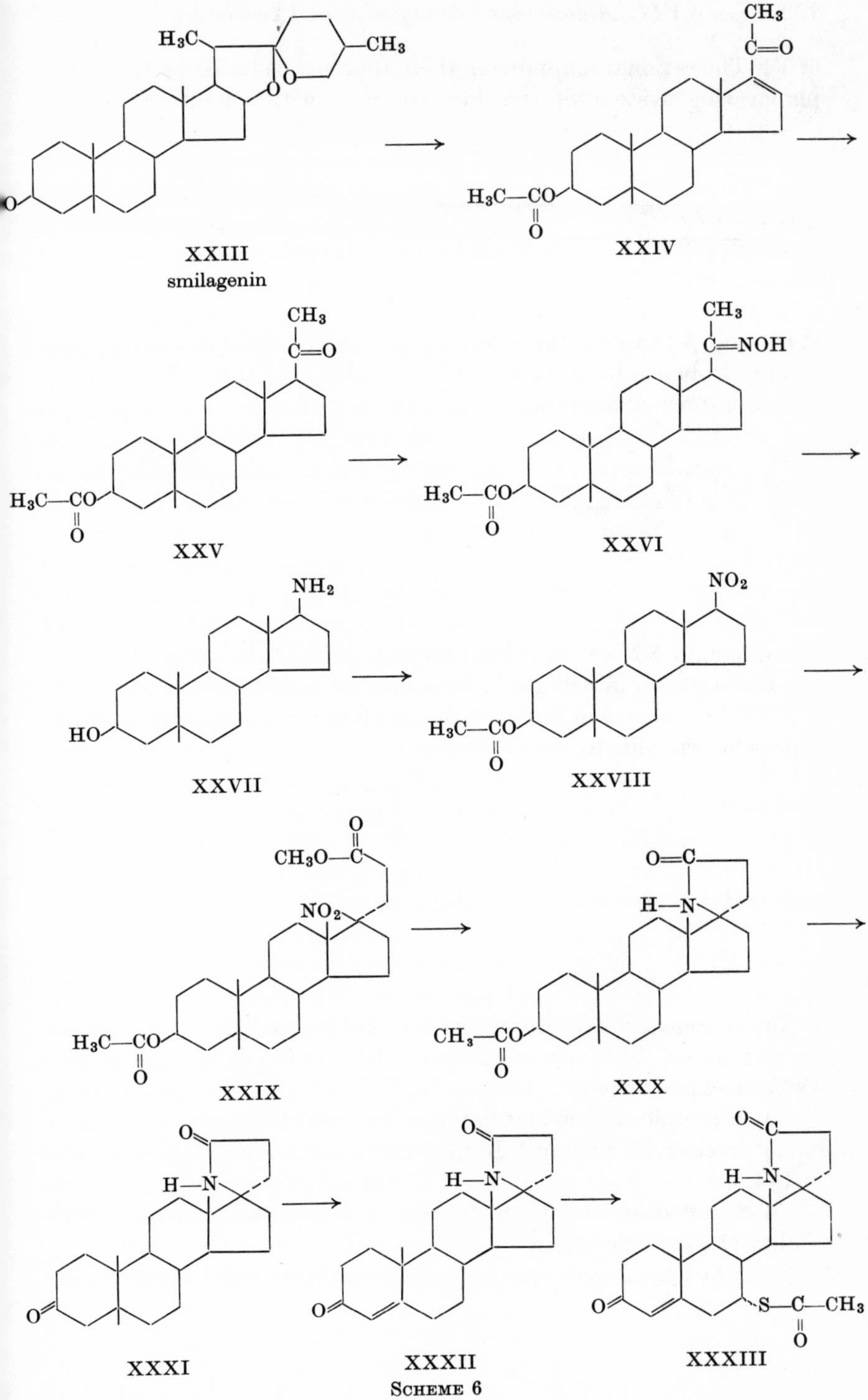

XXIII
smilagenin

XXIV

XXV

XXVI

XXVII

XXVIII

XXIX

XXX

XXXI

XXXII

XXXIII

SCHEME 6

of VI. The rationale supporting their approach is based on the nearly planar ring system of steroids (compare with "template"), e.g.,

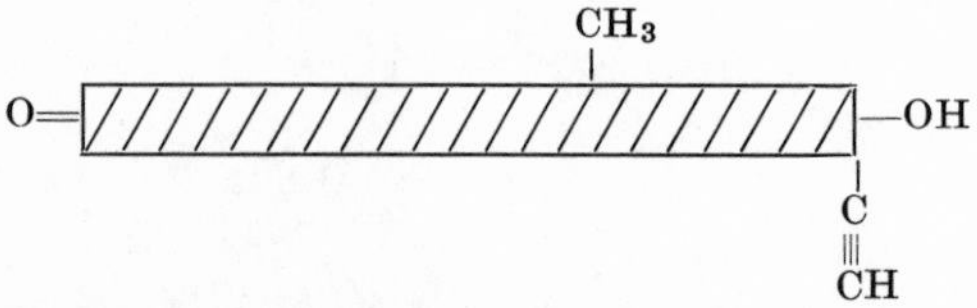

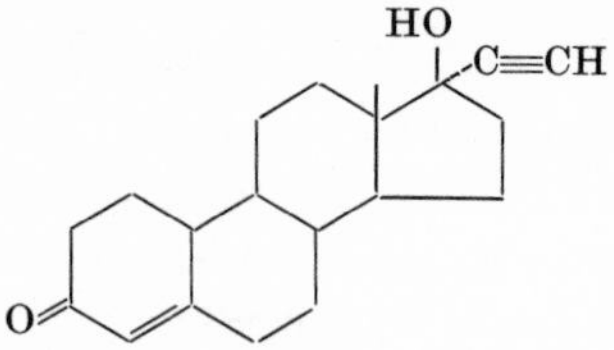

When ring A is missing as in *trans*-anti-*trans* 1,1-disubstituted 1,2,3,4-tetrahydrobenzo hydrindane, the "template" of the steroid appears to be compressed as shown.

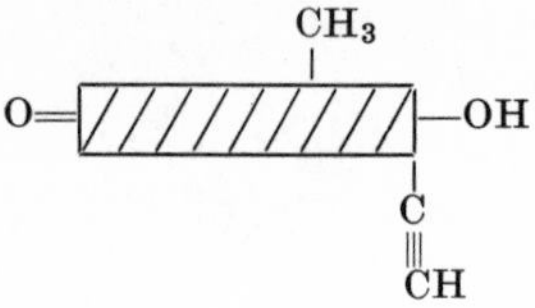

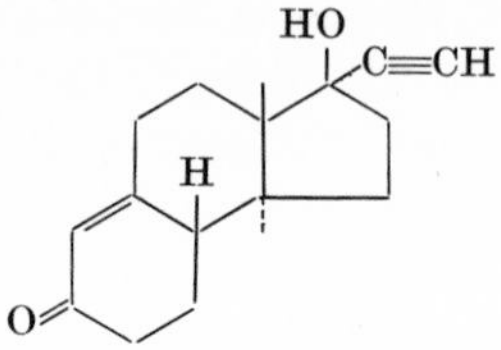

XXXIV

Compound XXXV was synthesized from XXXIV according to the method outlined in Scheme 1. When tested in adrenalectomized rats, XXXV was observed to block the sodium-retaining activity of the mineralocorticoids to some extent.

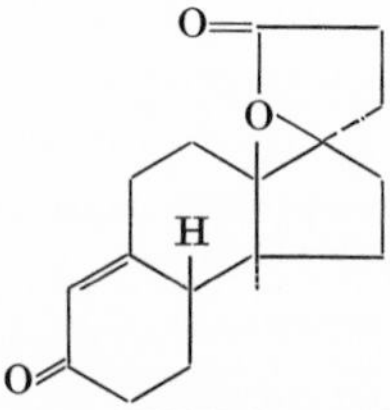

XXXV

The extensive structure–activity study on spirolactones has indicated the following essential structural requisites for optimal DCA blocking activity:

(*1*) A ketonic or incipient ketonic function at C-3.

(*2*) A relatively planar A/B ring juncture, preferably a double bond at C-4,5.

(*3*) Substitution only in the B ring to impart *significant* oral absorbability (7α-acylthio group).

(*4*) A five-membered spirolactone of specific configuration at C-17.

Spironolactone (SC-9420) was the most potent and effective compound prepared in the series. Pharmacologically, this substance as well as others in this genus were shown by Kagawa (33) to exert their effects on electrolytes by competing with aldosterone or similarly acting steroids at the kidney level. It follows, then, that in the absence of mineralocorticoids in the kidney, the spirolactones, acting as aldosterone antagonists, were found to be *ineffective* as diuretics. The clinical evaluation (34) of spironolactone confirmed animal experiments since this drug appears to exert its action with respect to the renal excretion of electrolytes only in the presence of hyperaldosteronism. Thus, the effectiveness of spironolactone is limited to those patients in which excessive aldosterone is a contributing factor to the disease. However, because of its specific aldosterone blocking effect in the distal tubules, spironolactone does have the important quality of causing marked sodium diuresis without potassium excretion. Consequently, clinical interest has been focused on the use of this drug in the treatment of cirrhosis with ascites, a condition in which the use of other diuretics would inevitably lead to the excretion of abnormally large amounts of potassium. Some successful clinical studies have also been carried out on the use of spironolactone in combination with hydrochlorothiazide in overcoming resistant edemas. This combination brings about a strong saluretic effect with minimum potassium loss. The sodium diuresis is believed to occur from a simultaneous pharmacological antagonism of aldosterone in the distal tubule by spironolactone and inhibition of sodium reabsorption in the proximal tubule by hydrochlorothiazide (35). Spironolactone is orally effective at dosages of 100 to 200 mg three or four times daily.

2. 2-(Naphthyl)cyclopentanes

Since it was shown that compound XXXV antagonizes aldosterone, and, thus, the tetracyclic ring system of the steroid was not absolutely essential for activity, Chinn (36) undertook the synthesis of some further structural modifications of steroids. This led to the synthesis of some 2-(naphthyl)cyclopentanes which are neither steroids nor do they have the spirolactone system incorporated in their structures. However, if they are written in a certain spatial form, their relationship to steroids is apparent. Those substances which were found to be active are outlined in Table II.

The hydroxymethyl ketone derivative is effective when administered both orally and subcutaneously. Replacement of the primary hydroxy group of the methyl ketone with halogen had a variable effect; the fluoromethyl ketone derivative shows blocking activity only when given subcutaneously, whereas the chloromethyl ketone derivative exhibited weak antimineralocorticoid effects as compared to the hydroxymethyl ketone derivative.

TABLE II

2-(NAPHTHYL)CYCLOPENTANES (36)

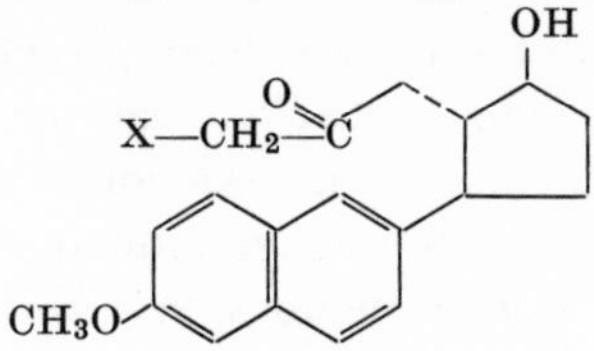

X	M.E.D.[a] Subcutaneous	Oral
OH	0.36–1.0	3.0–7.8
F	1.2	> 4.8
Cl	> 2.4	—

[a] The M.E.D. value is defined as the "medium effective dose (total mg/rat) which when used with 12 mg of deoxycorticosterone acetate (DCA) in adrenalectomized rats produces the same urinary sodium–potassium ratio as that which results from the use of 6 mg of DCA alone."

Some simpler analogs in the benzene series have also been reported by Chinn (37) to be diuretics. However, no biological data are available on this group of compounds.

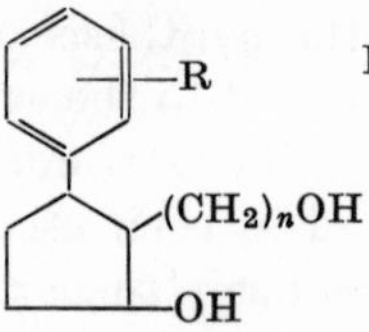

R = H, lower alkyl, alkoxy

n = 1,2,3

3. AMINOPTERIDINES

The collaborative effort of Professor E. C. Taylor of Princeton and J. Weinstock of Smith, Kline and French has resulted, not only in some novel methods for the preparation of aminopteridines but also in the development of a compound in this heterocyclic class with interesting diuretic properties. Since the synthesis of numerous substituted aminopteridines by these investigators is the subject of several patents (38–42), herein only the synthesis of triamterene (XXXVII) will be illustrated, the most active compound in this class which has received extensive pharmacological and clinical evaluation. Essentially the reaction involves the condensation of 2,4,6-triamino-5-nitroso pyrimidine (XXXVI) with benzylcyanide in dimethylformamide with sodium methoxide as a catalyst.

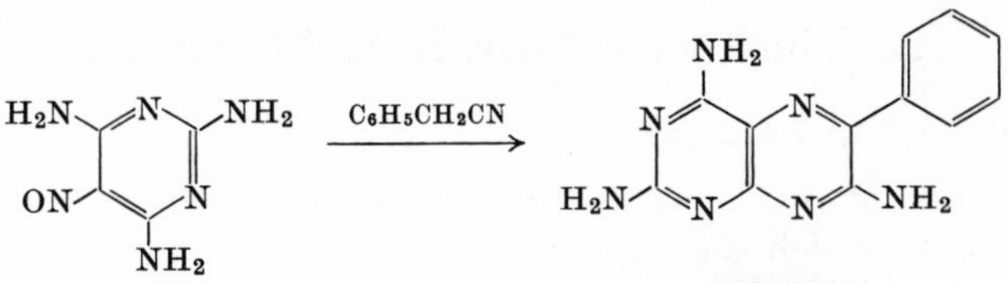

H_2N, N, NH_2, ON, N, NH_2
XXXVI

$\xrightarrow{C_6H_5CH_2CN}$

NH_2, N, N, H_2N, N, N, NH_2
XXXVII
SKF-8542
triamterene

The initial pharmacology on this compound was reported by Wiebelhaus and collaborators (43) in 1961. Triamterene was shown to be a potent orally effective diuretic in the saline-loaded rat. In the sodium-deficient rat it also produced a profound diuresis without any effect on potassium. This group then found that triamterene completely antagonizes both the sodium-retention and potassium-losing effects of crystalline aldosterone in the adrenalectomized rat. These results were also reproduced in dogs receiving relatively high doses of aldosterone. Consequently, it appeared to these investigators that triamterene functioned as an aldosterone antagonist. Clinical studies by Crosley *et al.* (44) and Laragh and his group (45) revealed that triamterene causes a significant natriuresis in man. Laragh presented the following evidence that triamterene inhibits aldosterone:

(*1*) It produced natriuresis and chloruresis and reduced potassium excretion.

(*2*) It was more effective when aldosterone secretion was elevated.

(*3*) It corrected hypokalemic alkalosis of aldosteronism.

(*4*) It increased sodium excretion while producing little change in urine flow suggesting distal tubular action.

On the other hand, Ball and Greene (45a) and Wiebelhaus *et al.* (45b) have recently shown that triamterene very definitely causes a natriuresis in adrenalectomized rats and dogs suggesting that the drug acts by mechanisms other than aldosterone antagonism.

Laragh and Crosley *et al.* (46) indicated that triamterene in doses of 150 mg per day acted more rapidly and appeared to be more potent than 1200 mg per day of spironolactone. However, Laragh reported four cases of reversible granulocytopenia in his study. Extensive clinical trials are still in progress with this compound in the United States, but it has been introduced into clinical medicine in Great Britain and West Germany.

C. Inhibitors of Aldosterone Biosynthesis

1. Amphenone and Metyrapone

Allen and Corwin (47) in 1950 synthesized a pinacolone-type ketone (XXXIX) to which they appended the trivial name amphenone B. The structure XXXIX was assigned by these workers on the basis of

$$H_2N{-}C_6H_4{-}C(OH)(CH_3){-}C(OH)(CH_3){-}C_6H_4{-}NH_2 \xrightarrow{H_2SO_4} H_2N{-}C_6H_4{-}C(CH_3)_2{-}C(=O){-}C_6H_4{-}NH_2$$

XXXVIII → XXXIX

an apparent negative iodoform test and a rather drastic alkali fission of its *N*,*N*′-tetramethyl derivative to afford a very small amount of *p*-dimethylaminobenzoic acid. Within the next few years, amphenone B was evaluated in a number of biological test systems and it was shown to produce a variety of effects. Hertz and co-workers (48) reported it to have weak antiestrogenic activity, progestational activity, antithyroid activity, and a suggestion of general suppression of adrenal corticosteroid synthesis in the rat. It subsequently became clear that in the dog and in man amphenone interferes with the biosynthesis of all or most of the adrenal corticoids, probably by interfering with the enzymic mechanisms responsible for the later stages of steroid synthesis (49). Rosenfeld and Bascom (50) located these inhibitions as specifically involving 11β-, 17α, and 21-hydroxylations. In addition, Thorn (51) and Renold and collaborators (52) showed that amphenone inhibited the secretion of aldosterone in man leading to a marked diuresis in normal patients or those with Cushing's syndrome but not in adrenalectomized patients (49). This established that amphenone was acting as an inhibitor of aldosterone biosynthesis in the adrenal cortex. However, because of the variety of other effects which this substance manifested some of which were quite toxic, its use for clinical purposes was precluded (53).

At about this time (1956), Bencze and Allen of the CIBA Laboratories began a series of investigations to prepare amphenone analogs which showed fewer of the side effects and less toxicity than amphenone, yet which still had the ability to suppress adrenal cortical secretion. In looking for new potential routes to the synthesis of amphenone-like compounds, the original amphenone synthesis was restudied. Bencze and Allen (54) by means of stepwise degradation and spectral data found that the original structure XXXIX proposed was in error and that, in fact, under the conditions of the reaction (refluxing the glycol XXXVIII in dilute hydrochloric acid or concentrated sulfuric acid) only the *p*-aminophenyl group undergoes migration to form 3,3-bis(*p*-aminophenyl)-butanone-2 (XL), the correct constitution of amphenone B.

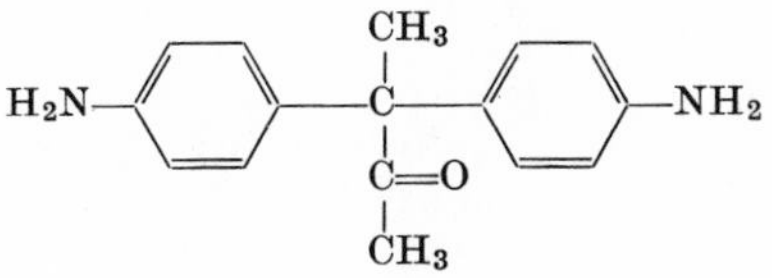

CH_3
H_2N— C₆H₄ —C— C₆H₄ —NH_2
C=O
CH_3

XL

amphenone B

A diversity of monosubstituted compounds related to XL were prepared by this method or from the parent substance by Sandmeyer-type exchange reactions (55). Table III lists these compounds and their adrenocortical inhibitory action.

Several pertinent structure–activity relationships are revealed by the substituted 3,3-diphenylbutanones. The *N*,*N*′-tetramethyl compound showed some activity, whereas shifting the amino groups of amphenone to the *m*-position caused a complete loss of biological activity. Substitution of other functional groups at the *para* position also gave inactive compounds. Oximation or reduction of the carbonyl group of amphenone to the secondary alcohol derivative did not yield a substance which showed improvement over the parent compound. Furthermore, the exchange of the two methyl groups of amphenone for ethyl radicals (XLI) proved to be of no advantage since the adrenal cortical inhibitory activity was diminished.

TABLE III

SUBSTITUTED 3, 3-DIPHENYLBUTANONES (55)

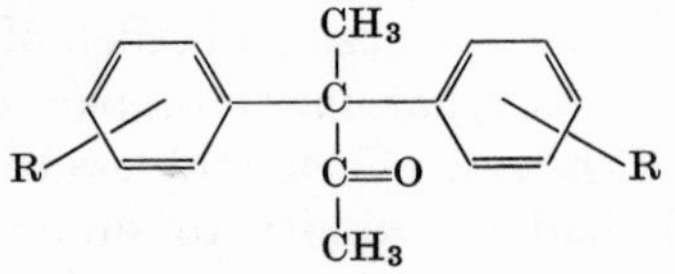

R	Activity[a]
4-NH_2[b]	Active
3-NH_2[b]	Inactive
4-$(CH_3)_2N$-[b]	Slightly active
N-$^{+}(CH_3)_3I^{-}$	Inactive
H[b]	
4-OCH_3[b]	
4-COOH[b]	
4-CN[c]	
4-F[c]	
4-Cl[c]	Moderately active
4-SO_2NH_2[c]	Inactive
4-I[c]	
4-Br[c]	
4-NO_2[b]	

[a] Adrenal cortical suppression was determined by the reduction of concentration of 17-hydroxysteroids in adrenal vein blood (56).

[b] Prepared from the corresponding *p*-substituted acetophenones via pinacol reduction and rearrangement.

[c] Obtained from amphenone by Sandmeyer-type exchange reactions.

It was next of interest to prepare and evaluate the deoxybenzoin-type compounds. Since the ketone (XXXIX), isomeric with amphenone, could not be obtained from the parent pinacol (XXXVIII), it

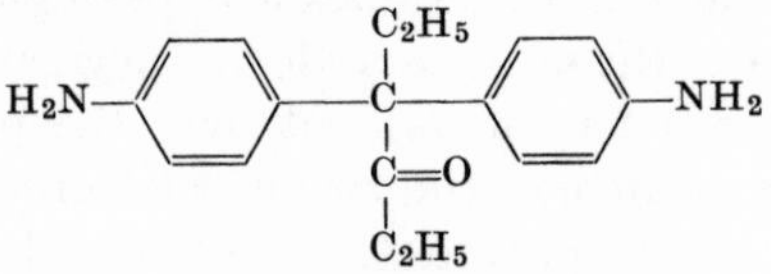

XLI

was necessary to devise a new synthesis of this substance (57) (see Scheme 7).

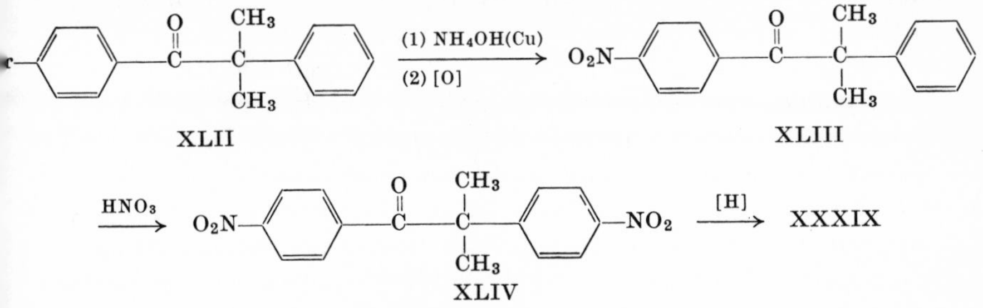

XLII $\xrightarrow[\text{(2) [O]}]{\text{(1) } NH_4OH(Cu)}$ O_2N—C_6H_4—CO—$C(CH_3)_2$—C_6H_5 (XLIII) $\xrightarrow{HNO_3}$ O_2N—C_6H_4—CO—$C(CH_3)_2$—C_6H_4—NO_2 (XLIV) $\xrightarrow{[H]}$ XXXIX

Scheme 7

Treatment of di-(*p*-bromophenyl)cadmium with α-phenylisobutyryl chloride yielded 1-(*p*-bromophenyl)-2-methyl-2-phenyl-1-propanone XLII.

The bromine was exchanged for an amino group which was in turn oxidized to a nitro group. Nitration of compound XLIII followed by catalytic reduction led to the desired diaminopinacolone (XXXIX). The structure of this substance was confirmed through its degradation to a substance of known constitution. The compounds listed in Table IV were prepared by this scheme. Thus, the presence of an amino group *para* to the carbonyl was sufficient to impart to the compound activity comparable to amphenone. An amino group *para*

TABLE IV

p, p'-Disubstituted α-Dimethyldeoxybenzoins (55)

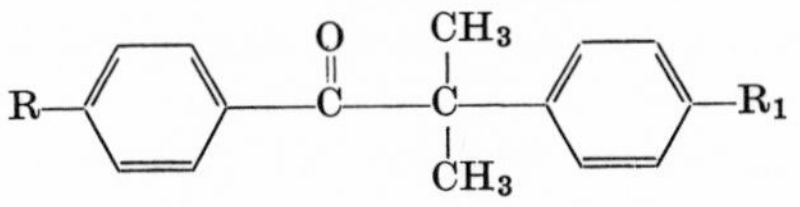

R—C_6H_4—CO—$C(CH_3)_2$—C_6H_4—R_1

R	R_1	Activity
H	H	Active
H	NH_2	Activity of short duration
NH_2	H	Equal to amphenone
NH_2	NH_2	Equal to amphenone
Cl	Cl	Inactive
Cl	H	Transient activity
Br	Cl	Inactive
Cl	NH_2	Activity of short duration

to the α,α-dimethyldeoxy group had little effect. The *p,p'*-diamino compound again was as active as amphenone. The halogen group did not have a beneficial effect. Finally, the compounds described in Table IV were found to be even more toxic than amphenone.

Bencze and co-workers (58, 59) then turned their attention to amphenone-type compounds containing pyridine rings. The main procedure for the preparation of the pyridine amphenone analogs was essentially the same as previously described. The 2,3- and 4-acetylpyridines were reduced electrolytically (47) or photochemically (59) to their corresponding pinacols, and these were rearranged in concentrated sulfuric acid to yield the following pinacolone-type ketones.

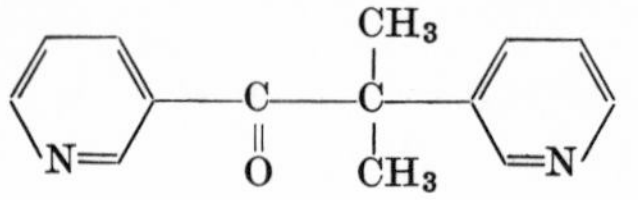

XLV
Su-4885—Metyrapone

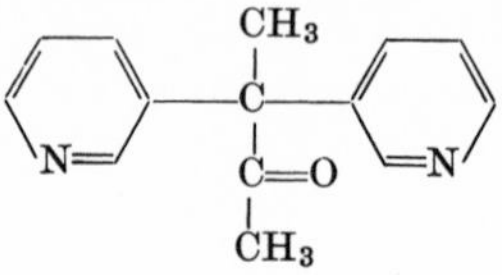

XLVI

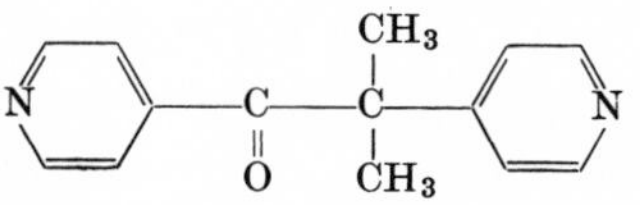

XLVII

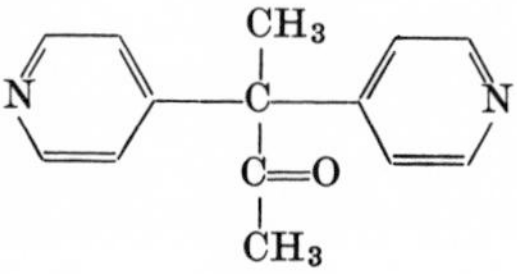

XLVIII

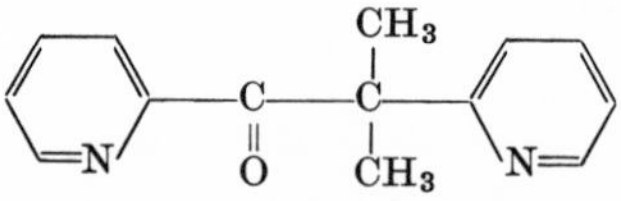

XLIX

Compounds XLV through XLVIII showed the highest amphenone-like activity encountered, whereas XLIX possessed only moderate activity. Compound XLV, 1,2,-bis-(3-pyridyl)-2-methyl-1-propanone (Metyrapone or Su-4885), was chosen for broad biological and clinical investigation (60). It was first noted in dogs that in acute experiments this compound reduced the total 17-OH secretion. It was also observed, and for a time inexplicably, that when given to dogs over a long period of time, Su-4885 did not cause adrenal insufficiency and, in fact, under some conditions caused a retention of sodium, suggesting excessive biosynthesis of a mineralocorticoid. The explanation of this paradox turned out to be, as shown independently by Liddle *et al.* (61) and Jenkins and co-workers (62), as well as others, that the predominant effect of *moderate* doses of Su-4885 was to block 11β-hydroxylation and hence to inhibit the secretion of the main natural corticoids—hydrocortisone, corticosterone, and aldosterone (see Scheme 8) (63).

If the action of the drug stopped at this point, then it might have been of some value as a diuretic. Unfortunately, the suppression of

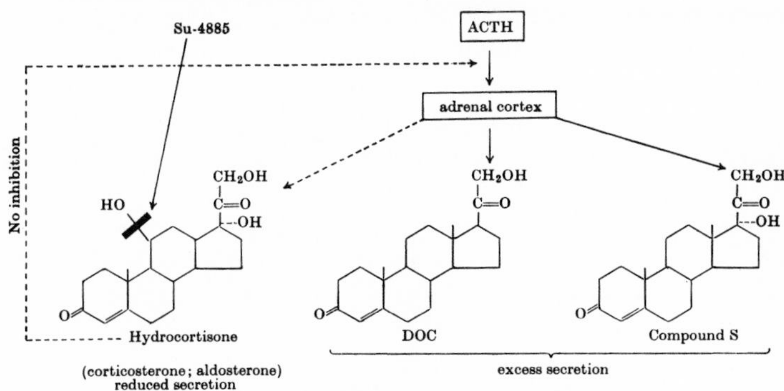

SCHEME 8. Su-4885 causing sodium retention (63)

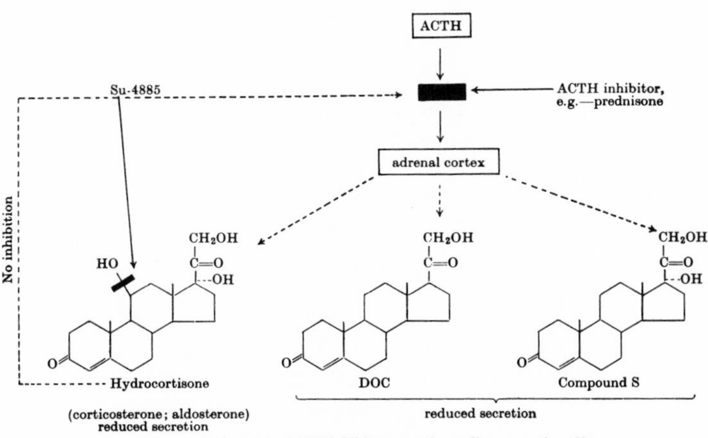

SCHEME 9. Su-4885—ACTH inhibitor—causing sodium excretion (63)

hydrocortisone secretion resulted in greatly increased secretion of ACTH. The consequent excess of ACTH acting on the adrenals, whose main pathways of steroidogenesis are blocked, causes an outpouring of two steroids normally secreted only in very small amounts: 11-deoxyhydrocortisone (Reichstein's Compound S) and 11-deoxycorticosterone (DOC). The latter substance is a potent salt-retaining hormone. In fact, the amount of this mineralocorticoid produced is such that sodium retention of ten times resulted despite the lack of aldosterone. However, Liddle (64) has shown that if an ACTH inhibitor such as prednisone is given with Su-4885, then the compensatory increase in Compound S and DOC is prevented and a sodium diuresis occurs (see Scheme 9). This type of diuretic regimen is of limited value and is used only in those cases where other forms of therapy are inapplicable. However, Su-4885 is finding wide use as a diagnostic tool in determining various endocrine diseases (i.e., pituitary deficiency).

2. Indenes and Tetralones

During the study of the amphenone synthesis, it was observed that treatment of the various pinacols with concentrated hydrochloric acid led to the formation of substituted indenes. Some of these substances also exhibited 17-OH inhibition when tested in dogs (see Table V). Reduction of these substances to indane derivatives did

TABLE V

Indene Derivatives (55)

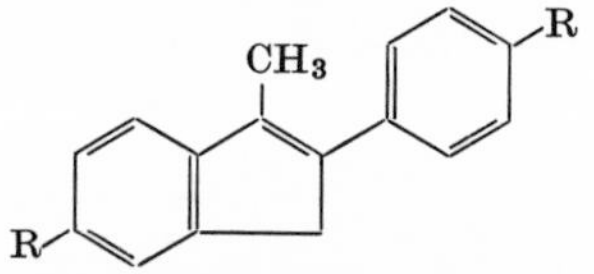

CH_3 R R

R	Activity
NH_2	Slight activity
$N(CH_3)_2$	Active
$—N^+—(CH_3)_3I^-$	Inactive, toxic
Cl	Inactive

not alter the activity substantially. The pyridine analog (L) of these compounds was also obtained and it also had activity similar to

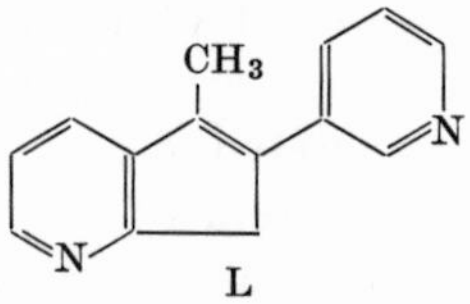

CH_3 N N

L

Su-4885 (59). These findings then prompted Bencze and co-workers (65) to synthesize some 2-aryl-substituted tetralones. The general synthetic route by which these compounds were prepared is shown in

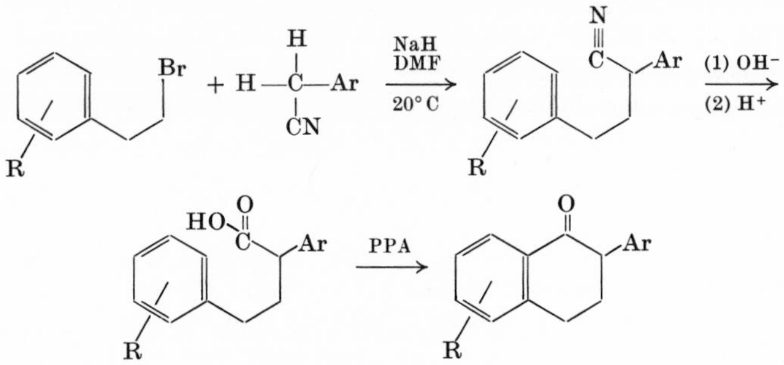

R = Cl, OCH_3, OH
Ar = phenyl, substituted phenyl, 3-pyridyl

SCHEME 10

Scheme 10. From these studies emerged two new 17α-hydroxylase inhibitors, their code names being Su-9055 and Su-10,603.

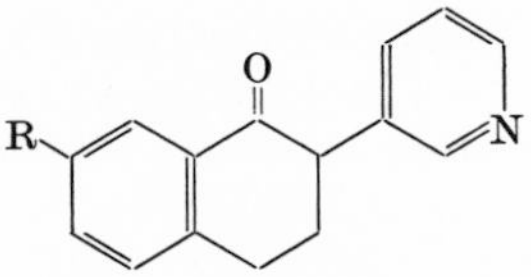

R = H — Su-9055 — LI
R = Cl — Su-10,603 — LII

Studies in dogs indicate that these compounds inhibit the conversion of progesterone to its 17α-derivative. More recently, Kahnt and Neher (66) have found that in the presence of nicotinamide, Su-9055 primarily inhibits aldosterone formation and 17α-hydroxylation to a lesser extent, whereas Su-10,603 shows the converse affect in addition to inhibiting 18-hydroxylation. As yet, it is difficult to assess whether or not these substances will be of any practical value.

REFERENCES

1. O. Wintersteiner, H. M. Vars, and J. Pfiffner, *J. Biol. Chem.* 105, c (1934).
2. E. C. Kendall, H. L. Mason, W. M. Hoehn, and B. F. McKenzie, *J. Biol. Chem.* 119, IVII (1937).
3. F. A. Hartman and H. J. Spoor, *Endocrinology* **26**, 871 (1940).
4. J. A. Luetscher, Jr., Q. B. Deming, and B. B. Johnson, "CIBA Foundation Colloquia on Endocrinology" (G. E. W. Wolstenholm and M. P. Cameron, eds.), p. 530. Churchill, London, 1952.

5. S. A. Simpson and J. F. Tait, *Endocrinology* **50**, 150 (1952).
6. S. A. Simpson, J. F. Tait, A. Wettstein, R. Neher, J. von Euler, O. Schindler, and T. Reichstein, *Helv. Chim. Acta* **37**, 1163 (1954); *Experientia* **10**, 132 (1954).
7. (a) A. Wettstein, *Verhandl. Deut. Ges. Inn. Med.* **62**, 214 (1956). (b) J. Schmidlin, G. Anner, J. R. Billeter, and A. Wettstein, *Experientia* **11**, 365 (1955).
8. K. Heusler, P. Wieland, H. Ueberwasser, and A. Wettstein, *Chimia (Aarau)* **12**, 121 (1958).
9. E. Vischer, J. Schmidlin, and A. Wettstein, *Experientia* **12**, 50 (1956).
10. D. H. R. Barton and J. M. Beaton, *J. Am. Chem. Soc.* **82**, 2641 (1960).
11. J. F. Tait, S. A. S. Tait, B. Little, and K. R. Laumas, *J. Clin. Invest.* **40**, 72 (1961).
12. F. C. Bartter, G. W. Liddle, L. E. Duncan, and C. Delea, *J. Clin. Invest.* **35**, 688 (1956).
13. J. A. Luetscher and B. J. Axelrod, *Proc. Soc. Exptl. Biol. Med.* **87**, 650 (1954).
14. B. B. Johnson, A. H. Lieberman, and P. J. Mulrow, *J. Clin. Invest.* **36**, 757 (1957).
15. J. W. Conn, *J. Lab. Clin. Med.* **45**, 6 (1955). (a) J. W. Conn, *J. Am. Med. Assoc.* **172**, 1650 (1960).
16. J. H. Laragh, *J. Chronic Diseases* **11**, 292 (1960).
17. J. A. Cella and C. M. Kagawa, *J. Am. Chem. Soc.* **79**, 4808 (1957).
18. J. A. Cella, E. A. Brown, and R. R. Burtner, *J. Org. Chem.* **24**, 743, (1955).
19. J. A. Cella and R. C. Tweit, *J. Org. Chem.* **24**, 1109 (1959).
20. E. A. Brown, R. D. Muir, and J. A. Cella, *J. Org. Chem.* **25**, 96 (1960).
21. J. A. Cella, *in* "Edema" (J. H. Moyer and M. Fuchs, eds.), pp. 303–309. Saunders, Philadelphia, Pennsylvania, 1960.
22. C. M. Kagawa, J. A. Cella, and C. G. Van Arman, *Science* **126**, 1015 (1957).
23. R. M. Dodson and R. C. Tweit, *J. Am. Chem. Soc.* **81**, 1224 (1959).
24. P. Striebel and C. Tamm, *Helv. Chim. Acta* **37**, 1094 (1954). (a) F. Sallman and C. Tamm, *Helv. Chim. Acta* **39**, 1340 (1956).
25. N. W. Atwater, R. H. Bible, Jr., E. A. Brown, R. R. Burtner, J. S. Mihina, L. N. Nysted, and P. B. Sollman, *J. Org. Chem.* **26**, 3077 (1961).
26. R. C. Tweit, F. B. Colton, N. L. McNiven, and W. Klyne, *J. Org. Chem.* **27**, 3325 (1962).
27. H. J. Hess, *J. Org. Chem.* **27**, 1096 (1962).
28. L. N. Nysted and R. R. Burtner, *J. Org. Chem.* **27**, 3175 (1962); R. R. Burtner and L. N. Nysted, U.S. Pat. 3,001,986 (Sept. 26, 1961).
29. G. P. Mueller, *Nature* **181**, 771 (1958).
30. A. A. Patchett, F. Hoffman, F. F. Giarrusso, H. Schwam, and G. E. Arth, *J. Org. Chem.* **27**, 3822 (1962).
31. Reported by A. A. Patchett in a lecture at the Gordon Conference meeting on "Steroids and Other Natural Products," New Hampton, New Hampshire, July 31, 1961.
32. L. J. Chinn, H. L. Dryden, Jr., and R. R. Burtner, *J. Org. Chem.* **26**, 3910 (1961).
33. C. M. Kagawa, *in* "Edema" (J. H. Moyer and M. Fuchs, eds.), pp. 309–316. Saunders, Philadelphia, Pennsylvania, 1960.
34. R. M. Salassa, V. R. Mattox, and M. H. Power, *J. Clin. Endocrinol. Metab.* **18**, 787 (1958).
35. C. M. Kagawa and V. A. Drill, *Arch. Intern. Pharmacodyn.* **136**, 3–4, 283 (1962).
36. L. J. Chinn, *J. Org. Chem.* **27**, 1741 (1962).
37. L. J. Chinn, U.S. Pat. 3,019,233 (Jan. 30, 1962).

38. J. Weinstock, U.S. Pat. 2,963,233 (Jan. 30, 1962); U.S. Pat. 2,998,420 (Aug. 20, 1961); U.S. Pat. 3,028,387 (April 3, 1962).
39. E. C. Taylor, U.S. Pat. 2,963,479 (Dec. 6, 1960); U.S. Pat. 3,012,034 (Dec. 6, 1961).
40. E. C. Taylor and J. Weinstock, U.S. Pat. 2,963,480 (Dec. 6, 1960).
41. T. S. Osdene and E. C. Taylor, U.S. Pat. 2,975,180 (March 14, 1961).
42. J. Grannells and J. Weinstock, U.S. Pat. 2,963,481 (Dec. 6, 1960).
43. V. D. Wiebelhaus, J. Weinstock, F. T. Brennan, G. Sosnowski, and T. S. Larsen, *Federation Proc.* **20**, I, 409 (1961).
44. A. P. Crosley, Jr., L. M. Ronquillo, and F. Alexanders, *Federation Proc.* **20**, 410 (1961).
45. J. H. Laragh, E. B. Reilly, T. B. Stites, and M. Angers, *Federation Proc.* **20**, 410 (1961).
45a. G. M. Ball and J. A. Greene, *Proc. Soc. Exptl. Biol. Med.* **113**, 326 (1963).
45b. V. D. Wiebelhaus, F. T. Brennan, G. Sosnowski, J. Weinstock, G. Gessner, and M. Ayeff, *The Pharmacologist* **5**, *no.* 2, 267 (1963).
46. A. P. Crosley, Jr., L. M. Ronquillo, W. H. Strickland, and F. Alexanders, *Annals Internal Med.* **56**, 241 (1962).
47. M. J. Allen and A. H. Corwin, *J. Am. Chem. Soc.* **72**, 114, 117 (1950).
48. R. Hertz, W. W. Tullner, J. A. Schricker, F. G. Dhyse, and L. F. Hallman, *Recent Progr. Hormone Res.* **11**, 119 (1955).
49. A. E. Renold, J. Crabbé, L. Hernando-Avendano, D. H. Nelson, E. J. Ross, K. Emerson, Jr., and G. W. Thorn, *New Engl. J. Med.* **256**, 16 (1957).
50. G. Rosenfeld and W. D. Bascom, *J. Biol. Chem.* **222**, 565 (1956).
51. G. W. Thorn, A. E. Renold, A. Goldfien, D. H. Nelson, W. J. Reddy, and R. Hertz, *New Engl. J. Med.* **254**, 547 (1956).
52. A. E. Renold, J. Crabbé, E. J. Ross, L. Hernando-Avendano, D. H. Nelson, and G. W. Thorn, *J. Clin. Invest.* **35**, 731 (1956).
53. R. Hertz, J. A. Pittman, and M. M. Graff, *J. Clin. Endocrinol. Metab.* **16**, 705 (1956).
54. W. L. Bencze and M. J. Allen, *J. Org. Chem.* **22**, 352 (1957).
55. W. L. Bencze and M. J. Allen, *J. Med. Pharm. Chem.* **1**, No. 5, 395 (1959).
56. J. J. Chart and H. Sheppard, *J. Med. Pharm. Chem.* **1**, No. 5, 407 (1959).
57. W. L. Bencze, L. I. Barsky, M. J. Allen, and E. Schlittler, *Helv. Chim. Acta* **41**, 882 (1958).
58. W. L. Bencze and M. J. Allen, *J. Am. Chem. Soc.* **81**, 4015 (1959).
59. W. L. Bencze, C. A. Burckhardt, and W. F. Yost, *J. Org. Chem.* **27**, 2865 (1962).
60. J. J. Chart, H. Sheppard, M. J. Allen, W. L. Bencze, and R. Gaunt, *Experientia* **14**, *4*, 151 (1958).
61. G. W. Liddle, D. Island, E. M. Lance, and A. P. Harris, *J. Clin. Endocrinol. Metab.* **18**, 906 (1958).
62. J. S. Jenkins, J. W. Meakin, D. H. Nelson, and G. W. Thorn, *Science* **128**, 478
63. R. Gaunt, *in* "Diuresis and Diuretics" (H. Schwiegk, ed.), pp. 174–175. Springer, Berlin, 1959.
64. W. S. Coppage, Jr., D. Island, M. Smith, and G. W. Liddle, *J. Clin. Invest.* **38**, 2101 (1959).
65. W. L. Bencze and L. I. Barsky, *J. Med. Pharm. Chem.* **5**, No. 6, 1298 (1962).
66. F. W. Kahnt and R. Neher, *Experientia* **18**, 499 (1962).

CHAPTER VIII

Miscellaneous Group

In this chapter it is intended to discuss briefly a variety of substances which have found some use in the past in diuretic therapy. Among those to be considered are the osmotic and acidotic diuretics, antidiuretic hormone inhibitors, and plant extracts. In addition, other compounds which have recently been reported to show diuretic effects in animals and in man will also be presented. Some of these newer compounds have been selected from a growing list of substances primarily because of their unusual structural features or because of their clinical utility. In any event, these substances are structurally unrelated to previously described systems.

A. Osmotic Diuretics

The osmotic diuretics are those which mobilize fluid by increasing the osmotic pressure of extracellular or tubular fluid. Thus, if soluble inorganic salts or low molecular weight organic compounds enter the glomerular filtrate in concentrations sufficiently high to exceed tubular reabsorption, then an osmotic equivalent of water is also excreted. Usually, diuresis of this type is evoked by the intravenous administration of hypertonic solutions of electrolytes such as sodium sulfate, potassium chloride, and potassium nitrate and nonelectrolytes such as urea, sucrose, glucose, and mannitol. Of these only urea has had some clinical application but its use has gradually diminished. The administration of urea leads to its excessive concentration in the extracellular fluid as well as in the tubular urine. This then causes inhibition of tubular reabsorption of water, in proportion to the concentration of the urea in the blood. Electrolytes also are retained in the tubules and thus edematous fluid and electrolytes are removed together. Urea is no longer used clinically because of its disagreeable taste which is emphasized by its high dosage (20–100 gm daily by mouth) (1). Urea derivatives (alkyl ureas, urethanes, and ureides) have also been studied but do not show any marked advantage over the parent substance (2, 3).

A similar effect can be obtained with mannitol, its advantage over other sugars being that it is only slightly metabolized. However, mannitol has to be given intravenously in daily doses of 25–100 gm as a 25% solution (1).

B. Acidotic Diuretics

The acidotic diuretics which have been used clinically are ammonium chloride and ammonium nitrate, and calcium chloride and calcium nitrate. These substances exert their diuretic effect by altering the acid–base balance to a condition of acidosis; thus, they have also been termed *acidifying salts*. The diuretic effect of the ammonium salts is due to the conversion of the ammonium ion in the liver to urea leaving the excess chloride or nitrate free to displace bicarbonates. Although their displacement does not cause a change in the total ion content, the proportion of chloride is increased in the extracellular fluid and in the glomerular filtrate. Some of the excess chloride is filtered and, in turn, reabsorbed in the tubules; but an appreciably greater amount also escapes reabsorption, carrying with it an equivalent amount of sodium and an osmotic equivalent of water. This saluretic response is effective for 1 or 2 days but then the sodium reserve becomes depleted and the disturbed acid–base balance in the body must be restored. This calls for the excretion of chloride unaccompanied by sodium. The kidney then produces ammonia which combines with hydrogen ion to form the ammonium ion which in turn is excreted with chloride ion. Thus, within a 3- or 4-day period, the amount of ammonium chloride excreted begins to equal the amount ingested and the diuretic action ceases (4). The clinical observation of the rapid disappearance of the diuretic effect of the acidifying salts thus has a rational explanation in their mode of action. The acidifying salts are effective at doses of 8–12 gm daily, concentrations which cause gastrointestinal irritations. Their most important therapeutic application has been to potentiate the action of organomercurials (5).

C. Inhibitors of Antidiuretic Hormone

The posterior pituitary gland secretes into the blood stream the antidiuretic hormone, vasopressin, in response to the need for the conservation of water. Vasopressin acts directly on the kidney tubules to effect maximum reabsorption of water unaccompanied by electrolytes.

Water has long been considered *the* physiological diuretic. It is the medium whereby waste materials are eliminated from the body. If water is ingested in large amounts it leads to a suppression of the secretion of the antidiuretic hormone since the threshold reabsorption of water has been acceded. A water diuresis without electrolyte excretion then follows until the water level returns to normal whereupon the secretion of vasopressin is resumed. However, for obvious reasons water is not an effective agent for alleviating clinical edema.

Ethyl alcohol, given orally or intravenously, also causes suppression of vasopressin secretion resulting in a moderate water diuresis without any effects on electrolytes. The lack of salt elimination plus its general effect on the nervous system and circulation has precluded its clinical use as a diuretic.

In 1959 Levine and Weller (6) clinically observed that pyrathiazine (I) administered orally at a daily dose of 1.5 gm caused an increase in

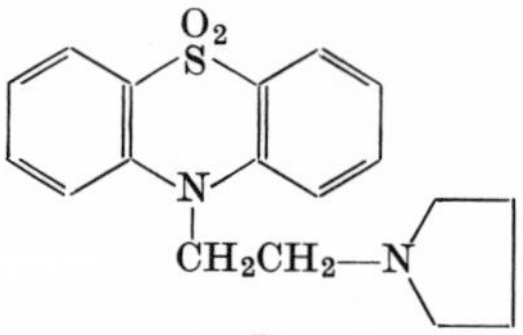

I
pyrathiazine

urine volume out of proportion to sodium and potassium loss, suggesting a selective decrease in water reabsorption. The same pattern of diuresis was noted previously by Parrish and Levine (7) in patients given chlorpromazine (II) intravenously. These investigators showed

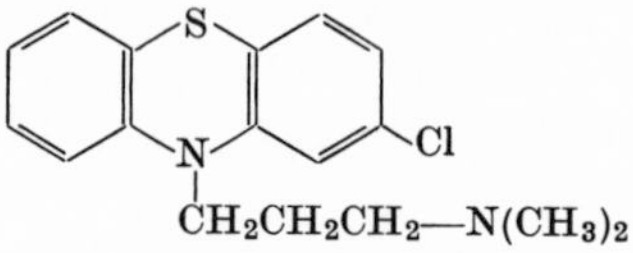

II
chlorpromazine

by bioassay an increased secretion of antidiuretic hormone, thus suggesting the participation of the posterior pituitary in phenothiazine-induced diuresis. Pontidas and Mills (8) were not able to confirm these findings with pyrathiazine in their clinical studies.

Many phenothiazines related to chlorpromazine have been tested for diuretic effects but, as yet, none have achieved clinical importance.

D. Plant Extracts

Numerous papers have been published on plant extracts exhibiting diuretic effects. An evaluation of many of these has indicated that the materials isolated and tested are grossly impure, the controls used are inadequate, and much of the work is not reproducible. However, reports on the extracts of the following plants may be of interest for further investigations: *Betula alba* (9), *Mikania hirsutissima* (10) *Coix lacryma jobi* (11), *Orthosiphon staminens* (12), *Cymbopogon proximus* (13), and *Phytolacca esculenta* (14).

A review of diuretics would not be complete without mentioning the group associated with digitalis. Digitalis refers to a group of closely related complex steroids that occur in the leaves of *Digitalis purpurea* (purple foxglove), *Digitalis lanata*, and *Strophanthus kombè* or *hispidus*. Chemical investigations on the active principles of the digitalis plants have been quite extensive and this area of research has already been thoroughly reviewed by Fieser and Fieser (15). Only a brief account of the essential features of these substances will be outlined here.

The cardiac glycosides are made up of two fundamental building blocks, namely, one or more *carbohydrate* residues (*D*-glucose or *L*-rhamnose) attached to a complex steroid usually referred to as the *aglycone* or *genin* through the oxygen at position 3 (β-configuration). The 17-position of the steroid nucleus is invariably substituted with an unsaturated lactone ring. All the active compounds in the digitalis group have a β-hydroxy group at carbon 14, whereas in the strophanthus group a β-hydroxy group is also usually present at C-5. The strophanthus group also contains a primary alcohol or aldehyde group at position 19. The stereochemistry of the CD and the AB rings is *cis* and the BC ring configuration is *trans*. Digitoxigenin (III) and strophanthidin (IV) are representative of the aglycone portion of the cardiac glycosides. The aglycone portion with the α,β-unsaturated 5-membered lactone ring at position 17 is usually referred to as a cardenolide.

Use of digitalis as a diuretic was introduced in 1785 by Withering and met with spectacular success. It has subsequently been shown that these substances exert their principal effect on the heart by increasing blood circulation. As a result, the renal blood flow and glomerular filtration rate are increased facilitating the removal of edema fluids and electrolytes. However, recently Mills *et al.* (16) have reviewed this matter and suggest that the digitalis drugs increase sodium and potassium excretion by direct action on the renal tubule.

Sugar(s) usually attached here ⟶ through C-1.

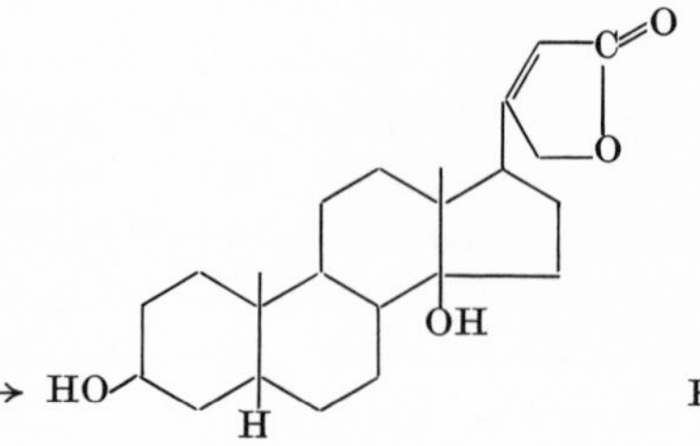

III
digitoxigenin

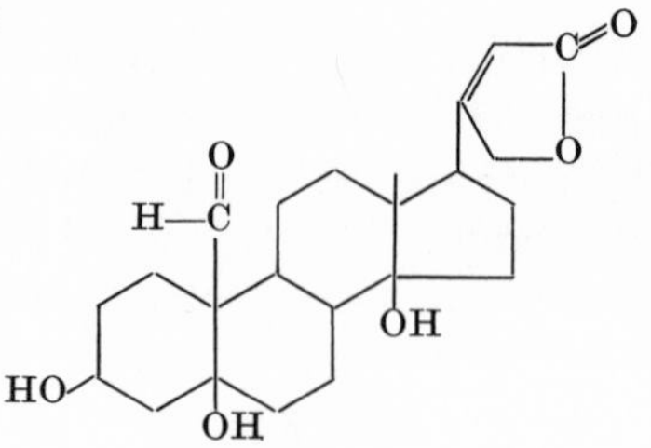

IV
strophanthidin

Consequently, extreme care must be exercised in administering the thiazide or hydrothiazide diuretics to the digitalized patient, otherwise hypokalemia and hepatocoma can result. These side effects are usually averted with potassium salt supplement.

E. Heterocycles

1. 8-Chloroalloxazines

As reported by Petering and Van Giessen (17) the condensation of 4-chloro-2-aminoaniline (V) with alloxan (VI) under acidic conditions affords 8-chloroalloxazine (VII) (see Scheme 1). This compound was

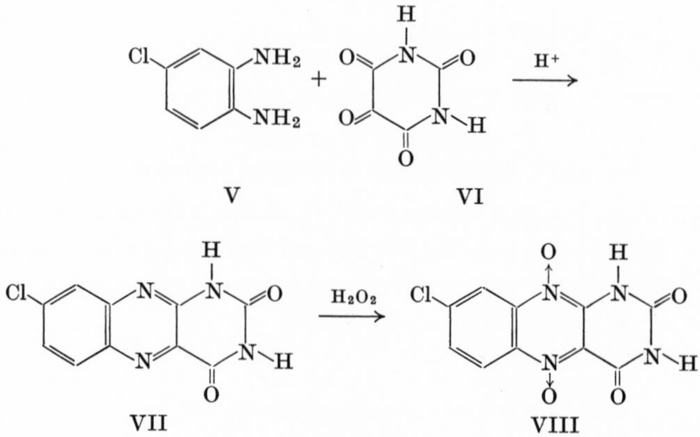

V VI

VII VIII

Scheme 1

found to elicit significant diuretic effects when administered orally to rats and dogs. Moreover, oxidation of this substance to the 5,10-dioxide derivative (VIII) led to a marked increase (30–50%) in the urine excretion. Sodium chloride excretion figures were not given (18).

2. 1, 2, 3-Benzothiadiazines

An inspection of the structures of hydralazine (IX), a potent antihypertensive agent (19), and of chlorothiazide led Schmidt and coworkers (20) to synthesize a compound which incorporated structural features of both drugs. This was readily done by allowing 2-cyano-5-ethoxybenzenesulfonylchloride (X) to react with hydrazine. As

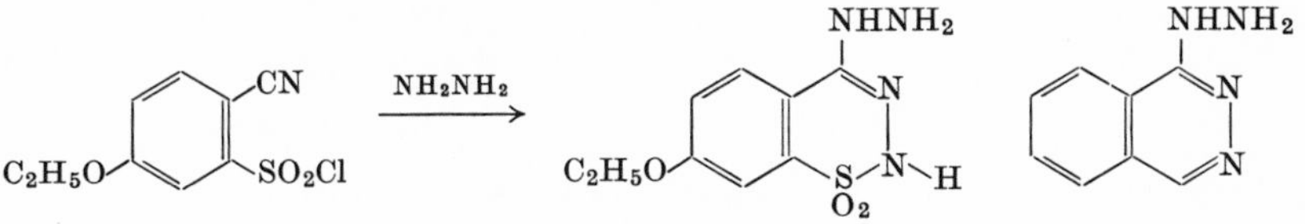

C_2H_5O–, CN, SO_2Cl $\xrightarrow{NH_2NH_2}$ $NHNH_2$, C_2H_5O–, S, O_2, N–H; $NHNH_2$

X XI IX
hydralazine

predicted, the resulting 4-hydrazino-7-ethoxy-2*H*-1,2,3-benzothiadiazine-1,1-dioxide (XI) caused an antihypertensive effect in animals comparable to hydralazine. Moreover, this compound had a diuretic effect about one-half that of chlorothiazide. These effects were also observed in humans, but the diuretic action was only manifest at much higher doses than those necessary to overcome hypertension. Compound XI also did not appear to have a significant influence on sodium excretion (21).

Many derivatives of XI were made; e.g., the 7-ethoxy was replaced with halogen and alkyls and the 4-hydrazino group was substituted with alkyl groups or modified to a pyrazole derivative. These changes did not yield a substance biologically superior to XI.

F. α,β-Unsaturated Ketone Derivatives

The most recent important contribution to emerge from the Sprague group (22) at Merck, Sharp and Dohme is concerned with a new class of diuretics; namely, α,β-unsaturated ketone derivatives of aryloxyacetic acids of the following general structure:

$$-\underset{|}{C}=\underset{|}{C}-\overset{\overset{O}{\|}}{C}-Ar-O-CH_2-COOH$$

Ar = phenyl, substituted phenyl or naphthyl

According to these investigators this general structure evolved from a search for biologically active compounds which would react selectively with functionally important sulfhydryl groups just as the organomercurials do. All of the compounds in this series with significant diuretic activity were also shown to have a high order of reactivity *in vitro* toward representative sulfhydryl-containing compounds.

Many structural variations of the above-described general structure were made but compounds (XII–XV) were reported to be most potent.

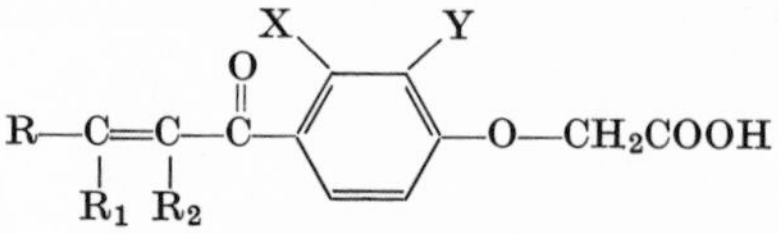

XII: $R = R_1 = Y = H; R_2 = C_2H_5; X = Cl$
XIII: $R = R_1 = H; R_2 = C_2H_5; X = Y = Cl$
XIV: $R = R_1 = H; R_2 = C_2H_5; X = Y = CH_3$
XV: $R = H; R_1 = CH_3; R_2 = C_2H_5; X = Y = Cl$

For maximum diuretic activity, one position in the aromatic nucleus *ortho* to the unsaturated ketone function must be substituted. Halogen and methyl groups were reported to be outstandingly effective. 2,3-Disubstitution further enhanced activity, but additional substitution may adversely effect activity.

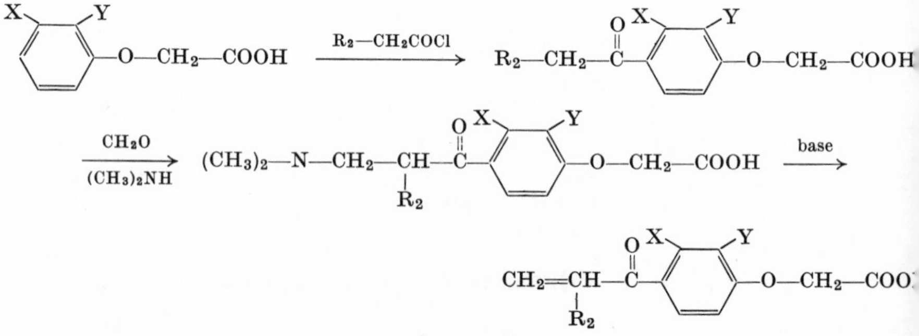

SCHEME 2

Those compounds having a terminal methylene group (XIII–XIV) were synthesized according to Scheme 2 or 3.

Friedel-Crafts acylation of the appropriate aryloxyacetic acid yielded the intermediate ketone. The Mannich reaction on this product followed by treatment with base gave the desired α,β-unsaturated ketone derivative.

For the preparation of compounds where the unsaturation is not in the terminal position (see XV), the procedure outlined in Scheme 3 was used. The acylphenoxyacetic acids were brominated and the resulting α-bromoketones were dehydrobrominated to form compounds related to XV.

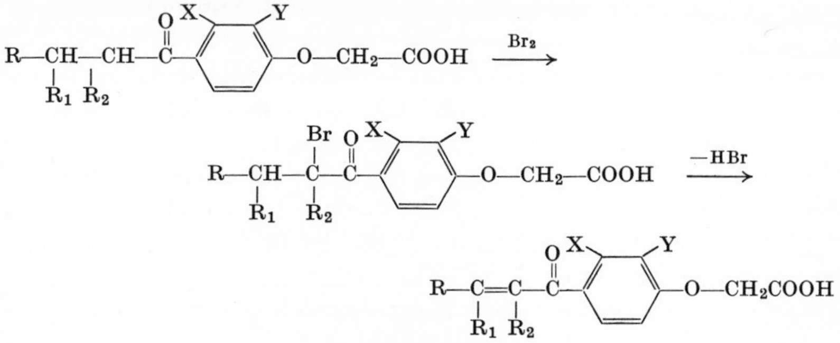

$$R{-}CH(R_1){-}CH(R_2){-}C({=}O){-}C_6H_2(X)(Y){-}O{-}CH_2{-}COOH \xrightarrow{Br_2}$$

$$R{-}CH(R_1){-}C(Br)(R_2){-}C({=}O){-}C_6H_2(X)(Y){-}O{-}CH_2{-}COOH \xrightarrow{-HBr}$$

$$R{-}C(R_1){=}C(R_2){-}C({=}O){-}C_6H_2(X)(Y){-}O{-}CH_2COOH$$

SCHEME 3

These compounds are reported to be highly active in the dog when administered orally, intravenously, or intramuscularly. They are inactive in the rat by all routes of administration. This species specificity is reminiscent of the organomercurials. In the dog, the excretion of sodium and chloride is increased by approximately equivalent amounts. In contrast to the thiazides, but similar to the mercurials, these compounds greatly increase the volume of urine. However, unlike the organomercurials, both the diuresis and saluresis caused by these compounds are very rapid in onset and occur even in bicarbonate-treated dogs. Several of these substances have an order of activity, on a dose basis, comparable to chlorothiazide and hydrochlorothiazide. Sprague *et al.* (22) and Baer and co-workers (23) have indicated that these substances have a pronounced effect on sodium chloride excretion accompanied by only a slight increase in the potassium excretion. When compound XIII (ethacrynic acid), the most effective compound in the series, was superimposed in animals receiving meralluride and chlorothiazide, an additional increment of saluresis was obtained, suggesting that XIII has a novel mode of action (24).

In a preliminary clinical study of ethacrynic acid, Folty (25) found it to be effective by the oral and intravenous route. Dose-response curves in normal subjects following oral administration showed increasing diuresis and saluresis from a minimum of 20 mg to 200 mg.

At 250 mg, no increase in total diuresis or saluresis was noted, but the onset of activity was earlier and of greater intensity initially.

In patients with edema associated with congestive heart failure, cirrhosis, and the nephrotic syndrome, diuresis with major saluretic effects has followed single daily doses of 50 mg to a total of 400 mg when these patients had become refractory to thiazide and mercurial agents.

In another clinical study, Melvin, Farrelly, and North (26) compared the action of etahcrynic acid with that of hydrochlorothiazide. In normal patients they found the diuresis induced by ethacrynic acid to be more intense but less prolonged. However, this drug produced in edematous patients a greater diuresis than hydrochlorothiazide, each at a dose of 150 mg daily, but the potassium loss was reported to be correspondingly greater. These investigators have cautioned that the dramatic diuresis induced in some cases by this potent diuretic could be dangerous. One patient was reported to have excreted 8590 ml of urine containing 952 meq of sodium on the first day of treatment with ethacrynic acid. However, they have also noted that some patients resistant to hydrochlorothiazide, respond quite well to ethacrynic acid. Further clinical trials will establish the value of this substance in diuretic therapy.

References

1. L. Werko, *in* "Edema" (J. Moyer and M. Fuchs, eds.), pp. 183–191. Saunders, Philadelphia, Pennsylvania, 1960.
2. H. T. A. Hass, *Pharmazie* **3**, 97 (1948).
3. W. L. Lipschitz and Z. Hadidian, *J. Pharmacol. Exptl. Therap.* **81**, 84 (1944).
4. L. S. Goodman and A. Gilman, "The Pharmacological Basis of Therapeutics," p. 845. Macmillan, New York, 1960.
5. H. L. Friedman, *in* "Medicinal Chemistry" (A. Burger, ed.), pp. 641–649. Interscience, New York, 1960.
6. E. H. Levine and J. W. Weller, *Univ. Mich. Med. Bull.* **25**, 234 (1959).
7. A. E. Parrish and E. H. Levine, *J. Lab. Clin. Med.* **48**, 264 (1956).
8. E. Pontidas and L. C. Mills, *Antibiot. Med. Clin. Therapy* **6**, 715 (1959).
9. H. Leclerc, *Presse Med.* **45**, 1270 (1937).
10. J. Gomez da Cruz and C. H. Liberalli, *Boll. Chim. Farm.* **77**, 693 (1938).
11. N. Tashima, R. Kawanishi, S. Sugita, and T. Kushefuchi, *Chem. Abstr.* **55**, 14,834 (1961).
12. F. Kurzen, German Pat. 1,065,132 (Sept. 10, 1959).
13. Z. F. Ahmed, H. Royahem, and I. R. Fahmy, *Egypt. Pharm. Rept.* **39**, 167 (1957).
14. H. Masuyawa, *Okayama Igakkai Zasshi* **52**, 1664 (1940).
15. L. F. Fieser and M. Fieser, "Steroids," pp. 727–809. Reinhold, New York, 1959.
16. L. C. Mills, J. H. Moyer, and G. Faludi, *in* "Edema" (J. H. Moyer and M. Fuchs, eds.), pp. 325–333. Saunders, Philadelphia, Pennsylvania, 1960.

17. H. G. Petering and G. J. Van Giessen, *J. Org. Chem.* **26**, 2818 (1961).
18. H. G. Petering, U.S. Pat. 2,973,359 (Feb. 28, 1961).
19. J. Druey and B. H. Ringier, *Helv. Chim. Acta* **34**, 204 (1951).
20. P. Schmidt, K. Eichenberger, and M. Wilhelm, *Helv. Chim. Acta* **45**, 996 (1962).
21. Unpublished reports from CIBA Clinical Investigation Division.
22. E. M. Schultz, E. J. Cragoe, Jr., J. B. Bicking, W. A. Bolhofer, and J. M. Sprague, *J. Med. Pharm. Chem.* **5**, 660 (1962).
23. J. E. Baer, H. F. Russo, J. K. Michaelson, and K. H. Beyer, *The Pharmacologist*, **4**, *no.* 2, 158 (1962).
24. J. E. Baer, J. K. Michaelson, H. F. Russo, and K. H. Beyer, *Federation Proc.* **22**, 598 (1963).
25. E. J. Folty, *Federation Proc.* **22**, 598 (1963).
26. K. E. W. Melvin, R. O. Farrelly, and J. D. K. North, *British Med. J.* p. 1521 (1963).

CHAPTER IX

Therapeutic Use of Diuretics in the Treatment of Hypertension

The pressure arising from the flow of blood through the arteries results from the pumping action of the heart and the resistance to the flow of blood in the peripheral vessels. This is a balanced hemodynamic state which remains fairly constant in normal individuals from day to day. However, an increase in peripheral resistance upsets this hemodynamic balance, the consequence of which is abnormally high blood pressure or *hypertension*. Many factors may cause this disturbance, some of which are known and others unknown. In many cases, there is no clearly defined structural disease or disorder to account for the high blood pressure, and this condition is usually referred to as *essential* or *primary hypertension*. This is distinguished from *secondary hypertension* which is usually the result of another pathological condition (e.g., tumor of the adrenal or pituitary glands, congenital defects, or renal impairment). However, it is now generally accepted that many types of human and experimental hypertension are associated with changes in electrolyte balances, especially as regards sodium ion concentration (1). Consequently, the maintenance of normal blood pressure is associated closely but not exclusively with normal kidney function.

The earliest observations on the role of sodium and other electrolytes in hypertension resulted from the use of a low salt diet in the therapeutic management of patients with high blood pressure. The original advocates of such diets were Ambard and Beaujard (2) in France in 1905, and later Allen and Sherrill in 1922 (3) and also Volhard (4). However, the beneficial effect of these diets was attributed to the restriction of the chloride ion rather than sodium. This misconception was enforced by the observation that the addition of large amounts of salt to the normal diet did not cause an increase in blood pressure either of the normal or the hypertensive patient. It was concluded, accordingly, that the intake of salt was not associated to any great extent with increased blood pressure. This was an unfortunate erroneous notion since the acceptance of salt-free dietotherapy was held up for many years.

Grollman and Harrison (5, 6) in 1945 demonstrated the effectiveness of maximum sodium restriction in lowering blood pressure first in experimental animals and then in hypertensive patients. Moreover, they showed unequivocally for the first time that it was the sodium rather than the chloride ion which was responsible for the hypotensive effects of salt restriction. In addition, it was revealed that sodium phosphate or sodium bicarbonate, which previously were permitted in the diet of hypertensive patients, counteracted the beneficial effects of a salt-free diet.

Finally, these studies supported the findings of Kempner (7) concerning the effectiveness of rice in lowering blood pressure. Whereas it had been thought previously that the rice per se contained a factor which was responsible for the antihypertensive effect, Grollman (8) was able to show that this effect of rice was owing to its low sodium content. Moreover, he concluded that a hypotensive effect could be induced by the use of any salt-restricted diet. However, it should not be surmised from these studies that ingestion of large amounts of salt is responsible for the hypertensive syndrome, but only that salt aggravates and enhances this condition. Several detailed reviews have been written on this subject to which the reader is referred (1, 9, 10).

For over a decade following the report of Grollman and Harrison, low salt dietotherapy was an essential factor in the treatment of high blood pressure. Even the introduction of effective antihypertensives (see Chart I) between the years 1952 and 1958 did not alter the necessity of sodium restriction.

Although Megibow and colleagues (11) reported in 1948 that mercurial diuretics significantly reduced blood pressure in a small group of hypertensive patients, it is surprising that this form of antihypertensive therapy did not gain much favor in the subsequent 10-year period. It was not until the advent of chlorothiazide and hydrochlorothiazide that diuretic drugs achieved the prominence they now enjoy in the treatment of hypertension.

The use of chlorothiazide in the treatment of hypertension was first

CHART I

ANTIHYPERTENSIVE DRUGS (31)

$(CH_3)_3N^+—(CH_2)_6—N^+(CH_3)_3$

hexamethonium

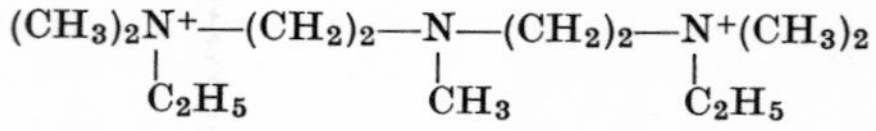

$(CH_3)_2N^+(C_2H_5)—(CH_2)_2—N(CH_3)—(CH_2)_2—N^+(CH_3)_2(C_2H_5)$

azamethonium

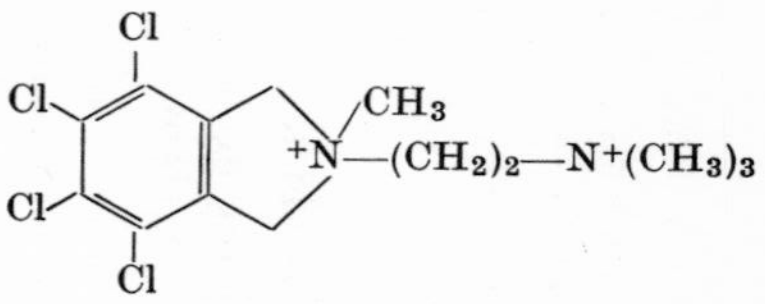

chlorisondamine

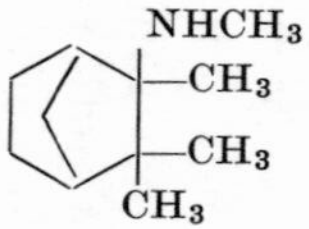

mecamylamine

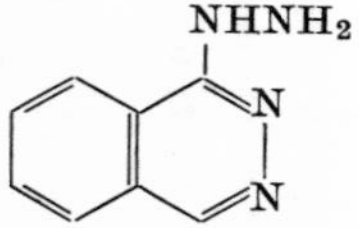

hydralazine

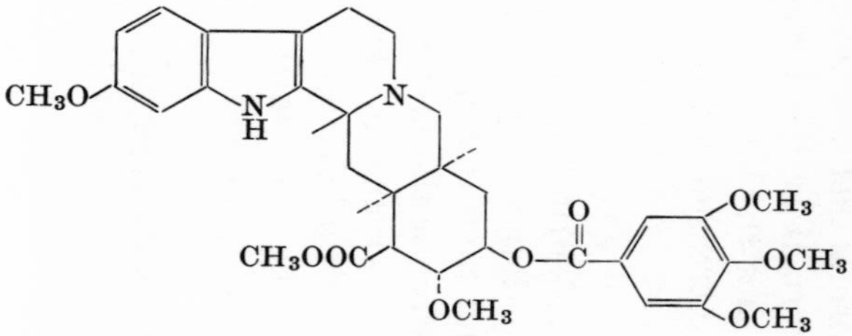

reserpine

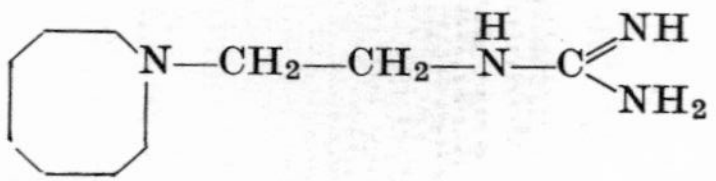

guanethidine

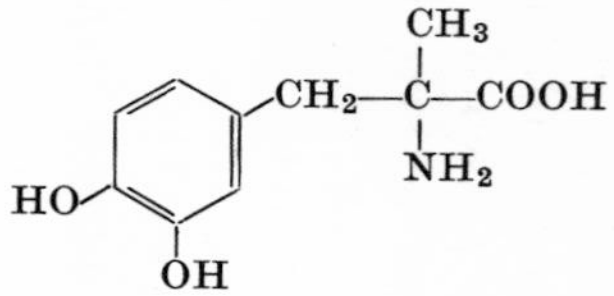

α-methyldopa

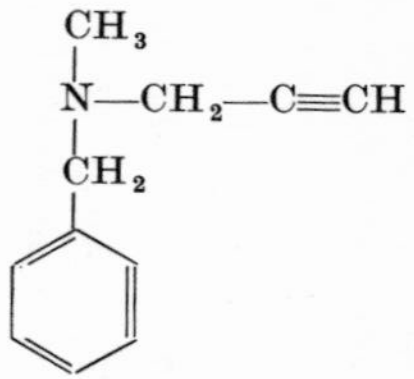

pargyline

reported independently by Wilkins and Hollander (12) and Freis and Wilson (13). They demonstrated that this compound enhanced the antihypertensive effects of ganglionic blockers and reserpine. In a minority of patients chlorothiazide seemed to be effective when used as the sole antihypertensive agent. Shortly thereafter, Hollander *et al.* (14) compared the effect of hydrochlorothiazide with chlorothiazide in over fifty hypertensive subjects. In Fig. 1 and Table I the

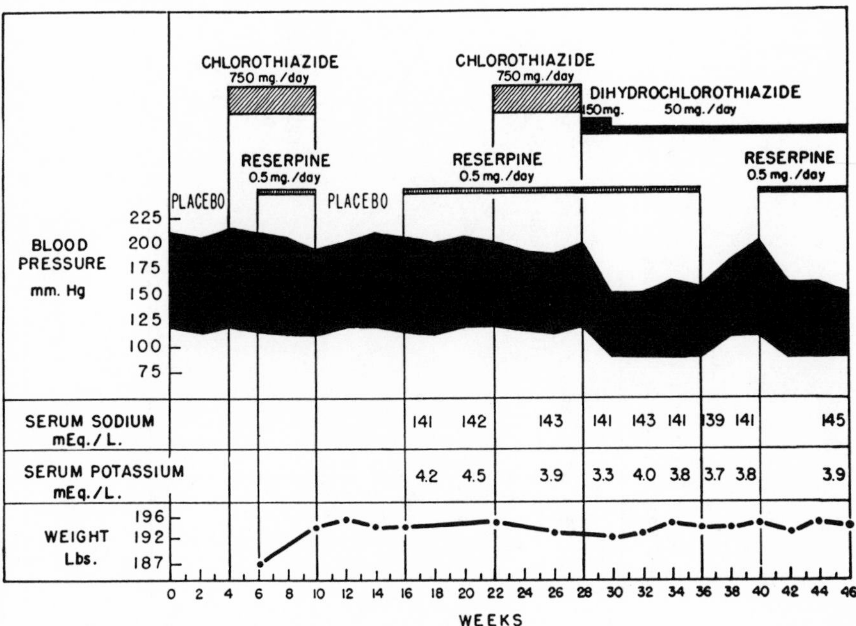

FIG. 1. Chart showing the comparative effects of chlorothiazide and dihydrochlorothiazide on the blood pressure, serum electrolytes, and weight in a hypertensive subject.

blood pressure responses to these compounds are compared. In a dose one-tenth that of chlorothiazide, hydrochlorothiazide alone and in combination with other drugs appeared to be slightly more antihypertensive than chlorothiazide. Hollander *et al.* reported that, in general, about one in ten subjects appeared to have a definitely greater blood pressure lowering response to hydrochlorothiazide than to chlorothiazide. Additional clinical studies (15–17) have indicated that these two drugs as well as other members of the thiazide and

TABLE I

COMPARATIVE EFFECTS OF CHLOROTHIAZIDE AND DIHYDROCHLOROTHIAZIDE ON THE BLOOD PRESSURE OF 56 HYPERTENSIVE SUBJECTS (14)

Drugs	No. of cases	No. of responders (B.P. + = > $\frac{14}{9}$)	Average B.P. reduction (mm. Hg)	Range of B.P. reduction (mm. Hg)	Average diuretic dosage (mg/day)	Diuretic dose range (mg/day)
Chlorothiazide alone	16	7	18/10	20/10–60/25	750	375–1000
Dihydrochlorothiazide alone	16	9	24/14	20/10–70/30	75	37.5–100
Rauwolfia + hydralazine						
+ Chlorothiazide	32	20	30/16	20/15–60/25	750	375–1000
+ Dihydrochlorothiazide	32	23	37/20	20/15–70/30	75	37.5–100
Ganglion blocker + *Rauwolfia*						
+ Chlorothiazide	8	5	34/16	20/10–80/30	375	375–750
+ Dihydrochlorothiazide	8	6	40/21	20/10–80/40	37.5	37.5–75

hydrothiazide groups are effective in mild hypertension. Much discussion and debate has followed on how these compounds act to reduce blood pressure. It appears that, in general, these compounds cause sodium depletion which in turn results in a reduction of plasma volume. This subject has been succinctly reviewed by Corcoran only recently (18).

These findings have prompted the study of other diuretics in the treatment of hypertension. Gifford (19) has evaluated amisometradine in a group of patients with mild to moderate, uncomplicated hypertension. The results of his study are shown in Table II. These patients

TABLE II

EFFECT OF DIURETIC AGENTS ADMINISTERED ALONE IN THE TREATMENT OF HYPERTENSION (19)

Diuretic	Patients	Average dose (mg/day)	Average B.P. (sitting) (mm Hg) Before treatment	During treatment	Reduction (%) of mean blood pressure[a]
Chlorothiazide	38	1000	$\frac{187}{111}$	$\frac{166}{102}$	10.0
Hydrochlorothiazide	20	100	$\frac{176}{104}$	$\frac{150}{94}$	12.9
Amisometradine	5	1200	$\frac{184}{106}$	$\frac{168}{102}$	6.9

[a] Mean blood pressure $= \frac{\text{systolic} + \text{diastolic}}{2}$.

were treated for periods that varied from 6 weeks to 6 months at a daily dosage of 1200 mg. A hypotensive effect was noted in all five patients, but it was less than that observed in the larger series of patients treated with chlorothiazide and hydrochlorothiazide. Moreover, Gifford also noted that amisometradine is much less effective in potentiating the effects of either hydralazine or a ganglionic blocking drug than are the thiazide compounds.

Finnerty and co-workers (20) have reported that acetazolamide has a modest hypotensive effect for relatively short periods when given to women with toxemia of pregnancy. Again the antihypertensive effect of acetazolamide is less than that of thiazides. In addition, carbonic anhydrase inhibitors are rendered ineffective after several days of continuous therapy, and this has made them unsuitable for the prolonged treatment of hypertension.

Ford *et al.* (21) have shown that chlorazinil and amanozine enhance the potency of reserpine and mecamylamine, but this effect is less pronounced than that observed with thiazide or mercurial diuretics. Ford has suggested that chlorazinil may have a nephrotoxic effect since it frequently causes elevation of blood urea.

Hollander *et al.* (22) also have reported on the clinical effects of spironolactone in subjects with uncomplicated essential hypertension. In Fig. 2 are shown the results of this on one subject of this study. A combination of reserpine, hydralazine, and hydrochlorothiazide had produced a moderate reduction in blood pressure along with a depression of serum potassium. Following the addition of spironolactone, there followed a further reduction in blood pressure but an increase in serum potassium to normal. In the last part of the study satisfactory control of the blood pressure and serum electrolytes was achieved with spironolactone alone, as well as in combination with hydrochlorothiazide. This latter combination is useful in those states where hypopotassemia is already a complicating factor. Unlike hydrochlorothiazide, the hypotensive action of spironolactone is gradual in onset, a maximum effect being attained only after 2 or 3 weeks following the administration of the drug. However, extensive clinical trials with reserpine, hydralazine, hydrochlorothiazide combination has proven this to be a most effective preparation for reducing high blood pressure. It is presently a most important drug for overcoming moderate-to-severe hypertension.

Hydrochlorothiazide combined with guanethidine (23) has been found to be remarkably effective in eliciting an antihypertensive effect. Schultz (24) reported his results on a group of twenty-five patients with moderate-to-severe hypertension receiving daily doses of guanethidine averaging 21–25 mg plus 25 mg of hydrochlorothiazide. In all cases blood pressure reductions were approximately 38/20 mm mercury supine and 44/18 mm of mercury standing. This investigator noted that side effects were reduced with the combination and that blood pressure control was smoother especially in the supine position.

Brest and Moyer (25) also observed that the hypotensive potency of guanethidine is markedly enhanced by hydrochlorothiazide. This potentiation is illustrated in Fig. 3. The antihypertensive response

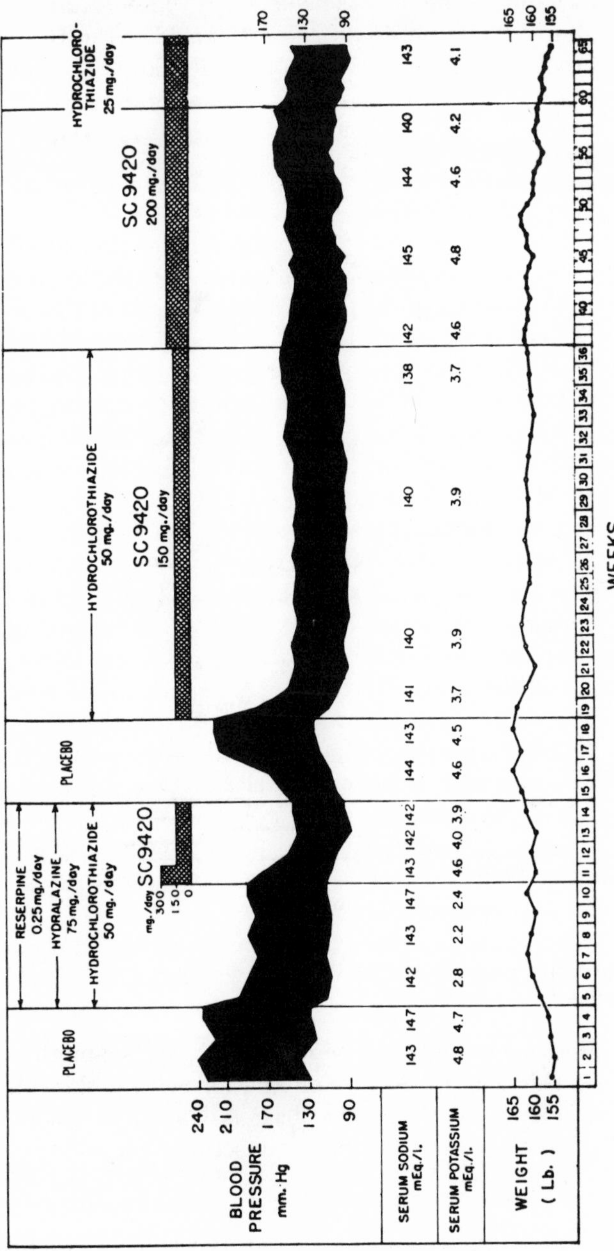

FIG. 2. Clinical effects of spironolactone (SC-9420) and hydrochlorothiazide in a hypertensive subject.

obtained with guanethidine was conspicuously potentiated by the concomitant administration of hydrochlorothiazide at the 16th week of therapy. Moreover, the daily dosage of guanethidine was reduced by one-half without a blood pressure rise. Similar findings have been recorded by Blanshard and Essigman (26), Ford (27), Klapper and Richard (28), and Maronde *et al.* (29).

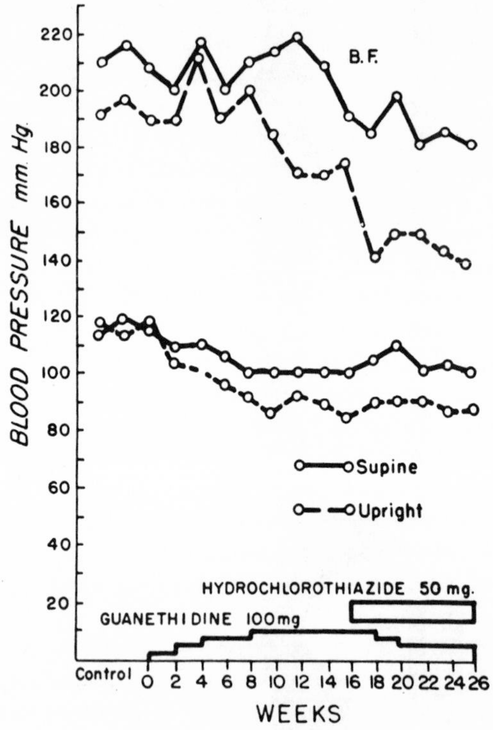

FIG. 3. Clinical effects of guanethidine in combination with hydrochlorothiazide in a hypertensive subject.

Another antihypertensive drug recently introduced is α-methyldopa (30). The use of this compound in combination with a thiazide has become almost mandatory since the drug is known to cause fluid retention. This combination has been prescribed for all forms of hypertension, but it is as yet too early to affirm this broad clinical application.

Finally, the most recent addition to antihypertensive therapy is pargyline, a substance which also behaves as a monoamine oxidase inhibitor. Brest and co-workers (32) suggest that this drug reduces blood pressure primarily by decreasing peripheral vascular resistance, whereas cardiac output seems not to be significantly affected. They also report that renal vascular resistance is similarly reduced, and therefore renal blood flow and glomerular filtration rate are affected only to a moderate extent. They have recommended pargyline as a drug for the treatment of severe hypertensive states.

Bryant and his group (33) have also reported on the clinical utility of pargyline alone and in combination with a hydrothiazide diuretic (methychlothiazide). They found that a greater antihypertensive response was obtained when the combination was used, and in addition there was a 91% reduction in side effects. The effective daily dosage of the combination was 12.5 mg of pargyline and 10 mg of methychlothiazide.

In summary then, the effectiveness of the thiazide and hydrothiazide drugs, given alone or in conjunction with other antihypertensive drugs in the treatment of hypertension, has been well established. More than any of the other diuretic drugs presently in use (see Table III), they are most suited for the long-term treatment of hypertension for the following reasons:

(*1*) They are the most potent, orally effective natriuretic and diuretic agents available and thus have a greater hypotensive action than any of the other diuretics when given orally.

(*2*) They are consistently effective, resistance to their action seldom occurring.

(*3*) They are relatively nontoxic.

(*4*) In contrast to the mercurials and the carbonic anhydrase inhibitors, their activity is not affected by changes in the acid–base balance.

The chief disadvantage of treatment with thiazide and hydrothiazide diuretics for edema, hypertension, or any other clinical condition for which they may be prescribed is their tendency to cause some potassium depletion. However, this side effect is usually asymptomatic and rarely does the serum potassium level go below 2.5 meq/liter if the patient has adequate food intake and normal kidney and liver function. Administration of supplements of potassium and the liberal consumption of fluids by patients taking these drugs over any length of time may be a necessary corollary to therapy in some individuals.

TABLE III

COMPARATIVE ADVANTAGES AND DISADVANTAGES OF VARIOUS DIURETIC AGENTS IN THE TREATMENT OF HYPERTENSION

Diuretic	Hypotensive potency	Effective orally	Resistance develops	Hypopotassemia	Azotemia	Other electrolyte disturbance	Nephrotoxicity
Acetazolamide	+	Yes	+++	+	0	++	0
Amisometradine	+	Yes	+	0	0	0	0
Chlorazinil	+	Yes	0	0	+++	0	?
Mercurials	++	No[a]	0	0	±	++	?
Thiazides	+++	Yes	0	+++	++	0	0

[a] Oral use is about 50% as effective as parenteral use.

References

1. H. A. Schroeder, *in* "Edema" (J. H. Moyer and M. Fuchs, eds.), pp. 379–386. Saunders, Philadelphia, Pennsylvania, 1960.
2. L. Ambard and E. Beaujard, *Semaine Med.* **25**, 133 (1905).
3. F. M. Allen and W. J. Sherrill, *J. Metab. Res.* **2**, 429 (1922).
4. F. Volhard, "Handbuch der inneren Medezine," Vol. 6, p. 1753. Springer, Berlin,
5. A. Grollman and T. R. Harrison, *Proc. Soc. Exptl. Biol. Med.* **60**, 52 (1945).
6. A. Grollman, *J. Am. Med. Assoc.* **129**, 533 (1945).
7. W. Kempner, *N. Carolina Med. J.* **5**, 125 (1944).
8. A. Grollman, *J. Am. Dietet. Assoc.* **22**, 864 (1946).
9. A. Grollman, *in* "Edema" (J. H. Moyer and M. Fuchs, eds.), pp. 375–378. Saunders, Philadelphia, Pennsylvania, 1960.
10. J. H. Moyer, *in* "Hypertension" (J. H. Moyer, ed.), pp. 299–318. Saunders, Philadelphia, Pennsylvania, 1959.
11. R. S. Megibow, H. Pollak, G. H. Stollerman, E. H. Roston, and J. J. Bookman, *J. Mt. Sinai Hosp. N.Y.* **15**, 233 (1948).
12. W. Hollander and R. W. Wilkins, *BMQ Boston Med. Quart.* **8**, 69 (1957).
13. E. D. Freis and I. M. Wilson, *Med. Ann. District Columbia* **26**, 468, 516 (1957).
14. W. Hollander, A. V. Chobanian, and R. W. Wilkins, *in* "Hypertension" (J. H. Moyer, ed.), pp. 570–580. Saunders, Philadelphia, Pennsylvania, 1959.
15. M. R. Hejtmancik, G. R. Herrmann, and F. W. Kroetz, *Texas State J. Med.* **54**, 854 (1958).
16. J. A. Spittel, Jr., R. W. Gifford, Jr., and R. W. P. Achor, *Proc. Staff Meetings Mayo Clinic* **34**, 256 (1959).
17. R. V. Ford, *Ann. N.Y. Acad. Sci.* **88**, 809 (1960).
18. A. C. Corcoran, *in* "Edema" (J. H. Moyer and M. Fuchs, eds.), pp. 387–391. Saunders, Philadelphia, Pennsylvania, 1960.
19. R. W. Gifford, Jr., *in* "Edema" (J. H. Moyer and M. Fuchs, eds.), pp. 392–397. Saunders, Philadelphia, Pennsylvania, 1960.
20. F. A. Finnerty, Jr., J. H. Buchholz, and J. Tuckman, *J. Am. Med. Assoc.* **166**, 141 (1958).
21. R. V. Ford, A. C. Bullock, and J. B. Rochelle, III, *G. P. J. Am. Acad. Gen. Pract.* **18**, 116 (1958).
22. W. Hollander, A. V. Chobanian, and R. W. Wilkins, *Ann. N.Y. Acad. Sci.* **88**, 975 (1960).
23. R. A. Maxwell, R. P. Mull, and A. J. Plummer, *Experientia* **15**, 267 (1959).
24. F. B. Schultz, *J. Med. Assoc. State Alabama* **31**, No. 6, 1 (1961).
25. A. N. Brest and J. H. Moyer, *Symp. Guanethidine* (*Ismelin*), *Memphis, Tenn.* (April 22, 1960).
26. G. Blanshard and W. Essigman, *Lancet* **2**, 334 (1961).
27. R. V. Ford, *Geriatrics* **16**, 577 (1961).
28. M. S. Klapper and L. Richard, *Southern Med. J.* **55**, 75 (1962).
29. R. F. Maronde, L. J. Haywood, and B. Barbour, *Am. J. Med. Sci.* **242**, 228 (1961).
30. L. Gillespie, Jr., *Ann. N.Y. Acad. Sci.* **88**, 1011 (1960).
31. E. Schlittler, A. Marxer, and J. Druey, *Progr. Drug Res.* **4**, 295 (1962).
32. A. N. Brest, G. Onesti, C. Heider, and J. H. Moyer, *Ann. N.Y. Acad. Sci.* **107**, 1016 (1963).
33. J. M. Bryant, N. Schwartz, S. Torosday, H. Fertig, J. Fletcher, Jr., M. S. Schwartz, and R. B. Quan, *Ann. N. Y. Acad. Sci.* **107**, 1023 (1963).

APPENDIX I

Comparison of Mode of Action of Various Diuretics

Effect	Xanthines and pyrimidines	Triazines	Mercurials	Sulfonamides	Thiazides and hydrothiazides	Aldosterone antagonists and inhibitors
Na^+ excretion	Slight	Little	Marked	Marked	Marked	Greater than Cl^-
Cl^- excretion	—	—	Marked	—	Marked	—
K^+ excretion	Little	Little	Little	Marked	Minimum at low doses	None
HCO_3^- excretion	Little	—	Little	Very marked	Little	Little
Acidosis	Less effective	—	Effective	Ineffective	Effective	Effective
Alkalosis	—	—	Ineffective	—	Effective	Effective
Free water clearance	—	Increased	Increased	No increase	No increase	—
Carbonic anhydrase inhibition	None	None	None	Marked	Weak to moderate	None
Onset of action	Moderate	—	Delayed	Rapid	Rapid	Delayed
Steroid excretion pattern	—	—	—	Unaltered	Unaltered	Altered

APPENDIX II

Generic and Trade Names of Principal Diuretics

Compound Class	Generic name	Trade name
Xanthines:	Theophylline–ethylenediamine	Aminophylline
	Theophylline–ethylenediamine + aluminum hydroxide	Amindrox, Cardalin
	Theobromine–sodium salicylate	Diuretin
	Theophylline–methylglucamine	Glucophyllin
	Theophylline–piperazine	Piperophyllin
	Theophylline–ethanolamine	Monotheamin
Pyrimidines:	Aminometradin	Mictine
(aminouracils):	Amisometradin	Rolicton
Triazines:	Chlorazanil	Daquin
Organomercurials:	Merbaphen	Novasural
	Mersalyl	Salyrgan
	Merethoxylline	Dicurin
	Mercumatilin	Cumertilin
	—	Esidron
	Mercurophylline	Mercuzanthine
	Mercaptomerin	Thiomerin
	Meralluride	Mercuhydrin
	Chlormerodrin	Neohydrin
	Merbiurelidin	Meterox
	Diglucomethoxane	Mersoben
	WY-1204	Oradon
Sulfonamides:	Acetazolamide	Diamox
	Ethoxzolamide	Cardrase
	Methazolamide	Neptazane
	(Butyl analog of acetazolamide)	Butamide
	Carzenide	Dirnate
	Chlosudimeprimylium	Brinaldix
Compound XXX*II*	—	Nirexon
(Chapter V):	Dichlorphenamide	Daranide
Compound XX*II* (Chapter V):	5-Chloro-2, 4-disulfamylaniline	Salamid, Ferrosan
	Disulfamid	Disamide
Compound X*V*	—	Haflutan
(Chapter V):	Chlorthalidone	Hygroton

APPENDIX II—*continued*

Compound Class	Generic name	Trade name
Thiazides and hydrothiazides:	Chlorothiazide	Diuril
	flumethiazide	Ademol
	Benzthiazide	Naclex
	Hydrochlorothiazide	Esidrix, Hydrodiuril, Oretic
	Hydroflumethiazide	Saluron
	Thiabutazide	Saltucin
	Quinethazone	Hydromox
	Benzhydroflumethiazide	Naturetin
	Trichloromethiazide	Naqua, Esmarin, Fluitran
	Methychlothiazide	Enduron
	Polythiazide	Renese
	Cyclothiazide	Anhydron
	Cyclopenthiazide	Navidrix
Aldosterone: Antagonists and secretory inhibitors	Spironolactone	Aldactone
	Metyrapone	Metopirone
	Triamterene	Dytac
Miscellaneous: compounds Compound XIII (Chapter VIII)	Ethacrynic acid	—

Author Index

Numbers in parentheses are reference numbers and are inserted in the index to enable the reader to locate a reference when the authors' names do not appear in the text. Numbers in italic indicate the pages on which the complete references are listed.

F

G

H

Y

Z

Subject Index

D

I

K

L

M

N

O

P